Recognition, Evaluation, and Control of Workplace Health Hazards

Joel M. Haight, Editor

American Society of Safety Engineers
Des Plaines, Illinois, USA

Library of Congress Cataloging-in-Publication Data

Recognition, evaluation, and control of workplace health hazards / Joel M. Haight, editor.
p. ; cm.
Includes bibliographical references.
ISBN 978-1-885581-68-6 (alk. paper)
I. Haight, Joel M. II. American Society of Safety Engineers.
[DNLM: 1. Occupational Health--standards--United States. 2. Safety Management--organization & administration--United States. 3. Equipment Safety--standards--United States. 4. Hazardous Substances--standards--United States. 5. Occupational Health--legislation & jurisprudence--United States. 6. Workplace--organization & administration--United States. WA 485]

363.11--dc23

2012043222

Managing Editor: Michael F. Burditt, ASSE
Editor: Jeri Ann Stucka, ASSE
Text design and composition: Cathy Lombardi
Cover Design: Image Graphics

Printed in the United States of America

18 17 16 15 14 6 5 4 3

Recognition, Evaluation, and Control of Workplace Health Hazards

Contents

FOREWORD

SIGNIFICANT CHANGES TO FEDERAL occupational health regulations followed with the passage of the Occupational Safety and Health Act in 1970. Section 6(a) of OSHA authorized the adoption of any national consensus standard, any established federal standard, and any established federal standard as an occupational safety or health standard, unless OSHA determined a standard would not result in improved health and safety. The following year, in issuing the *Compliance Operations Manual*, OSHA set priorities for inspections in the following order:

1. Inspection of fatalities and catastrophes
2. Response to employee complaints
3. Inspection of target industries and facilities with targeted health hazards
4. Random inspections.

The Target Health Hazards Program included asbestos, cotton dust, silica, inorganic lead, and carbon dioxide. In 1971 OSHA also moved forward with the inclusion of standards for noise, personal protective equipment (PPE), and nearly 500 permissible exposure limits (PELs) for approximately 400 chemical substances, based largely on threshold limit values (TLVs) developed earlier by the American Conference of Governmental Industrial Hygienists (ACGIH). While some of the PELs were later removed under a DOL ruling, the modern era of federal enforcement of occupational health was underway.

The OSH Act also gave OSHA the authority to issue emergency temporary standards (ETS) if the secretary determines that

- employees are exposed to grave danger from exposure to substances of agents determined to be toxic or physically harmful or from new hazards, or
- the emergency standard is necessary to protect employees from such danger.

An ETS is immediately effective as of the date of its publication in the *Federal Register.* OSHA issued an ETS for asbestos, vinyl chloride, and DBCP (1, 2,-dibromo-3-chloropropane).

The health of American workers is also protected under a provision of the OSH Act known as the General Duty Clause Section 5(a), which requires employers to: ". . .furnish to each of his employees employment and a place of employment which are free from recognized hazards that are causing or likely to cause death or serious physical harm to his employees."

Two years after the passage of the OSH Act, a new process of standards adoption was implemented by OSHA. This involves the now-familiar process that begins with the publication of the proposed standard in the *Federal Register*, followed by a comment period and a period in which objections to the proposed law may filled. Specific time periods apply to each phase of the rule-making process. Eighteen separate health standards were issued by OSHA from inception through 1984.

The issue of cost-benefit analysis in OSHA rule making is discussed in the chapter on regulations, including the Supreme Court's ruling on the OSHA benzene PEL. OSHA issued standards on a number of chemical substances, as well as the many notices and standards promulgated on asbestos. The involvement of the Organization Resources Counselors, Inc., the American Chemistry Council (ACC), and the American Petroleum Institute (API) in attempts to change OSHA PELs is also discussed. Other important OSHA standards discussed are the ventilation, respirator, noise, hearing conservation, and ionizing radiation.

The important first chapter also provides an introduction to occupational health regulations developed by MSHA, the Mine Safety and Health Administration, and the EPA.

The second chapter discusses applied science and engineering principles of recognition, evaluation, and control of health hazards. As the authors note at the outset, "Hazards—whether chemical, physical, biological, or mechanical—are the sources of risk." The EPA and OSHA have set different levels of acceptable risk for some chemical substances, as noted in an interesting comparison. Finally, the authors note that *risk communication* is a ". . .necessary and powerful component of the risk function because people are much more likely to *buy in* to a decision in which they have participated."

The traditional approach in the U.S. for controlling worker exposure to hazardous airborne chemicals has been to compare the results of an exposure assessment to the occupational exposure limits (OELs). The UK's Control of Substances Hazardous to Health (COSHH) regulations, based on risk assessment and the EPA's evolving risk-assessment approaches, are reviewed. The remainder of the chapter is focuses on exposure-assessment aspects of industrial hygiene.

Understanding the risks of and controlling exposure to chemicals and particulates in the workplace is the subject of the third chapter. Chemistry is an essential basic science that plays an important role in the understanding of occupational health hazards that may occur when handling or working with industrial and commercial chemical products in a variety of occupations. Often diseases or health conditions of exposed workers are the result of direct exposures or from secondary effects of exposures to chemicals found in the workplace or the work environments. The safety and health professional is often required to evaluate the potential for injury or illness when working with chemicals, as well as to determine safe working levels for worker exposures. Therefore, a basic understanding of chemistry and other related fields is required.

There are a number of professional fields that deal with these issues, such as industrial hygiene (IH), which focuses on the means to identify, evaluate and control these exposures in the workplace; toxicology, which studies the mode and effect of the exposure on living species; or epidemiology, which looks at the effects of disease manifestation statistically to develop both historical and predictive models of the effects. Safety and health professionals are generally not considered experts or practitioners in these fields, but they are expected to understand the methodologies and applications of the information, which is generated and available from various studies conducted both in controlled studies and field assessments.

The purpose of this chapter is to provide safety and health professionals, including students studying in this field, with a basic understanding of some of the specific terms and methodologies used in generating and understanding chemical data. Without an understanding of the terms used in published data or an appreciation for the limitations of the data as presented in studies, the safety and health professional may be unable to fully characterize a potential chemical hazard and, therefore, may compromise the approach to eliminate or control hazards through the methods listed in the chapter.

Safe work practices are often prescribed by government regulations and also through consensus standards of best practices, but the application of these practices requires an understanding of chemical properties, such as physical state, chemical composition, and possible degradation products. Also, solubility of the product in liquids, volatility in air, plus characteristics that make the products flammable or corrosive, are important when considering safe storage and spill control measures.

This chapter provides a summary description of how properties of chemicals affect these issues, as well as the inherent toxicity of the material in use. A short list of definitions used in descriptions, as well as references to applicable standards and terms, is included as a lexicon for practical use in understanding these properties and sources of information. Sample questions focus on best practices for methods of controlling hazards through an understanding of the terms introduced in the chapter.

The fourth chapter discusses the recognition and control of physical hazards. The history of exposure guidelines and regulations for physical agent stressors in the workplace reads like a checkerboard of disconnected events, each with its own cultural biases. The guidelines and standards were generally set by content experts working in areas affected by signal incidents. These standards were described in the terminology available to and comfortable for each of the expert communities, some medical, some chemical, and some engineering or physics. There was no overarching mechanism for standardization. This is true even to the point that, not withstanding a national priority for using the SI system of units, many standards are written in terms of units deprecated by NIST guidelines for use of the SI system in the U.S. Where that is true, this chapter has attempted to make conversions to the SI system units to keep the presentation uniform.

Philosophically, the chapter is organized around the first law of thermodynamics: Energy is conserved in all interactions but it may change form. The forms of energy of interest are internal energy (of a target organ), and the transfer of energy to the target organ by means of work (force pushing tissue around) or heat (photons pushing molecules around). Conceptually, most physical agents pose a risk when they deliver energy to a target organ or tissue at a rate that causes a damaging accumulation of internal energy (as does radiofrequency (RF) energy) or mechanical breakage (as does auditory energy and mechanical vibration).

For some physical agents, including ionizing radiation, the damage is cumulative and the standards are set for total energy of that sort over a short period, ranging from seconds to weeks, and for long periods of weeks, months, years, and a lifetime. For other physical agents, including lasers and impulse noise, the damage is nearly instantaneous, and the standard limits energy per pulse and power levels.

For many physical agents, resonance effects exist that make some frequencies more damaging than others. This is an important organizing concept for electromagnetic radiation, noise and vibration. In these cases not only do the standards limit both energy and power levels, they do so as a function of frequency with the lowest allowed levels occurring at and near the resonant frequency. Full understanding of the resonant features of these standards is facilitated by the application of Fourier and LaPlace Transforms to the time history of the forces applied to the target tissue, and these topics are deemed beyond the scope of this handbook.

The exercises are designed to further illustrate concepts presented in the text of the chapter and the serious reader is encouraged to spend time with those. To your author's knowledge, this chapter represents a first attempt at a coherent presentation of physical agent standards. If you find errors or better ways to present a topic, please address these to Dr. Rock in care of the publisher.

The subject of the next chapter is biological hazards. The primary focus of the book is on clinical testing and microbiological research facilities. Routes of transmission are discussed. These include oral ingestion and respiratory intake, and risk exposures for both are discussed. The author then discusses the types of biological agents—bacteria, viruses, and fungi. How to conduct facility hazard assessments and control of biological hazards are then discussed, followed by the important subject of training. The author notes as well that the NIH recommends that, "all individuals, corporations, or institutions not strictly covered by the *NIH Guidelines* establish a properly constituted institutional biosafety committee (IBC)." The author concludes the chapter with a thoughtful analysis of personal and environmental sampling and interpretation.

The final chapter is fittingly on best practices. Anticipation of hazards requires the most technical knowledge, skill and experience. A best practice in anticipation is the review of all new chemicals and processes (including significant modifications of processes) in advance of their use. For potential high-hazard processes, best practice is to use one of many available tools, such as the hazard and operability (HAZOP) approach. Best practice is also to review all new chemicals and processes or major process modifications for risk at the local level (where it is used) and at the organizational level (when they are to be implemented at multiple sites). Another best practice is to perform a quantitative or qualitative risk assessment of all processes and procedures at least annually.

Recognition is the second tenant of industrial hygiene. Best practice is to develop a dossier (file or database) containing all the legal requirements and recommended practices for the substances and processes of concern. From this file, inspection and monitoring procedures can be developed, with best practice being to risk rank operations and establish an assessment or audit plan and frequency based on this ranking.

Evaluation is the third tenant of industrial hygiene. Best practice is to have a justifiable exposure assessment strategy. The actual evaluations must be detailed and documented in a standardized way. Records of these exposure assessments should be kept indefinitely, subject to the legal restrictions of the organization and statutory requirements.

Prevention is the next tenant of industrial hygiene, and it is a best practice to have an effective hazard communication program. Effective hazard communication requires education and training, which is also effective. It is a best practice to demonstrate the effectiveness of all safety and health training since this is such a critical part of prevention. An example is the testing of fork-lift drivers for both knowledge (paper test) and skill (driving test).

Control is the last tenant. A best practice for control is to follow the hierarchy of controls (elimination, substitution, engineering controls, administrative controls, personal protective controls). Another best practice is to have an active product stewardship program. Within the product stewardship concept is the best practice of having an active customer support program, which may include specialized use training and auditing. The final best practice is to develop and implement a recognized management systems approach. The best practices listed in this summary are not all inclusive but they are well recognized in the profession as being associated with the "best programs."

ABOUT THE EDITOR

In 2009, Joel M. Haight, Ph.D., P.E., was named Branch Chief of the Human Factors Branch at the Centers for Disease Control and Prevention (CDC)—National Institute of Occupational Safety and Health (NIOSH) at their Pittsburgh Office of Mine Safety and Health Re search. He continues in this role. In 2000, Dr. Haight received a faculty appointment and served as Associate Professor of Energy and Mineral Engineering at the Pennsylvania State University. He also worked as a manager and engineer for the Chevron Corporation domestically and internationally for eighteen years prior to joining the faculty at Penn State. He has a Ph.D. (1999) and Master's degree (1994) in Industrial and System Engineering, both from Auburn University. Dr. Haight does human error, process optimization, and intervention effectiveness research. He is a professional member of the American Society of Safety Engineers (where he serves as Federal Liaison to the Board of Trustees and the ASSE Foundation Research Committee Chair), the American Industrial Hygiene Association (AIHA), and the Human Factors and Ergonomics Society (HFES). He has published more than 30 peer reviewed scientific journal articles and book chapters and is a co author and the editor in chief of ASSE's *The Safety Professionals Handbook* and the John Wiley and Sons, *Handbook of Loss Prevention Engineering*.

ABOUT THE AUTHORS

Susan F. Arnold, MSOH, CIH, is Principal of EH&S, LLC. Susan received her Master's degree in Occupational Hygiene from the Medical College at Ohio at Toledo.

Michael A. Charlton, Ph.D., CHP, CIH, CHMM, CSP, is Assistant Vice President for Risk Management & Safety, Environmental Health & Safety Department, and Adjunct Associate Professor in the Radiological Sciences Program at the University of Texas Health Science Center at San Antonio, Texas.

S. Z. (Zack) Mansdorf, Ph.D., CSP, CIH, QIP, in Environmental Engineering from the University of Kansas, School of Engineering, with Masters' degrees in Environment and Safety from the University of Michigan and Central Missouri State. Zack is currently a consultant in EHS and sustainability.

Gayla J. McCluskey received her M.B.A. in engineering management in 1984 from the University of Dallas and is a Certified Industrial Hygienist, Certified Safety Professional, Qualified Environmental Professional, and Registered Occupational Hygienist. She currently is principal of Global Environmental Health Services and clinical instructor of emergency medicine at Drexel University College of Medicine. She formerly was a managing consultant at Sun Oil Company and director of health, safety, and environmental affairs for North American and Pacific Rim operations at Rhone Poulenc Rorer. She served for ten years on the Board of the American Industrial Hygiene Association and was its President in 2002 and 2003.

Sheryl A. Milz, Ph.D., CIH, is Chair and Associate Professor of Public Health and Preventive Medicine at the University of Toledo.

Deborah Imel Nelson, Ph.D., CIH, is Safety, Health and Emergency Management Program manager for EPA, Office of Criminal Enforcement, Forensics and Training.

William Piispanen, CIH, CSP, CEA, CM IOSH, is the Senior Director for Environmental, Safety, and Health for the Washington Division of URS, in Boise, Idaho.

James C. Rock, Ph.D., P.E., CIH, is Vice President for Research and Engineering of TUPE, Inc.

Regulatory Issues

1

Gayla McCluskey

LEARNING OBJECTIVES

- Obtain a historical overview of the federal regulation of occupational safety and health.
- Learn about the various federal agencies responsible for workplace safety and health, with a focus on OSHA.
- Learn about the formation of OSHA and the health standards it has promulgated to date.

THE U.S. GOVERNMENT was slow to respond to the changing occupational environment in the late nineteenth and early twentieth centuries when the country developed into a leading industrial nation. Industrialization introduced new chemicals, dusts, and dangerous machines into factories, mines, and cities. Workers began experiencing diseases such as silicosis in workplaces that had inadequate ventilation and unsanitary conditions (MacLaury 1981).

The regulation of health and safety initially fell to state labor agencies. The Massachusetts Bureau of Statistics urged the development of legislation that dealt with "the peril to health from lack of ventilation." Massachusetts passed the nation's first factory inspection law in 1877, which required equipment guarding and emergency fire exits. By 1890, nine states had factory inspection laws, thirteen required machine guarding, and twenty-one had narrow provisions for health hazards.

Prince Otto von Bismarck initiated the first Workers' Compensation system in Germany in 1884 for the purpose of compensating injured workers. In the United States, organized labor opposed the system because it was not a preventive measure, until the Pittsburgh Survey was released in 1907–08. This survey detailed lives and working conditions in Allegheny County, Pennsylvania. It found that injured workers and the survivors of those killed bore the economic brunt of accidents, even though most accidents were thought to be the fault of the employer. The study's authors suggested that employers should bear a substantial share of the economic burden, thus giving them an incentive to reduce the causes of injury.

The Pittsburgh Survey was supported by both labor and business, and as a result, a limited Workers' Compensation law was passed in 1908 for federal employees. Wisconsin established the first state workers' compensation program in 1911 and, by 1921, most states had established programs. However, there was little incentive for a company to invest in safety improvement because insurance premiums were so low. In addition, very few states included compensation for disease, despite what was known at the time about occupational illness.

Federal Regulation of Health and Safety

The federal government began investigating industry-related diseases early in the twentieth century. The Bureau of Labor published the first studies of death and disease in the dusty trades in 1903. In 1910, it published a study of the horrors of phosphorus necrosis, a disfiguring and sometimes fatal disease of workers in the white phosphorus match industry (MacLaury 1981).

The U.S. Commissioner of Labor, Charles Neill, met Dr. Alice Hamilton[1] at a 1910 European conference on occupational accidents and disease. As Director of the Illinois Commission on Occupational Diseases, Dr. Hamilton was conducting a study of lead exposure. Neill invited Hamilton to work for the Bureau of Labor and, in that capacity, she traveled around the country until 1921, visiting lead smelters, storage battery plants, and other hazardous workplaces (MacLaury 1981). Her findings were so scientifically persuasive that they resulted in sweeping reforms, both voluntary and regulatory, leading to the reduction of occupational exposure to lead. Other investigations for which she is best known include studies of carbon monoxide poisoning in steelworkers, mercury poisoning in hatters, and "dead fingers" syndrome among laborers who used jackhammers (NIOSH 2006).

Congress created the Department of Labor in 1913, appointing William B. Wilson, a former coal miner and union official, as Secretary. The Bureau of Labor Statistics started to compile accident statistics, initially in the iron and steel industry. In 1914, federal responsibility for industrial safety and health was placed in the Office of Industrial Hygiene and Sanitation under the Public Health Service (MacLaury 1981).

The United States' entry into World War I worsened the health and safety conditions found in the factories that were trying to meet the wartime needs of the military. In response, Congress created a service to inspect war production sites, advise companies on reducing hazards, and help the states to develop and enforce safety and health standards.

In 1933, President Franklin D. Roosevelt selected Frances Perkins[2] as Secretary of Labor, the first woman appointed to the Cabinet. Perkins was appointed to the New York Industrial Commission in 1918 and later was named its Commissioner by Roosevelt when he was governor of the state. Perkins created the Bureau of Labor Standards in 1934, the first permanent federal agency to promote health and safety for all workers. However, the Bureau's efforts continued to focus on helping state governments improve their administration of state health and safety laws.

Industrial hygiene evolved significantly after the passage of the Social Security Act of 1935, which allocated funds to the Public Health Service for research and grants to states for industrial hygiene programs. Before 1935, only five state health departments contained industrial hygiene units; by 1936, seventeen units existed in state and local health departments (Corn 1992).

The Walsh-Healy Act of 1936 enabled the federal government to establish health and safety standards for federal contractors. In spite of this act, enactment of safety and health laws were largely left to the states until 1958, when Congress gave the authority to set safety and health standards for longshoremen to the Department of Labor (MacLaury 1981).

The Department of Labor issued mandatory health and safety standards under the Walsh-Healy Act in December 1960. These were the first federal regulations that applied to the whole range of industry. Until that time, most of these standards had previously been used as informal guidelines to aid federal and state inspectors. The business community was caught by surprise, since the regulations were enacted without hearings or prior announcement. Business community criticism caused the department to announce revisions to the standards, and a hearing on the new federal guidelines was held in March 1964. The Department of Labor decided to examine all of its safety programs in order to develop a more coordinated health and safety policy. An outside consultant's (identity not given) review recommended all of the safety programs be consolidated under a single agency.

In 1965, the U.S. Public Health Service issued a report entitled, "Protecting the Health of Eighty Million Americans." The report noted that a new chemical enters the workplace every twenty minutes, cited evidence showing a strong link between cancer and the workplace, and concluded that old problems were far from being solved. The report called for a national occupational health effort centered in the Public Health Service.

World War II

In 1940, in a speech at the Air Hygiene Foundation's Fifth Annual Meeting, Dr. Ernest Brown of the Navy Medical Corps commented that one of the most important concerns in the Navy for years was industrial hygiene. At that time, enormous expansion in naval construction was occurring. Industrial hygiene had been listed as a specialty of the naval medical officer, along with other specialties outside of clinical practice. The object of his presentation was to outline the administration of industrial hygiene in the naval yards. At that time, there were only eleven naval yards (Brown 1940).

The United States was ill-equipped to fight, much less win, a war prior to World War II. In 1940, Congress approved large sums of money to build a two-ocean navy, as well as thousands of planes and equipment for an immense army. The U.S. Navy and the U.S. Maritime Commission, which administered shipbuilding activities, became two of the largest industrial employers in the early 1940s. Under Maritime Commission contracts, 5601 vessels were delivered. As production demands rose, shortages of materials and qualified workers became more widespread. Faced with these labor shortages, the two government agencies had to define a policy to keep workers safe, healthy, and productive.

The Secretary of the Navy required that shipyards establish an industrial health office in each naval district and enlarge the safety engineering organization as soon as personnel were available. The Navy then turned to the Division of Industrial Hygiene in the newly created National Institutes of Health (NIH) and asked for it to provide industrial hygiene services. At the time, the Division of Industrial Hygiene had neither staff nor funds to respond favorably to this request.

The Maritime Commission hired two consultants: Phillip Drinker, a professor of industrial hygiene at Harvard University, and John Roche, an industrial safety engineer from the National Safety Council (NSC), to make health and safety surveys at the various shipyards. They completed their respective reports and made a series of recommendations. Drinker and Roche recommended the preparation of minimum standards of health and safety at the shipyards. A conference was held, and the minimum requirements were presented to safety, medical, and labor representatives from the shipyards. The Minimum Requirements for Safety and Industrial Health were approved in January of 1943 (Corn and Starr 1987).

When the war ended, the soldiers returned home, and little more was done to improve health and safety conditions in the workplace for two decades.

OSHA's Beginning

In 1968, President Lyndon B. Johnson's administration submitted a bill to the 90th Congress to create the first federal comprehensive safety and health program. The Occupational Safety and Health Bill was introduced in the House by James O'Hara (D-Michigan) and in the Senate by Ralph Yarbrough (D-Texas). The bill contained provisions to conduct research to determine a basis for standard-setting, granted authority to the Secretary of Labor to set and enforce standards and impose sanctions for violation of the standards, and provided resources to the states to develop and strengthen their programs (Ashford 1976).

Congressional hearings were held during which Secretary Wirtz cited two casualty lists facing the country at that time: the military toll in Vietnam and the industrial toll at home. Wirtz asked "whether Congress is going to act to stop a carnage" which, he said, continued because people "can't see the blood on the food that they eat, on the things that they buy, and on the services they get." Labor supported the bill, but the business community argued that it vested the Secretary of Labor with too broad a power and undermined the role of the states (MacLaury 1981).

The Johnson proposal did not reach the floor of either body of Congress. After President Richard Nixon was elected and confirmed, he asked Secretary of Labor James C. Hodgson to prepare a health and safety bill for introduction in 1969.

The Republicans introduced bills sponsored by Congressman William Ayres (R-Ohio) and Senator Jacob Javits (R-New York). The Democrats introduced Occupational Health and Safety Bills HR 3809, sponsored by James O'Hara (D-Michigan), and S 2193, sponsored by Harrison A. Williams (D-New Jersey), that included similar provisions to the legislation previously introduced (Ashford 1976).

The Republican-sponsored bills differed from those sponsored by the Democrats by vesting the authority to set and enforce standards to a new safety board, consisting of members appointed by the president, rather than vesting the authority in the Department of Labor. In addition, the Nixon administration's proposal limited the Labor Department's role to workplace inspection.

Hearings were held on the Nixon proposal, during which Secretary of Labor George Shultz asked Congress to "work out our differences and get something done." Organized labor opposed the new safety board, arguing that the program should be in the Labor Department. The U.S. Chamber of Commerce, the National Association of Manufacturers, and other industry groups supported the Nixon proposal (MacLaury 1981).

The Senate approved a compromise version of S 2193 in November 1970, in which an independent review commission charged with final review of enforcement activities would be created, while standards-setting and initial enforcement authority were given to the Secretary of Labor. The bill also included a proposal to elevate the status of the former Bureau of Occupational Safety and Health and give it the authority to perform research and make recommendations to the Department of Labor (Ashford 1976).

The House approved HR 19200, a revised administration bill sponsored by William A. Steiger (R-Wisconsin) and Robert Sikes (D-Florida). The House bill proposed an independent board to set standards, with enforcement to be provided by an independent appeals commission. The Labor Department would then share enforcement responsibilities and conduct inspections.

The two bills were sent to a Congressional conference committee and the resulting compromise version became the Occupational Safety and Health (OSH) Act of 1970. The legislation was signed into law by President Nixon on December 29, 1970, and became effective 120 days later.

The Occupational Safety and Health Administration (OSHA) was created within the Department of Labor to implement the requirements of the act. George C. Guenther, at the time Director of the Labor Standards Bureau, was named as OSHA's first Assistant Secretary (MacLaury undated). The agency set up 10 regional offices and 49 area offices to cover the 50 states, the District of Columbia, Puerto Rico, the U.S. Virgin Islands, Guam, and American Samoa (Showlater 1972).

Initial Standards Setting

Section 6(a) of the OSH Act required OSHA to promptly set up a regulatory framework by adopting any national consensus standard and any established federal standard as an occupational safety or health standard, unless OSHA determined a standard would not result in improved health and safety. This authority was allowed for a period from the effective date of the act until two years after the effective date (U.S. Congress 1970) .

On April 28, 1971, OSHA issued the *Compliance Operations Manual*, which set policies. In it, OSHA set priorities for inspections in the following order:

1. Inspection of fatalities and catastrophes
2. Response to employee complaints
3. Inspection of target industries and facilities with targeted health hazards
4. Random inspections

The Target Health Hazards Program included asbestos, cotton dust, silica, inorganic lead, and carbon dioxide (Ashford 1976).

On May 29, 1971, OSHA adopted a body of voluntary consensus standards. These took effect on August 27, 1971, and in some cases, on February 15, 1972. The

CASE STUDY

George Guenther Administration, 1971–1973: A Closely Watched Start-up (USDOL, n.d.)

The Occupational Safety and Health Act of 1970 heralded a new era in the history of public efforts to protect workers from harm on the job. This act established for the first time a nationwide, federal program to protect almost the entire work force from job-related death, injury, and illness. Secretary of Labor James Hodgson, who had helped shape the law, termed it "the most significant legislative achievement" for workers in a decade.[1] Hodgson's first step was to establish within the Labor Department, effective April 28, 1971, a special agency, the Occupational Safety and Health Administration (OSHA) to administer the act. Building on the Bureau of Labor Standards as a nucleus, the new agency took on the difficult task of creating from scratch a program that would meet the legislative intent of the OSH Act.

Secretary Hodgson selected George Guenther, an experienced public official who was then director of the Labor Standards Bureau, to head OSHA as Assistant Secretary of Labor for Occupational Safety and Health. Guenther had come to the Labor Department from the post of deputy secretary of the Pennsylvania Department of Labor and Industry. Before that he headed a hosiery manufacturing firm in Pennsylvania.

At Senate hearings on April 2, 1971, on his nomination to head OSHA, Guenther stressed that under him the agency would strive to be "responsive and reasonable" in its administration of the act. Senator Jacob Javits, a New York Republican who had played a major role in the passage of the OSH Act, told Guenther:

> I hope you will remember one thing. . . . We have not finished with the occupational safety law and . . . (Y)ou have the lives of millions of workers in your hands. . . . Don't be afraid of anybody who tries to intimidate you, whether it is business or labor or politics (sic). You have got friends here and advocates. Come to us.[2]

During OSHA's start-up phase some of its actions and policies were reasonably successful, others were less so. The organizing and establishment of the agency within the Labor Department went smoothly. A decision to seek voluntary compliance and avoid a punitive approach to enforcement was well-received by the business community. Because of limitations on resources to protect workers in five million workplaces nationwide, OSHA loosely targeted its enforcement in a worst-case-first approach which emphasized investigation of catastrophic accidents and employers' compliance in the most dangerous and unhealthy workplaces. Partly at the urging of organized labor, OSHA tried to emphasize the "H" (for Health) in its name. The first standard that it set was for asbestos fibers.

On the other hand, a move that brought OSHA long-lasting notoriety as a "nitpicker" was the verbatim adoption and sometimes unreasonable enforcement of a body of voluntary consensus standards developed by industry associations. While adoption was specifically mandated by the OSH Act, OSHA chose to promulgate the rules en masse and immediately, having them take effect in August 1971 instead of using the full two-year phase-in period that the law allowed. Another unsuccessful early move was the decision to develop state programs as the primary means of realizing the goals of the act. Counting on the bulk of the states to participate, OSHA limited the development of its own staff of enforcement officers. It quickly became apparent that the states were not going to participate as extensively as OSHA had hoped. As a result, the agency soon found itself inadequately prepared to directly enforce the law on a nationwide basis. A damaging legacy from the start-up period came to light during the 1974 Watergate investigations in the form of an internal memorandum that sought ideas on ways to tailor OSHA's program that would increase business' support of President Nixon's reelection campaign in 1972. There is no evidence that this "responsiveness" program affected OSHA significantly at the time, but its revelation in 1974 did considerable damage to the agency's reputation.[3]

OSHA's principal client groups–organized labor and the business community–played active roles during the start-up phase and throughout the agency's history. Organized labor had been instrumental in the passage of the OSH Act. Labor leaders and workers' advocates, from AFL-CIO president George Meany to Ralph Nader, spoke out frequently on OSHA's conduct and policies. In June 1971 Meany told a special union meeting on workers' safety and health that when the OSH Act passed, "the AFL-CIO served notice that we were going to be watching over the government's shoulder. . . . We warned that if this law isn't fully and effectively implemented, we would scream bloody murder."[4] In April 1972 Nader announced the completion of "Occupational Epidemic," a study he sponsored condemning government, business, and labor for failing to deal with illness and injury on the job. Published later under the title *Bitter Wages*, it was prepared at his Center for the Study of Responsive Law by a task force of lawyers, law students, and graduate students in medicine and engineering. Nader and his report had harsh words for the Labor Department, which he called a "hostile environment" for enforcement of the OSH Act.

While organized labor and its supporters agreed that OSHA's initial effort to enforce the act was not effective, the business community did not have a uniform position on OSHA. Many in the small business community strongly opposed the agency. On the other hand, the National Association of Manufacturers (NAM), *Fortune* magazine, and other entities associated with large enterprises were relatively tolerant of it. Their equanimity resulted to a large extent from the fact that, unlike most small businesses, large corporations were used to dealing with federal regulation and usually had long-standing safety programs of their own.

This is not to say that big business had no concerns about the OSH Act or its implementation. Leo Teplow, a safety expert from the steel industry, called the

OSH Act "the most extensive federal intervention into the day-to-day operation of American business in history."[5] Employers were concerned about the competence of OSHA inspectors, the costs of compliance with federal standards, and the burden on business of meeting the act's requirements to report and record injuries, illnesses, and deaths on the job. The consensus standards that OSHA adopted were familiar to large employers, but it was a different matter to employers now that these rules were to be enforced as law.

OSHA took several steps to meet business objections. In January 1972, after receiving numerous petitions from employers for exceptions from record-keeping and reporting rules, OSHA eased the requirements somewhat. The previous September the agency granted the Boeing Co. the first interim variance under the OSH Act, which allows temporary exemption from a standard if an employer can convince OSHA that he can provide equivalent protection. OSHA also started to revise its consensus rules. This was part of a three-phase standards development program consisting of corrections of minor mistakes in the consensus standard, changes in these standards, and adoption of new safety and health rules.[6]

Despite such accommodations to business, however, for many smaller employers OSHA loomed as a threat to their economic well-being and even survival. In the spring of 1972 a movement centered in Wyoming developed among small businessmen who sought to curtail enforcement of the OSH Act. They flooded their congressmen with letters about alleged harsh tactics by OSHA inspectors, such as forcing businessmen to close because of safety violations and threatening employers with jail sentences.

This campaign had a tremendous effect on Congress in an election year. More than 80 bills were introduced to limit OSHA's powers, principally by exempting small businesses from the act. Committees held hearings on OSHA. Congressmen spoke out against it. Senator Carl Curtis of Nebraska said that attempts to limit OSHA were a reply to those who would allow the "arrogance of power" to run over small businessmen.[7]

Organized labor strongly opposed exemptions, but was sympathetic to the problems of small businesses. Jacob Clayman of the AFL-CIO, testifying before a House committee in June 1972, said that stories of harassment were blown out of proportion, but charged that inept administration was causing real problems for small businesses. He said that OSHA had made special efforts to inform large corporations about the act but failed to include small businesses. George Taylor, also from the AFL-CIO, charged before later hearings that OSHA had been "unpardonably" remiss in its failure to tell small businessmen about their rights and duties under the OSH Act.[8]

The Labor Department worked hard to defeat the growing movement to exempt small employers. On Capitol Hill, OSHA spokesmen denied charges that the agency fined ranchers and farmers in Wyoming, ordered the closing of a public school, or drove a company out of business because of violations. These claims, they said, were based on nothing but rumors. Guenther told a House committee that he strongly opposed across-the-board exemptions of small businesses, but indicated that OSHA would support a move to give it the authority to omit inspections of very small employers at its discretion. He also told the committee that OSHA would soon exempt employers with eight or fewer employees from certain reporting requirements. OSHA was also willing to provide consultation visits, if given the legal authority to do so.[9]

Despite vigorous efforts by the Labor Department and labor unions, exemptions of small employers twice came within a presidential veto of enactment in 1972. In June the House passed an amendment to the Labor-HEW appropriations bill exempting employers with 25 or fewer employees from the act. The Senate passed a narrower exemption for places with fifteen or fewer workers. The conference committee adopted the Senate version of the amendment and sent the appropriations bill to the White House for President Nixon's signature. Nixon, concerned about the size of the appropriations for the departments, vetoed the bill. In the fall, Congress again included an exemption amendment in the new appropriations bill that it sent to the President. However, Congress and the President were still at odds over the budget, and Nixon once again vetoed the Labor-HEW appropriations bill, ending efforts for exemption for the time being.[10]

1. Safety Standards, March 1971.
2. U.S. Senate, Committee on Labor and Public Welfare, Hearings on the Nomination of George Guenther, Washington, 1971, p.11.
3. See discussion of "Watergate memo" below in text.
4. *National Journal* (*NatJ*), Dec. 4, 1971.
5. *Wall Street Journal* (*WSJ*), Dec. 1, 1971.
6. *Daily Labor Report* (*DLR*), Sept. 23, 1971, Jan. 22, March 3, 1972.
7. *DLR*, June 21, 1972.
8. *New York Times* (*NYT*), June 29, Sept. 28, 1972.
9. *DLR*, June 14, 21, 1972; *NYT*, Oct. 3, 1972; *WSJ*, June 32, 1972.
10. *NatJ*, July 1, 1972; *NYT*, June 16, 28, 29, Oct. 8, 1972; *DLR*, June 23, Aug. 18, 23, 1972; *Occupational Safety and Health Reporter* (*OSHR*), Nov. 2, 1972.

consensus standards included over 400 pages of standards from the American National Standards Institute (ANSI) and from the National Fire Protection Association (NFPA)—both national consensus organizations.

On August 13, 1971, OSHA made effective immediately those standards having an effective date initially set for February 1972. These included standards for noise, personal protective equipment, and nearly 500 permissible exposure limits (PELs) for approximately 400 chemical substances (Ashford 1976).[3]

These PELs were largely based upon the 1968 American Conference of Governmental Industrial

Hygienists' (ACGIH)[4] threshold limit values (TLVs) that had been included as part of the Walsh-Healy Public Contracts Act of 1969. ACGIH had separated out the chemicals it considered to be carcinogenic and included them as an appendix to the TLV list, with zero as a recommended exposure limit. The Department of Labor concluded the appendix was not part of the Walsh-Healy Act and was, therefore, not a federally established standard that OSHA could adopt.

After the two-year start-up period, OSHA was required to follow Section 6 (b) of the Act to promulgate any new standard. This section requires OSHA to publish the standard in the *Federal Register* as a proposed rule and allows interested persons a period of 30 days after publication to submit written data or comments. Within the comment period, any interested person may file written objections to the proposed rule and request a public hearing to be held to hear these objections. Within 60 days after the comment period expires, or within 60 days after a hearing is held, OSHA is required to decide whether or not to issue the rule. The rule may contain a provision delaying the effective date, not to exceed ninety days, as determined by the Secretary, to allow employers and employees to become familiar with the provisions of the standard (U.S. Congress 1970).

Standards that apply to toxic materials or harmful physical agents, also must fulfill these requirements:

> The Secretary, in promulgating standards dealing with toxic materials or harmful physical agents under this subsection, shall set the standard which most adequately assures, to the extent feasible, on the basis of the best available evidence, that no employee will suffer material impairment of health or functional capacity even if such employee has regular exposure to the hazard dealt with by such standard for the period of his working life. Development of standards under this subsection shall be based upon research, demonstrations, experiments, and such other information as may be appropriate. In addition to the attainment of the highest degree of health and safety protection for the employee, other considerations shall be the latest available scientific data in the field, the feasibility of the standards, and experience gained under this and other health and safety laws. Whenever practicable, the standard promulgated shall be expressed in terms of objective criteria and of the performance desired.

The act also gave OSHA the authority to issue emergency temporary standards (ETS) if the Secretary determines that:

- employees are exposed to grave danger from exposure to substances of agents determined to be toxic or physically harmful or from new hazards
- the emergency standard is necessary to protect employees from such danger.

An ETS is immediately effective on the date of its publication in the *Federal Register*.

OSHA's first ETS was issued for asbestos in 1971. It was not challenged in court (Martonik, Nash, and Grossman 2001). Subsequent ETSs for vinyl chloride and DBCP (1,2,-dibromo-3-chloropropane) were also not challenged. However, when the second ETS for asbestos was issued in 1983, four other ETSs had been rejected. The second asbestos ETS was also rejected, and OSHA has not issued an ETS for any hazard since that time, although there have been many petitions requesting them (e.g., diacetyl).

General Duty Requirements

The OSH Act contains a broad-based provision to be used when a standard has not been promulgated to address a particular serious hazard. That provision, known as the General Duty Clause, is found in Section 5(a) of the act, which states: "Each employer shall furnish to each of his employees employment and a place of employment which are free from recognized hazards that are causing or are likely to cause death or serious physical harm to his employees" (U.S. Congress 1970).

An early use of the General Duty Clause involved a citation dated July 7, 1971, issued to the American Smelting and Refining Company's (ASARCO) plant in Omaha, Nebraska. The 1971 citation was issued in July before the adoption of the TLVs in August of that year (see earlier discussion); otherwise, the citation would have listed a violation of 29 CFR 1910.1001. The citation read:

> Airborne concentrations of lead significantly exceeding levels generally accepted to be safe working levels,

have been allowed to exist in the breathing zones of employees working in the lead-melting area, the retort area, and other work places. Employees have been, and are being exposed to such concentrations. This condition constitutes a recognized hazard that is causing or likely to cause death or serious physical harm to employees." (NIOSH 1973)

ASARCO contested the citation, and the case was heard by the Occupational Safety and Health Review Commission. ASARCO argued that the lead levels in excess of the threshold limit value of 0.2 milligrams per cubic meter (mg/m^3) in its plant did not constitute a recognized hazard causing, or likely to cause, death or serious physical harm, because its employees used respirators and were part of a biological sampling program. The company said there was no evidence that any of its employees had been injured by the airborne concentrations of lead.

The Hearing Examiner found that ASARCO's first responsibility was to reduce the airborne levels to 0.2 mg/m^3, or as close to that figure as possible. The Hearing Examiner determined that proof of violating Section 5(a)(1) of the OSH Act does not depend upon proof that injury has occurred. The original citation was upheld and the proposed penalty of $600 was affirmed.

In previous years, OSHA's position was that exposures above other exposure limits could be cited under Section 5(a)(1). In 1983, then-Assistant Secretary Thorne Auchter wrote in a letter of interpretation that pesticide exposures above the TLV could be cited as 5(a)(1) (OSHA 1983).

After the 1989 Air Contaminants Standard was vacated in 1992 (see further discussion in section entitled "PEL Update"), OSHA issued an interpretation to the compliance staff that Section 5(a)(1) could be used to cite exposures to the 164 substances that were not previously regulated by OSHA. This section could also be used to cite exposures between the 1989 proposed PELs and the original limits adopted in 1971 (OSHA 1993).

The guidance provided by the 2009 *Field Operations Manual* is as follows:

A standard provides for a permissible exposure limit (PEL) of 5 ppm. Even if data establish that a 3 ppm level is a recognized hazard, Section 5(a)(1) shall not be cited to require that the lower level be achieved. If the standard has only a time-weighted average permissible exposure level and the hazard involves exposure above a recognized ceiling level, the Area Director shall consult with the Regional Administrator or designee, who shall discuss any proposed citation with the RSOL (Regional Solicitor).

NOTE: An exception to this rule may apply if it can be proven that "an employer knows a particular safety or health standard is inadequate to protect his employees against the specific hazard it is intended to address." See, Int. Union UAW v. General Dynamics Land Systems Division, *815 F.2d 1570 (D.C. Cir. 1987). Such cases shall be subject to pre-citation review.* [Emphasis in original] (OSHA 2009)

Hierarchy of Control

Long before OSHA was formed, health and safety professionals ranked controls by their reliability and efficiency in controlling hazards. This ranking was referred to as the hierarchy of control, and includes (in order of preference), engineering controls, work practices, and personal protection equipment.

National consensus organizations have also long supported the concept of the hierarchy of controls. In its consensus standard of 1959, the American National Standards Institute (ANSI) wrote:

Respirators are used to supplement other methods of control of airborne contaminants rather than to substitute for them. Every effort should be made to prevent the dissemination of contaminants into the breathing zone of workers. In some instances, it is necessary to use respirators only until these control measures have been taken; in others, such measures are impracticable, and the continued use of respirators is necessary. (ANSI 1959)

In 1963, the American Conference of Government Industrial Hygienists (ACGIH) and the American Industrial Hygiene Association (AIHA) jointly published a guide to respiratory protection that made clear the preferred methods of controlling occupational health hazards:

In the control of those occupational diseases caused by breathing air contaminated with harmful dusts, fumes, mists, gases, or vapors, the primary objective should be to prevent the air from becoming contaminated. This is accomplished as far as possible by accepted engineering control measures. . . . (ACGIH and AIHA 1963)

When OSHA was formed, the initial standards from consensus organizations adopted under Section 6(a) included three provisions establishing the hierarchy of control:

- The respiratory protection standard, 29 CFR 1910.134, included language from the 1969 ANSI consensus standard that stated the primary objective was to prevent atmospheric contamination. This was to be accomplished as far as feasible[5] by engineering controls. When engineering controls were implemented or where they were not feasible, respirators could be used per the requirements of this regulation. The current standard contains the same language.
- The noise standard, 29 CFR 1910.95, requires employers to comply with the permissible exposure limit through the use of feasible administrative or engineering controls.
- The air contaminants standard, 29 CFR 1910.1000, indicates that, in order to achieve compliance with the permissible exposure limits, administrative and engineering controls must first be determined and implemented whenever feasible (U.S. Congress, Office of Technical Assessment 1985).

All substance-specific standards issued by OSHA have required the use of engineering controls and administrative work practices. These are to be used to reduce exposures to or below the permissible exposure limit, or as low as possible, before personal protective equipment can be used.

The use of respirators is generally allowed in the following circumstances:

- during the time it takes to install engineering controls or implement work practices
- when engineering and administrative controls are not feasible, such as during equipment repair
- when engineering and administrative controls are not sufficient in themselves to reduce exposures below the permissible exposure limits
- for some specific substance standards, for cases of intermittent or short-term exposure
- where they are worn to further reduce exposures even when exposures are below the permissible exposure limits
- in emergencies

Health Standards

The Early Years (Start-up to 1984)

As previously mentioned, any new standards issued after the two-year start-up period must follow the multistep process described in Section 6(b) of the act. Through 1984, OSHA issued eighteen separate health standards. The average time it took OSHA to finalize the rule after initial notification was about two years. These standards are listed in Figure 1.

Ten of these regulations established new permissible exposure limits (PELs) and included requirements for monitoring and medical surveillance (for asbestos, vinyl chloride, coke oven emissions, benzene, DBCP, arsenic, cotton dust, acrylonitrile, lead, and ethylene oxide). The carcinogen (fourteen carcinogens) standard contained work practices and medical surveillance requirements. The hearing conservation standard included monitoring, audiometric testing, training, and record-keeping requirements.

Regulation	Final Standard Issued
Asbestos	1972
Fourteen carcinogens	1974
Vinyl chloride	1974
Coke oven emissions	1974
Benzene	1978
1,2–dibromo-3-chloropropane (DBCP)	1978
Inorganic arsenic	1978
Cotton dust/cotton gins	1978
Acrylonitrile	1978
Lead	1978
Cancer policy	1980
Access to employee exposure and medical records	1980
–Modified	1988
Occupational noise exposure/hearing conservation	1981
Lead – reconsideration of respirator fit-testing requirements	1982
Coal tar pitch volatiles – modification of interpretation	1983
Hearing conservations reconsideration	1983
Hazard communication	1983
Ethylene oxide	1984

FIGURE 1. OSHA health standards issued from 1972 until 1984 (*Source:* Office of Technical Assistance, 1985)

The access to medical records standard provides employees and their authorized representatives access to medical and industrial hygiene monitoring records. The hazard communication standard, initially only applying to the manufacturing sector, is a very broad-based standard requiring containers of hazardous chemicals to be labeled. Chemical manufacturers must prepare material safety data sheets (MSDSs), provide the MSDSs to each purchaser of the material, and the purchaser must make them available to its employees. The cancer policy addressed future regulation of carcinogenic chemicals.

These standards resulted in new or revised requirements for 24 chemicals and for noise. The time frame for the development of these regulations (discussed above) did not include the time required to resolve legal challenges. The hearing conservation amendment, the benzene standard, and the requirements for one of the fourteen carcinogens were set aside by the courts (U.S. Congress, Office of Technical Assessment 1985).

Feasibility

From its very beginning, OSHA recognized the need to collect information concerning the technical feasibility of and costs associated with promulgating its standards in order to counter the arguments made by opponents of the regulations (U.S. Congress, Office of Technical Assistance 1985).

In its first full standard, OSHA proposed to lower the PEL for asbestos from 12 fibers per cubic centimeter (f/cc) to 5 f/cc in 1972, with a further lowering to 2 f/cc in 1976. The delayed effective date was "to allow employers to make the needed changes for coming into compliance." The Industrial Union Department of the American Federation of Labor--Congress of Industrial Organizations (AFL-CIO) brought suit challenging, among other issues, the use of economic factors in setting the limit. The Industrial Union Department argued that the phrase "to the extent feasible" in section 6(b)(5)[6] of the OSH Act should be interpreted to only mean whether or not the technology to control exposures was available. The District of Columbia Court of Appeals ruled that OSHA could take into account the costs of compliance with a new standard. The court said that a standard would be considered economically feasible if compliance with it would not threaten the viability of an industry as a whole, even if individual businesses might close.

Two subsequent decisions refined the two-pronged definition of feasibility. The AFL-CIO then challenged OSHA's decision to relax the requirements of the mechanical power press guarding standard because OSHA determined that it was infeasible to meet the requirements with current technology. The Third Circuit Court of Appeals upheld the decision, saying that while the OSH Act was a "technology-forcing piece of legislation," OSHA's determination that the standard was technologically infeasible was supported. In an industry challenge to the vinyl chloride standard, the Second Circuit Court of Appeals upheld a "technology-forcing" standard even if the technology necessary for compliance was not readily available. A standard would be considered infeasible only if meeting the standard was shown to be "clearly impossible."

President Gerald Ford issued the first Executive Order requiring inflationary impact statements during the same time frame as these decisions. OSHA came under pressure from the Council of Wage and Price Stability (CWPS) to base its decisions on cost-benefit analysis. The CWPS argued that a new standard on coke oven emissions was not worthwhile based on its economic analysis. CWPS also recommended OSHA consider allowing the use of respirators to comply with the standard.

Before the standard was finalized, Morton Corn[7] was appointed Assistant Secretary of Labor for OSHA (Figure 2 lists the persons who have served in this position since the Agency's beginning). Regarding cost-benefit analysis, he engaged in an in-depth review and concluded that the methodology for disease and death effects is very preliminary, and one can derive any desired answer. When OSHA issued the coke oven emissions standard, it rejected the use of cost-benefit analysis (MacLaury undated).

OSHA issued final standards for benzene, DBCP, arsenic, cotton dust, acrylonitrile, and lead in 1978. Four were challenged in the courts. The cases concerning benzene and cotton dust are particularly relevant

Asst. Secretary	Term
George Guenther	April 1971–January 1973
M. Chain Robbins (Acting)	January 1973–April 1973
John Stender	April 1973–July 1975
Bert Concklin and Marshall Miller (Acting)	July 1975–December 1975
Morton Corn	December 1975–January 1977
Bert Concklin (Acting)	January 1977–April 1977
Eula Bingham	April 1977–January 1981
David Zeigler (Acting)	January 1981–March 1981
Thorne G. Auchter	March 1981–April 1984
Patrick Tyson (Acting)	April 1984–July 1984
Robert A. Rowland (Recess appointment; never confirmed)	July 1984–July 1985
Patrick Tyson (Acting)	July 1985–May 1986
John A. Pendergrass	May 1986–March 1989
Alan C. McMillan (Acting)	April 1989–October 1989
Gerard F. Scannell	October 1989–January 1992
Dorothy L. Strunk (Acting)	January 1992–January 1993
David Zeigler (Acting)	January 1993–November 1993
Joseph A. Dear	November 1993–January 1997
Gregory R. Watchman (Acting)	January 1997–November 1997
Charles N. Jeffress	November 1997–January 2001
R. Davis Layne (Acting)	January 2001–August 2001
John L. Henshaw	August 2001–December 2004
Jonathan L. Snare (Acting)	January 2005–April 2006
Edwin G. Foulke, Jr.	April 2006–November 2008
No appointment	November 2008–December 2009
David Michaels	December 2009–Present

FIGURE 2. Occupational Safety & Health Administration Assistant Secretaries (Courtesy of the United States Department of Labor)

to OSHA's use of economic analysis (U.S. Congress, Office of Technical Assessment 1985).

Benzene – Significant Risk

The benzene PEL was initially set in 1971 as 10 ppm. OSHA issued a standard in 1978, which included the 1 ppm PEL and a 5 ppm ceiling limit. OSHA adopted 1 ppm based upon its "lowest feasible level" policy. Epidemiological studies indicated that human beings contracted leukemia at concentrations significantly below the 10 ppm PEL. OSHA said that higher exposures carried a greater risk and that the determination of a level that presents no hazard could not be determined. Thus, a safe level could not be determined. Therefore, OSHA felt prudent policy required that the lowest feasible level, 1 ppm, be selected in favor of employee protection (Corn 1992).

The petroleum industry challenged OSHA's more stringent standard for benzene exposure. The Court of Appeals for the Fifth Circuit ruled that the phrase "reasonably necessary or appropriate" contained in Section 3(8)[8] of the OSH Act meant OSHA could issue a more stringent regulation only if it estimated the risks addressed by the standard and determined that the benefits bore a "reasonable relationship" to the costs. The court invalidated the standard because it decided there was insufficient evidence that the new requirements would have any "discernible benefits" (U.S. Congress, Office of Technical Assessment 1985).

The decision was appealed to the Supreme Court, which voted 5 to 4 in 1980 to uphold the lower court's ruling, although it did not follow the same line of reasoning. Five separate opinions were issued by the court, but no single opinion had the support of more than four Justices. Justice Stevens presented the view of four of the Justices who voted to strike down the standard. In his opinion, the issue of whether the act required OSHA to follow a cost-benefit rule was not addressed and OSHA had not made a "threshold finding" that the risk presented by benzene exposure was "significant:"

> By empowering the Secretary to promulgate standards that are "reasonably necessary or appropriate to provide safe or healthful employment and places of employment," the Act implies that, before promulgating any standards, the Secretary must make a finding that the workplaces in question are not safe. But "safe" is not the equivalent of "risk-free" . . . a workplace can hardly be considered "unsafe" unless it threatens the workers with significant risk of harm.
>
> Therefore before he can promulgate any permanent health or safety standard, the Secretary is required to make a threshold finding that a place of employment is unsafe—in the sense that significant risks are present and can be eliminated or lessened by a change in practices.

The court ruled that the record before OSHA did not contain "substantial evidence" to support such a finding and that OSHA exceeded its authority in issuing a more stringent standard. The court did not rule on whether cost-benefit analysis was required in addition to this requirement to demonstrate "significant risk." It provided only limited guidance as to what was meant by "significant risk," and said in a footnote that OSHA's decisions concerning the acceptable level of risk "must necessarily be based on considerations of policy as well as empirically-verifiable facts."

The term "significant risk" does not appear in the language of the OSH Act. Justice Marshall wrote the dissenting opinion for the four judges who voted to uphold the standard. He argued that the plurality had improperly made its own findings about factual issues and had unfairly described OSHA's analysis. He said the requirement to demonstrate "significant risk" is a "fabrication bearing no connection with the acts or intentions of Congress and is based only on the plurality's solicitude for the welfare of regulated industries."

Cotton Dust – Significant Risk and Cost-Benefit Analysis

Cost-benefit and significant risk were taken up again in a case involving a more stringent standard for cotton dust exposure. OSHA issued a cotton dust standard in 1978 establishing various PELs for different textile operations. OSHA argued that the standard was designed to provide the highest degree of health and safety for workers, but it did not base exposure levels on a cost-benefit analysis. OSHA stated that:

> In setting an exposure limit for a substance, such as cotton dust, OSHA has concluded that it is inappropriate to substitute cost-benefit criteria for the legislatively determined directive of protection of all exposed employees against material impairment of health and bodily function (*Federal Register* 1978).

The textile industry representatives argued that OSHA had exceeded its statutory authority because it had not conducted a cost-benefit analysis or explicitly determined that the benefits of the standard justified the compliance costs. OSHA argued that the act did not require a cost-benefit analysis and it was required to issue the most protective standard where compliance was technologically and economically feasible once it determined that exposure to cotton dust presented a "significant risk" (U.S. Congress, Office of Technical Assessment 1985).

The United States Court of Appeals for the District of Columbia issued an opinion in 1979 upholding the standard, finding it to be economically and technically feasible. It said a formal cost-benefit analysis was not required. In 1981, the United States Supreme Court upheld the standard in a five to three decision. Justice Brennan, in the majority, said:

> In effect then, as the Court of Appeals held, Congress itself defined the basic relationship between costs and benefits by placing the "benefit" of worker health above all other considerations save that of making "attainment" of the "benefit" unachievable. Any standard based on balancing the costs and benefits by the Secretary that strikes a different balance than that struck by Congress would be inconsistent with the command set forth in Section 6(b)(5). Thus, cost-benefit analysis by OSHA is not required by the state because feasibility is (Corn 1992).

Standards Post–1984

From 1984 until the present, the time frame from start to completion of health standards has significantly increased due to administrative requirements imposed on OSHA and the complexity of risk assessment and cost-benefit analysis. Many of OSHA's health standards have resulted from petitions from labor organizations or public interest groups and from decisions mandated by the courts. Martonik commented on how quickly OSHA's first health standard, Asbestos, was developed, saying, "This timetable seems remark-

Regulation	Final Standard Issued
Asbestos standard revisions	1986
Formaldehyde	1987
Field sanitation	1987
Benzene	1987
Air contaminants update	1989
Chemical exposure in laboratories	1990
Cadmium	1992
MDA	1992
Asbestos standard revisions	1994
1,3–butadiene	1996
Methylene chloride	1997

FIGURE 3. OSHA health standards issued after 1984 (*Source:* USDOL-OSHA, Various and USDOL-OSHA, 1991)

able when compared with more recent OSHA rulemakings, which have taken from 4 years (e.g., benzene, arsenic) to more than 10 years (e.g., 1,3–butadiene, methylene chloride) from proposal to completion" (Martonik, Nash, and Grossman 2001).

The health standards that have been issued since 1984 appear in Figure 3.

1,3–Butadiene

The history of the 1, 3–butadiene standard is important because, as of the date of this writing, it is the only OSHA standard that was developed as a consensus standard. Interested stakeholders representing employers and employees worked together to outline a voluntary agreement that eventually led to the standard. The final standard was not challenged in court (OSHA 1997b).

The interest in 1,3–butadiene began when the National Toxicology Program released results on an animal study in 1983, indicating 1,3–butadiene (BD) caused cancer in rodents. OSHA and EPA jointly published a request for information in January 1984. Several labor unions[9] petitioned OSHA to issue an ETS of 1 ppm or less. OSHA denied the petitions on the grounds that it was evaluating health data to determine whether regulatory action was appropriate.

The EPA published an Advanced Notice of Public Rulemaking (ANPR) in May 1984 to announce the initiation of a regulatory action by the EPA to determine and implement the most effective means of controlling exposures to the chemical BD under the Toxic Substances Control Act (TSCA). EPA was working with OSHA because available evidence indicated that exposure to BD occurs primarily within the workplace. As a result of the information received, EPA designated BD as a probable human carcinogen and asked OSHA to consider regulating exposure in the workplace. In October 1986, OSHA published an ANPR and then published its proposed rule in August 1990. Hearings were held in 1991 and the comment period closed in 1992.

In the only mediated rule to the date of this writing (mediation had been tried, but failed, on the development of the coke oven and benzene standards), representatives[10] of the industry and labor groups involved in the production and use of BD developed and submitted a voluntary agreement that included provisions the industry/labor group wanted to have included in the standard. The agreement proposed a lower permissible exposure limit, additional provisions for exposure monitoring, and a program designed to reduce exposures below an action level.

In response to these recommendations, OSHA reopened the rule for further comment. The industry/labor group submitted examples of regulatory text that put their recommendations into specific requirements. OSHA adopted these recommendations and the standard became effective in 1997, thirteen years after the EPA-initiated rulemaking, despite cooperation from the regulated community and its employee representatives (OSHA 1997b).

Methylene Chloride

The background of the methylene chloride (MC) standard is illustrative of competing objectives between environmental protection and occupational health and how regulatory priorities can change.

OSHA established a PEL of 500 ppm, a ceiling limit of 1000 ppm, and a maximum peak of 2000 ppm for methylene chloride in 1971. In 1976, NIOSH recommended a reduction of the PEL to 75 ppm. The EPA classified methylene chloride as a probable human carcinogen in 1985. The Consumer Product Safety Commission (CPSC) and the Food and Drug Administration (FDA) took actions to ban the use of methylene chloride in consumer products and cosmetics (OSHA 1997a).

The International Union, United Automobile, Aerospace, and Agricultural Implement Workers (in short, the United Automobile Workers or UAW) petitioned OSHA in 1985 to publish a hazard alert,[11] issue an emergency temporary standard, and begin development of a permanent standard. In response to the scientific knowledge and the petition, OSHA issued guidelines in 1986 to control exposure. It denied the petition for an ETS, but began work on a permanent standard. OSHA issued an ANPR and began conducting site visits to assess how the standard would affect small business in response to comments received.

ACGIH lowered the TLV for methylene chloride to 50 ppm in 1988. The FDA banned the use of MC in cosmetic products in 1989, and in 1990 the CPSC required labels on products containing 1 percent or more of methylene chloride.

OSHA published a Notice of Public Rulemaking (NPRM) to address the risks of exposure to methylene chloride in late 1991, and a correction notice was published in January 1992. The proposal was turned over to an advisory committee and hearings were held.

In late 1990, the Clean Air Act Amendments (CAAA) were signed into law, requiring the phase-out of ozone-depleting chemicals, certain chlorofluorocarbons, and halons by 2000. The EPA was tasked to identify substitutes for these chemicals, and methylene chloride was one chemical being considered by the Agency. The CAAA also required EPA to address the residual risks of methylene chloride and other specified chemicals by establishing maximum achievable control technology (MACT) standards. In 1993, EPA issued a notice of proposed rulemaking on MACT rules for methylene chloride and other chemicals. In 1994, the EPA issued a final rule identifying methylene chloride as a substitute for ozone-depleting chemicals being phased out under the CAAA of 1990. The EPA found the use of methylene chloride acceptable in the production of flexible polyurethane foam and polyurethane integral skin foams, in metal cleaning, electronics cleaning, and precision cleaning, and in adhesives, coatings, and inks.

OSHA reopened the rulemaking several times as a result of EPA decisions and to receive comments on engineering controls and other matters. The standard was eventually issued on January 10, 1997.

Shortly thereafter, the UAW, the Halogenated Solvents Industry Alliance, Inc. (HSIA), and others filed a motion asking OSHA to reconsider three aspects of the standard. These three aspects were the decision not to include medical removal benefit protection, the start-up dates for engineering controls, and the decision allowing the use of respirators in some specific uses of methylene chloride

In response, OSHA decided to add some limited medical removal benefits.[12] OSHA also extended the final engineering control start-up date, which had been limited to employers with fewer than twenty employees. The extension now applied to employers in specific application groups who had 20 to 49 employees and to foam fabricators who had 20 to 149 employees (OSHA 1998a).

Asbestos

OSHA has issued 2 ETSs, 3 major notices of proposed rulemaking (NPRMs), 3 final standards, and 31 Federal Register notices related to asbestos regulation. These modifications introduced a framework for the content of toxic substance standards that followed. Medical removal protection was introduced in the 1972 standard. In the 1986 standard, the type of work performed, rather than type of business or product made, determined which of the two standards applied.

One innovation of the 1986 standard was the new approach for initial monitoring of employee asbestos exposure. Previously, every employer had to monitor each employee's asbestos exposure to make a determination for that employee. The 1986 standard allowed the use of "objective data"[13] for initial exposure determination. The use of objective data has been adopted in subsequent standards for cadmium, formaldehyde, 1,3–butadiene, and methylene chloride.

The 1994 standards differed from previous standards in many ways. Communication of hazards was required between employers, employees, and contractors. Mandatory work practices are specified for specific jobs and operations, regardless of exposure level (Martonik, Nash, and Grossman 2001).

OSHA initially regulated asbestos at a PEL of 12 f/cc when it adopted the ACGIH TLVs in 1971. In November 1971, shortly after the first asbestos PEL became effective, the Industrial Union Department of the AFL-CIO petitioned the agency for an ETS based upon a report (date not given) from Dr. Irving Selikoff and colleagues at Mt. Sinai Medical School (Martonik, Nash, and Grossman 2001). Dr. Selikoff recommended the enactment of a work practice standard to control exposure rather than a standard that simply set a PEL (OSHA 1994).

On December 7, 1971, OSHA issued an ETS that lowered the PEL to 5 f/cc instead of the 2 f/cc the union requested. The ETS did not include work practices or engineering controls, but did contain several specifications for respirator use. OSHA's first ETS was not challenged in court.

OSHA promulgated its first asbestos standard in only 183 days, issuing the new standard on June 7, 1972. It reduced the PEL to 5 f/cc immediately, with a PEL of 2 f/cc to become effective on July 1, 1976. The standard included additional provisions that were to serve as models for other health standards. These included methods of compliance, monitoring intervals, monitoring techniques, labels and warnings, and medical examinations.

The Industrial Union Department of the AFL-CIO petitioned for the court to review the standard, challenging the delay in requiring the lower PEL and objecting that the additional provisions were not sufficiently rigorous. The court upheld the standard, but asked OSHA for an explanation of the uniform application of 2 f/cc PEL in 1976 and the retention period for medical records.

OSHA published an NPRM in October 1975 to revise the asbestos standard and lower the PEL to 0.5 f/cc. Many comments were received in response to the notice and OSHA never adopted a standard based upon the 1975 proposal.

The International Association of Machinists and Aerospace Workers petitioned OSHA in June 1983 for a second ETS, asking that the PEL be reduced from 2 f/cc to 0.1 f/cc, work practices be modified, and other protective provisions be required in spite of exposure level. Sixteen other unions joined in this request.

In November 1983, OSHA granted the request and published an ETS that lowered the PEL to 0.5 f/cc. Included within the standard were numerical risk assessments as a result of the 1980 benzene decision discussed above. An industry trade association petitioned for judicial review and the ETS was vacated on March 7, 1984.

The next month, OSHA published an NPRM that included additional information. OSHA held hearings and in June 1986, issued two final standards—one applying to general industry and the second to construction operations. The approach OSHA took was unique in that the determination of which standard applied was based upon the work activities being conducted. Most activities involving previously installed materials were covered under the construction standard, including maintenance and repair. The construction standard also included specific work-practice requirements based upon the type of work being performed. Both standards included a PEL of 0.2 f/cc (*Federal Register* 1986).

The 1986 standards included a new approach for the initial monitoring of exposure. In previous health standards, employers were required to assess exposure through initial monitoring provisions. The asbestos standards allowed the use of "objective data"[14] in place of initial monitoring. This concept has been adopted in subsequent health standards.

Industry and labor petitioned the Court of Appeals for review of the standards. Labor argued that a lower PEL was both economically and technologically feasible. An industry trade association argued that the proposed PEL was neither.

The court upheld most of the provisions of the standards, but remanded some provisions back to OSHA for reconsideration. OSHA was asked to explain why a PEL of 0.1 f/cc was found to be infeasible and why certain provisions proposed by labor were not adopted.

OSHA next proposed revising the asbestos standard in June 1990 in response to the issues raised by the court. OSHA published two final standards on August 19, 1994, for construction and for general industry. OSHA lowered the PEL to 0.1 f/cc and required specific work practices for work activities regardless of exposure levels. The standard included provisions for hazard communications between building owners, employees, and contractors.

Industry and labor petitioned the court for judicial review. OSHA issued corrections to the 1994 rules that modified the provisions for working with roofing materials and exempted asbestos-containing asphalt roof coatings, cements, and mastics from the requirements of the standard.

PEL Update

Another novel approach was an attempt to update the PELs en masse when John Pendergrass[15] served as Assistant Secretary of Labor–Director of OSHA. As previously discussed, OSHA adopted approximately 400 PELs in 1971 for various substances that were largely based upon the 1968 ACGIH threshold limit values. Over the years, OSHA relied upon these values, although some of the guidelines from which the PELS were derived had been lowered.

To resolve this dilemma, OSHA undertook a major revision effort; in 1989, it published a final rule revising 212 existing exposure limits and establishing 164 new PELs. The new limits went into effect in September 1989, although engineering controls to comply with the limits were not required until January 1993. The use of respirators was allowed in the interim (de la Cruz and Sarvadi 1994).

Industry and labor groups challenged the proposed rule. The American Iron and Steel Institute argued that the agency did not demonstrate that the new limits would reduce or eliminate a significant risk or demonstrate the standard's economic and technological feasibility. Other arguments were made that the 7-month time frame in which the standard was developed did not allow for adequate review and comment. Other companies and trade associations were concerned about specific substances being regulated.

The AFL-CIO said that OSHA's evidentiary and factual findings were sound and lowered PELs should have been issued based upon these findings. The union objected to the short time frame the rulemaking took, the lack of specific monitoring or medical-surveillance requirements in the rule, and that the use of respirators was allowed for several years to comply with the reduced PELs instead of engineering controls.

In 1992, the 11th Circuit Court of Appeals vacated the entire air contaminants standard. The court found that OSHA could address multiple substances in one rulemaking, but that the agency did not sufficiently demonstrate the proposed changes were necessary or that they were economically or technologically feasible. This decision to vacate both the new and revised, more protective limits forced OSHA to return to the use of the original 1971 limits, still in effect today.

Additional Efforts to Update the PELs

After the court decision in 1992, a new effort to update PELs was begun by Organization Resources Counselors, Inc. (ORC) (now MERCER), the American Chemistry Council (ACC), and the American Petroleum Institute (API). The business supporters of a PEL update had believed that, while the court decision restricted OSHA's options in some crucial regards, it also left the door open to at least a few opportunities for expediting the process. The court had stated in its opinion that it had "no doubt that the agency acted with the best of intentions," and commenting further that "it may well be, as OSHA claims, that this was the only practical way of accomplishing a much needed revision of existing standards and of making major strides toward improving worker health and safety." Nevertheless, the 11th Circuit Court concluded that "before OSHA uses such an approach, it must get authorization from Congress. . . ."[16]

The ORC group opted to reform the existing OSHA rulemaking process rather than accepting the court's suggestion of enlisting Congress to step in. They advocated a new administrative approach to updating the limits, one that would have as its centerpiece an open and transparent forum for the collaborative collection and evaluation of scientific, technological, and economic data and information by OSHA and all affected stakeholders (White 2002).

The group proposed to establish a panel led by outside consultants, preferably one of the national laboratories, to help move the tedious PEL update process along. They met with then Assistant Secretary, Charles Jeffress, in 1999. At that point in time, Mr. Jeffress was in favor of changing the regulatory process to better deal with PELs. He also was considering asking Congress to open the Occupational Safety and Health Act (OSH Act) to help the agency speed up the regulatory process. The ORC group was opposed to opening the OSH Act.

The suggested process was that OSHA should:

- solicit, through a Federal Register notice, suggestions for chemicals to be considered, or develop a list of contaminants for the revision
- select a smaller list of high-priority substances
- choose a primary contractor, preferably a national laboratory, to manage the collection of information that will be reviewed by the agency
- assign staff members to act as liaisons to the committee (Speer 1999)

For a variety of reasons, this interindustry group was not successful in generating sufficient support for this new approach or for some alternative administrative process.

In 2001, the American Industrial Hygiene Association (AIHA) stepped forward to facilitate a new round of discussions among interested stakeholders and others about the subject of updating OSHA's PELs. The group included ORC, ACC, API, the AFL-CIO, and the United Auto Workers (UAW). After this group had developed a proposed process, meetings were held with the U.S. Chamber of Commerce, the National Association of Manufactures, and the National Federation of Independent Business. Other business groups participated as the process moved forward.

The proposed process would have involved a legislative process to open up the OSH Act for the sole purpose of updating the PELs, using current recommended exposure limits, including the TLVs, AIHA WEELs, NIOSH RELs, and German MAKs (Maximal Arbeits-platz-Konzentration). An advisory committee comprised of industrial hygienists, toxicologists, doctors, and other qualified persons would have been established under the Federal Advisory Committee Act, using a consensus process for its deliberations and recommendations. The deliberations of the committee would be open, transparent, and inclusive of all affected interests. Data and information would be solicited on science supporting the exposure limits, as well as technical and economic feasibility, so that the recommended limit would be supported. For this process to work, the evidentiary burden as to whether a proposed PEL was scientifically supported and capable of being achieved by affected industry sectors would have had to be less stringent than those under which OSHA was required to function. Only those contaminants where the supporting evidence was the strongest, most consistent, and least controversial would be considered. Once a PEL is recommended for issuance, there would be opportunity for further limited public input and, once issued in final form, a PEL should be subject to judicial review if challenged by adversely affected parties that participated in the process (White 2002).

Unfortunately, this effort also failed, but the proposed process was adopted by the California State OSHA in its update of PELs (Cal-OSHA 2011).

The current Assistant Secretary, David Michaels, is once again considering efforts to update at least some of the PELs. OSHA has asked for submissions of chemicals that should be considered, and over 100 have been submitted to the agency. OSHA has asked NIOSH to look at the list of priorities developed by an internal group, and OSHA may decide on a list for action. Another option under consideration would be to use the General Duty Clause when exposures over recommended exposure limits are found (OSHA 2010a).

Other Health Standards

Permissible Exposure Limits

The PELs adopted in 1971 appear in subpart Z of OSHA regulations, and are known as the Z-tables. These are expressed in terms of 8-hour time-weighted averages (OSHA 1971).

Most PELs are found in Table Z-1. Table Z-2 contains PELs for the substances listed in Figure 4.

Table Z-3 contains PELs for exposure to mineral dusts, including silica (crystalline and amorphous), silicates, graphite, coal dusts, and inert or nuisance dusts.

PELs for substance-specific standards are listed in Table 1. The more recent standards also include an action level (AL), which is generally half of the PEL. All PELs and ALs are calculated as 8-hour time-weighted averages. Certain requirements are triggered at exposure above the AL. Some standards also include excursion limits (EL) or ceiling limits (C)[17], which

Benzene	Formaldehyde
Beryllium and Beryllium compounds	Hydrogen Fluoride
Cadmium–dust and fumes	Hydrogen Sulfide
Carbon Disulfide	Methylene Chloride
Carbon Tetrachloride	Mercury
Chromic Acid and Chromates	Organo(alkyl)mercury
Ethylene Dibromide	Styrene
Ethylene Dichloride	Tetrachloroethylene
Fluoride as dust	Toluene
	Trichloroethylene

FIGURE 4. Substances regulated in Table Z-2 (*Source:* OSHA)

TABLE 1

Substances Regulated by Specific Standards

Material	Standard	PEL
Asbestos	1910.1001 1926.1001	0.1 f/cc
Vinyl chloride	1910.1017	1 ppm
Arsenic, inorganic	1910.1018	10 μg/M^3
Lead	1910.1025	50 μg/M^3
Cadmium	1910.1027	5 μg/M^3
Benzene	1910.1028	1 ppm
Coke oven emissions	1910.1029	150 μg/M^3
Cotton dust	1910.1043	200 μg/M^3
1,2-dibromo-3-chloropropane	1910.1044	1 ppm
Acrylonitrile	1910.1045	2 ppm
Ethylene oxide	1910.1047	1 ppm
Formaldehyde	1910.1048	0.75 ppm
Methylenedianaline	1910.1049	10 ppb
1,3–butadiene	1910.1051	1 ppm
Methylene chloride	1910.1051	25 ppm

(Source: OSHA 1991)

are higher than the PELs. The EL or C values are restricted by the time allowed for exposure and are not-to-exceed limits.

Ventilation Standard

The OSHA ventilation standard, 29 CFR 1910.94, applies to abrasive blasting; grinding, buffing, and polishing; and spray-finishing operations. Initially published in 1979, it was amended in 1993, 1996, and 1998.

Section A of the standard applies to operations where an abrasive is forcibly applied to a surface by pneumatic or hydraulic pressure or by centrifugal force. It is not applicable for steam blasting, steam cleaning, or other hydraulic cleaning methods that do not use abrasives.

Section B of the standard requires the use of enclosures and systems to remove dust, dirt, fumes, and gases generated through the grinding, polishing, or buffing of ferrous and nonferrous metals.

Section C of the standard applies to spray-finishing operations where organic or inorganic materials are used in dispersed form for deposit on surfaces to be coated, treated, or cleaned. Such methods of deposit may involve automatic, manual, or electrostatic deposition. The section does not apply to metal spraying or metallizing, dipping, flow coating, roller coating, tumbling, centrifuging, or spray washing and degreasing as conducted in self-contained washing and degreasing machines or systems (OSHA 1974a).

Respirator Standard

OSHA's original respirator standard, 29 CFR 1910.134, contained seven sections, the first six from ANSI Z88.2-1969, *Practices for Respiratory Protection*, and the seventh section from ANSI Standard K13.1-1969 (U.S. Congress, Office of Technical Assessment 1985). In late 1994, OSHA published a final rule revising the standard, which became effective in 1998.

The standard requires a Respiratory Protection Program that is managed by a qualified program administrator. Respirators must be certified by NIOSH. Pressure-demand supplied-air respirators must be used in atmospheres deemed to be immediately dangerous to life or health (IDLH) and respirators for non-IDLH atmospheres shall either be atmosphere-supplying or air-purifying with an end-of-service-life indicator.

Employees must undergo a medical examination before being assigned a respirator, and fit-testing must be performed prior to initial use and annually thereafter. The medical evaluation includes a mandatory questionnaire. The physician provides a written recommendation regarding the employee's ability to use the respirator. The recommendation should include any limitations on respirator use related to a medical condition the employee may have, or relating to the workplace conditions in which the respirator will be used, including whether or not the employee is medically able to use the respirator and any follow-up medical testing required.

The standard specifies the OSHA-accepted quantitative and qualitative fit-testing protocols. All respirators that rely on a mask-to-face seal need to be checked annually using either qualitative or quantitative methods to determine whether the mask provides an acceptable fit to a wearer. The qualitative fit-test procedures rely on a subjective sensation (taste, irritation, smell) of the respirator wearer to a particular test agent, while the quantitative test uses instruments to measure face-seal leakage. The relative workplace exposure level determines what constitutes an acceptable fit and which fit-test procedure is required. For negative-pressure air-purifying respirators, users may rely on either a qualitative or a quantitative fit-test procedure for exposure levels less than ten times the occupational exposure limit. Exposure levels greater than ten times the occupational exposure limit must use a quantitative fit-test procedure for these respirators. Fit-testing of tight-fitting, atmosphere-supplying respirators and tight-fitting, powered air-purifying respirators shall be accomplished by performing quantitative or qualitative fit-testing in the negative pressure mode.

Respirators must be maintained, cleaned, and disinfected. Respirator users shall be trained in specific provisions prior to initial use and annually thereafter (OSHA 1998b).

Noise and Hearing Conservation

The noise and hearing conservation standard, 29 CFR 1910.95, requires that engineering controls and work practices be used to reduce noise exposure below the levels published in its Table G-16, which appears as Table 2 in this chapter. If the controls and practices are insufficient to reduce levels to those in the table, personal protective equipment shall be used to do so (OSHA 1974c).

Monitoring shall be conducted when exposure levels are expected to meet or exceed an 85 dbA 8-hour, time-weighted average. A hearing conservation program is required for employees exposed at or above noise levels of 85 dbA, which includes audiometric testing, the use of hearing protectors, and employee training.

Noise

On October 19, 2010, OSHA issued a Federal Register notice requesting comments on its proposed official interpretation of workplace noise exposure controls. OSHA had planned to issue an interpretation of the term "feasible administrative or engineering controls," as used in the general industry and construction occupational noise exposure standards, and to amend its current enforcement policy to reflect the interpretation. For the purpose of enforcing compliance with these standards, the proposal states that *feasible* has its ordinary meaning of capable of being done.

OSHA's noise standards specify that feasible administrative or engineering controls must be used to reduce noise to acceptable levels and that personal protective equipment (PPE), such as ear plugs and ear muffs, must be used only as supplements when administrative or engineering controls are not completely effective. The preference for engineering and administrative controls over PPE is consistent with the approach taken in all of OSHA's health standards and reflects the fact that such controls are generally more effective. Under the agency's current enforcement policy, however, citations are issued by the agency for failure to use engineering and administrative controls only when they cost less than a hearing conservation program or when such equipment is ineffective.

OSHA currently proposes to interpret the term *feasible* in conformity with its ordinary meaning and with the safety and health purposes of the OSH Act. The Supreme Court has held that the term *feasible,* as used in the standard-setting provision of the Occupational Safety and Health Act, means capable of being done. The proposal aligns the interpretation of the noise standard with what the Court held and with OSHA's other standards that require feasible engineering controls.

TABLE 2

Permissible Noise Exposures*

Duration Per Day (in hours)	Sound level (dBA slow response)
8	90
6	92
4	95
3	97
2	100
1 1/2	102
1	105
1/2	10
1/4 or less	15

* When the daily noise exposure is composed of two or more periods of noise exposure of different levels, their combined effect should be considered, rather than the individual effect of each. If the sum of the following fractions: C(1)/T(1) + C(2)/T(2) C(n)/T(n) exceeds unity, then, the mixed exposure should be considered to exceed the limit value. Cn indicates the total time of exposure at a specified noise level, and Tn indicates the total time of exposure permitted at that level. Exposure to impulsive or impact noise should not exceed 140 dB peak sound-pressure level.

(Source: OSHA)

The agency intends to change its noise enforcement policy to authorize the issuing of citations requiring the use of administrative and engineering controls, when feasible, as indicated in the interpretation described in the Federal Register notice (OSHA 2010c).

In January 2011, OSHA withdrew this proposed interpretation. "Hearing loss caused by excessive noise levels remains a serious occupational health problem in this country," said Dr. David Michaels, Assistant Secretary of Labor for Occupational Safety and Health. "However, it is clear from the concerns raised about this proposal that addressing this problem requires much more public outreach and many more resources than we had originally anticipated. We are sensitive to the possible costs associated with improving worker protection and have decided to suspend work on this proposed modification while we study other approaches to abating workplace noise hazards" (OSHA 2011a).

Ionizing Radiation

Both OSHA and the Nuclear Regulatory Commission (NRC) have jurisdiction of U.S. facilities that manufacture or use nuclear materials. The two agencies have signed a memorandum of understanding that delineates these agencies' general areas of responsibility (OSHA 1989).

The NRC regulates radiation exposure under 10 CFR Part 20. The allowable exposure limits are found in Section 10.1201, Occupational Dose Limits. The annual dose limit for adults is 5 rem total effective dose (NRC 1991).

The OSHA *Ionizing Radiation Standard*, 29 CFR 1910.1096, sets forth the following limits of exposure that are for one calendar quarter of the year in its Table G-18, which appears as Table 3 in this chapter. A rem is a measure of the dose of any ionizing radiation to body tissue in terms of its estimated biological effect relative to a dose of 1 roentgen (r) of X-rays. The relation of the rem to other dose units depends upon the biological effect under consideration and upon the conditions for irradiation.

There are two exceptions to these limits. An employee may receive a dose to the whole body up to 3 rem in a calendar quarter or if his or her accumulated dose to the whole body does not exceed 5 ($N - 18$) rem, where N is the employee's age in years at his or her last birthday. The employer must maintain records that indicate the dose will not cause the individual to exceed the amount authorized.

The standard includes requirements for monitoring, provision of individual exposure monitoring devices, warning signs and labels, and an immediate evaluation warning signal.

The standard also requires that OSHA be immediately notified, for employees not under NRC jurisdiction, when an employee is exposed to a whole body dose of 25 rem (and other high doses) or when a release to the environment of a specified amount of radioactivity occurs. OSHA must also be notified within 24 hours when an employee is exposed to a whole body dose of 5 rem (and other doses).

OSHA Industrial Hygiene Inspections

Health inspections follow the same procedures as safety inspections, which are outlined in OSHA's *Field Inspection Reference Manual* (OSHA 2009). Industrial hygiene sampling procedures are found with the *OSHA Technical Manual* (OSHA 2008) and sampling and analytical procedures are located in a searchable database, maintained by the Salt Lake Technical Center, on the OSHA Web site (OSHA 2011b). Various manufacturers, such as SKC, Inc. (2011), provide a wealth of information on their Web sites and in the *NIOSH Pocket Guide* (NIOSH 2010).

OSHA compliance officers will generally perform air sampling to assess compliance with appropriate PELs. Once laboratory results are received, the compliance officer must consider sampling and analytical

TABLE 3

Allowable Quarterly Exposure

	Rems per Calendar Quarter
Whole body: Head and trunk, active blood-forming organs; lens of eyes, or gonads	1 1/4
Hands and forearms; feet and ankles	18 3/4
Skin of whole body	7 1/2

(Source: OSHA 1974b)

CASE STUDY

General and Health-Related Milestones from OSHA's Thirty-Five-Year Milestones
(USDOL, n.d.)

OSHA's mission is to send every worker home whole and healthy every day. Since the agency was created in 1971, workplace fatalities have been cut in half and occupational injury and illness rates have declined 40 percent. At the same time, U.S. employment has nearly doubled from 56 million workers at 3.5 million work sites to 105 million workers at nearly 6.9 million sites. The following milestones mark the agency's progress over the past 30 years in improving working environments for America's workforce.

December 29, 1970: President Richard M. Nixon signed the Occupational Safety and Health Act of 1970.

May 29, 1971: First standards adopted to provide baseline for safety and health protection in American workplaces.

January 17, 1972: OSHA Training Institute established to instruct OSHA inspectors and the public.

November–December, 1972: First states approved (South Carolina, Montana, and Oregon) to run their own OSHA programs.

May 20, 1975: Free consultation program created–nearly 400,000 businesses participated in past 25 years.

June 23, 1978: Cotton dust standard promulgated to protect 600,000 workers from byssinosis; cases of "brown lung" have declined from 12,000 to 700 in last 22 years.

January 20, 1978: Supreme Court decision setting staffing benchmarks for state plans to be "at least as effective" as federal OSHA.

April 12, 1978: New Directions grants program created to foster development of occupational safety and health training and education for employers and workers. (Nearly one million trained over 22 years.)

November 14, 1978: Lead standard published to reduce permissible exposures by three-quarters to protect 835,000 workers from damage to nervous, urinary, and reproductive systems. (Construction standard adopted in 1995.)

February 26, 1980: Supreme Court decision on Whirlpool affirming workers' rights to engage in safety and health-related activities.

May 23, 1980: Medical and exposure records standard finalized to permit worker and OSHA access to employer-maintained medical and toxic exposure records.

July 2, 1980: Supreme Court decision vacates OSHA's benzene standard, establishing the principle that OSHA standards must address and reduce "significant risks" to workers.

January 16, 1981: Electrical standards updated to simplify compliance and adopt a performance approach.

July 2, 1982: Voluntary Protection Programs created to recognize work sites with outstanding safety and health programs (nearly 700 sites currently participating).

November 25, 1983: Hazard communication standard promulgated to provide information and training and labeling of toxic materials for manufacturing employers and employees (Other industries added August 24, 1987).

November–December, 1984: First "final approvals" granted to state plans (Virgin Islands, Hawaii, and Alaska) giving them authority to operate with minimal oversight from OSHA.

April 1, 1986: First instance-by-instance penalties proposed against Union Carbide's plant in Institute, West Virginia, for egregious violations involving respiratory protection and injury and illness record keeping.

January 26, 1989: "Safety and Health Program Management Guidelines," voluntary guidelines for effective safety and health programs based on VPP experience, published.

March 6, 1989: Hazardous waste operations and emergency response standard promulgated to protect 1.75 million public- and private-sector workers exposed to toxic wastes from spills or at hazardous waste sites.

December 6, 1991: Occupational exposure to bloodborne pathogens standard published to prevent more than 9000 infections and 200 deaths per year, protecting 5.6 million workers against AIDS, hepatitis B, and other diseases.

October 1, 1992: Education Centers created to make OSHA training courses more available to employers, workers, and the public (12 centers have trained over 50,000 workers and employers to date.)

January 14, 1993: Permit-required confined space standard promulgated to prevent more than 50 deaths and more than 5000 serious injuries annually for 1.6 million workers who enter confined spaces at 240,000 workplaces each year.

February 1, 1993: Maine 200 program created to promote development of safety and health programs at companies with high numbers of injuries and illnesses.

June 27, 1994: First expert advisor software, GoCad, issued to assist employers in complying with OSHA's cadmium standard.

August 10, 1994: Asbestos standard updated to cut permissible exposures in half for nearly 4 million workers, preventing 42 cancer deaths annually.

September 4, 1995: Formal launch of OSHA's expanded Web page to provide OSHA standards and compliance assistance via the Internet.

June 6, 1996: Phone-fax complaint handling policy adopted to speed resolution of complaints of unsafe or unhealthful working conditions.

November 9, 1998: Strategic Partnership Program launched to improve workplace safety and health through national and local cooperative, voluntary agreements.

April 19, 1999: Site-Specific Targeting Program established to focus OSHA resources where most needed–on individual work sites with the highest injury and illness rates.

November 14, 2000: Ergonomics program standard promulgated to prevent 460,000 musculoskeletal disorders among more than 102 million workers at 6.1 million general industry work sites.

error in determining if a violation exists. The formulas used calculate the 95 percent confidence limits around the sample result and indicate the lower and upper confidence limits. These confidence limits are termed one-sided since the only concern is in being confident that the true exposure is on one side of the PEL (OSHA 2005).

Sampling and analytical errors (SAEs) have been developed for most materials. The current guidance is to contact the OSHA Salt Lake City Technical Center if no SAE is provided with sample results. OSHA personnel are to use the SAEs provided by an equipment manufacturer for detector tubes or direct-reading instruments.

Various examples are provided within the *OSHA Technical Manual* for single and multiple samples as well as for mixtures. The method used for one full-shift, continuous single sample is as follows:

1. Determine exposure severity (Y) by dividing the sampling result (X) by the PEL:

$$Y = X/PEL \quad (1)$$

2. Calculate the upper confidence limit:

$$UCL_{95\%} = Y + SAE \quad (2)$$

3. Calculate the lower confidence limit:

$$LCL_{95\%} = Y - SAE \quad (3)$$

These one-sided confidence limits are used to classify the sample result into one of three categories:

- in compliance—the result and the UCL both do not exceed the PEL
- in violation—the result and the LCL both exceed the PEL
- possible overexposure—the result does not exceed the PEL but the UCL does exceed the PEL, or the result exceeds the PEL but the LCL is below the PEL

In cases of possible overexposure, the compliance officer is directed to take additional samples. If further sampling is not conducted or the additional results fall into the same category, the compliance officer is directed to discuss the possible overexposure and encourage exposure reduction or additional sampling to determine if the exposure is below the PEL.

State Plans

The first state agency to deal with workplace safety was founded in 1867 in Massachusetts. By 1900, most heavily industrialized states had some form of legislation requiring employers to reduce or eliminate certain workplace hazards. Often a separate effort was being made by state health agencies to control disease (Ashford 1976).

The language of the OSH Act in Section 18 encouraged states to administer their own health and safety laws:

> (a) Nothing in this Act shall prevent any State agency or court from asserting jurisdiction under State law over any occupational safety or health issue with respect to which no standard is in effect under section 6.
>
> (b) Any State which, at any time, desires to assume responsibility for development and enforcement therein of occupational safety and health standards relating to any occupational safety or health issue with respect to which a Federal standard has been promulgated under section 6 shall submit a State plan for the development of such standards and their enforcement." (U.S. Congress 1970)

Alaska	New Mexico
Arizona	New York
California	North Carolina
Connecticut	Oregon
Hawaii	Puerto Rico
Indiana	South Carolina
Iowa	Tennessee
Kentucky	Utah
Maryland	Vermont
Michigan	Virgin Islands
Minnesota	Virginia
Nevada	Washington
New Jersey	Wyoming

FIGURE 5. Approved state occupational safety and health plans (*Source:* OSHA) *Note:* The plans for Connecticut, New Jersey, New York, and the Virgin Islands cover public-sector (state and local government) employment only.

The OSH Act goes on to say that the Secretary must approve a state plan if the plan:

> [P]rovides for the development and enforcement of safety and health standards relating to one or more safety or health issues, which standards (and the enforcement of which standards) are or will be at least as effective in providing safe and healthful employment and places of employment as the standards promulgated under Section 6 which relate to the same issues." (U.S. Congress 1970)

Currently, the states listed in Figure 5 have approved state plans.

Mine Safety and Health Administration

The Mine Safety and Health Administration (MSHA) is a separate federal agency within the Department of Labor, which develops standards and provides enforcement in mining operations. Prior to its formation, the Metal and Nonmetallic Mine Safety Act of 1966 provided for inspections and health and safety standards. In 1969, the Coal Mine Safety Act was enacted, which set mandatory health and safety standards, provided aid to states to improve compensation programs, and provided for research into coal workers' pneumoconiosis (black lung). The act also provided compensation to miners disabled by black lung or to their widows. In 1973, the responsibility for enforcing this act and the other Metal and Nonmetallic Mine Safety Act was transferred to a new Mining Enforcement and Safety Administration (Ashford 1976).

The Mine Safety and Health Administration was created by Public Law 95-164, the Federal Mine Safety and Health Act of 1977. Under the Act, the Secretary may "develop, promulgate, and revise as may be appropriate, improved mandatory health or safety standards for the protection of life and prevention of injuries in coal or other mines."

The agency has standards for exposure to respirable dust. The following MSHA standards adopted the 1973 TLVs by reference:

- 30 CFR, Part 56: Safety and health standards—surface metal and nonmetal mines
- 30 CFR, Part 57: Safety and health standards—underground metal and nonmetal mines

MSHA adopted the *Hazard Communication Standard* in 2000, which includes provisions similar to those contained in the OSHA standard. It amended its noise standard in 1999 to include hearing conservation provisions.

Environmental Protection Agency

The Environmental Protection Agency (EPA) was founded in 1970 during President Nixon's administration. Throughout the years, the EPA and OSHA have had many successes in working together while, in some cases, issues of jurisdiction have been troublesome.

The first jurisdictional battle occurred in the early 1970s concerning the regulation of pesticide exposure. OSHA issued a temporary emergency standard for 21 pesticides on May 1, 1973. The effective date of the standard was stayed by the court and the standard itself was vacated in 1974. Before the standard was vacated, two organizations and an individual filed suit against OSHA seeking a permanent standard. EPA issued its pesticide standard in 1974. The court decided that EPA had the authority for setting standards for pesticide exposure.

The EPA develops regulations under a number of statutes, including the Toxic Substances Control Act (TSCA), and recently began setting OELs using authority vested by that act (15 USC s/s 2601). Under Section 5 of the act, any person who plans to manufacture or import a new chemical substance must first submit notice to the EPA. The EPA conducts a risk assessment and, if the agency determines that the chemical may present an unreasonable risk of injury via inhalation exposure, it will set a new chemical exposure limit (NCEL). These limits are for informational purposes only and are not legally enforceable limits. However, chemical manufacturers are bound by a TSCA Section 5(e) Consent Order to follow the agency's recommendations. At the time of this writing, there are 35 limits posted on the EPA Web site with the title, Nonconfidential List of NCELs (EPA 2011).

OSHA at the End of the Twentieth Century

In 1991, The United Food and Commercial Workers Union (UCFW), along with the AFL-CIO and 29 other labor organizations, petitioned OSHA to publish an ETS on ergonomic hazards. OSHA concluded that there was not a sufficient basis to support issuance of an ETS, but agreed there was a need to initiate rulemaking to address ergonomic hazards. In 1992, OSHA published the ANPR requesting information for consideration in the development of an ergonomics standard. OSHA issued its first ergonomics guidelines in 1990 for meat-packing plants. In 1996, OSHA developed a strategy to address ergonomics through a four-pronged program including:

- training, education, and outreach activities
- study and analysis of the work-related hazards that lead to muscular-skeletal disorders
- enforcement
- rulemaking

OSHA's Transition into the Twenty-First Century

OSHA published the ergonomics program standard developed in the 1990s on November 14, 2000. The standard became effective on January 16, 2001 (OSHA 2000).

On March 6, 2001, the U.S. Senate passed a resolution of disapproval of the ergonomics program standard under the Congressional Review Act. The House of Representatives then passed a similar resolution the next day. President George W. Bush signed the resolution into law, forcing OSHA to remove the standard from the *Code of Federal Regulations* (OSHA 2001).

John Henshaw[18] was appointed as Assistant Secretary of OSHA in August 2001. OSHA's focus shifted further toward guidelines and compliance assistance in this century. OSHA has expanded the number of strategic partnerships with employers, associations, and labor unions, building a program that began in 1998.

Another focus is to expand the number of companies participating in Voluntary Protection Programs (VPP). VPP is an initiative to promote comprehensive safety and health programs through cooperative arrangements among management, labor, and OSHA (OSHA 2004).

Additional Focus in the Twentieth Century

In the mid-2000s, OSHA was forced to deal with Hurricane Katrina and the threat of pandemic flu. Edwin Foulke, named as head of OSHA in 2006, had formerly served on the Occupational Safety and Health Review Commission from 1990 to 1995. His focus was on what he termed the "balanced approach." This was comprised of three components: (1) strong, fair and effective enforcement; (2) outreach, education and compliance assistance; and (3) cooperative and voluntary programs (Foulke 2006).

The current Assistant Secretary, David Michaels, has outlined his focus for the agency. He wrote, "After forty years, OSHA needs a fundamental transformation in the way we address workplace hazards, and in our relationship to employers and workers" (Michaels 2010). He outlined the following ways in which OSHA would transform itself (Michaels 2010):

- strengthen enforcement, because some employers need incentives to do the right thing
- ensure that workers have a voice
- refocus and strengthen compliance assistance programs
- change workplace culture so that employers find and fix workplace hazards
- develop innovative approaches to addressing new and old hazards and improve intra-agency collaboration
- improve and modernize workplace injury and illness tracking
- strengthen OSHA's use of science
- strengthen state OSHA plans

Michaels has proposed the development of an injury and illness prevention program rule (I2P2). The Advisory Committee on Construction Safety and Health (ACCSH), sponsored by OSHA, held a series of stakeholder meetings in 2010 to solicit information and comments on a systematic process that would proactively address workplace safety and health hazards (ACCSH 2010). This initiative follows the lead of fifteen states, such as California and Minnesota, which have already implemented such programs.

Summary

Since its inception in 1970, OSHA has recognized the need to develop occupational health standards, with most of those developed under the 6(b) process directed to prevent occupational disease. However, OSHA has long exhibited a safety bias when it comes to enforcement. In 1973, the first full year of enforcement, OSHA conducted 48,409 inspections of which only 6.6 percent were health-related (Ashford 1976).

Not much was different in 2006, as OSHA planned to conduct 38,579 inspections, with the majority targeted to high-hazard industries (OSHA 2006). This was understandable in the beginning, when most of the initial compliance officers were predominantly safety-trained. OSHA employed 933 compliance officers in 1975, with a ratio of one industrial hygienist to five safety professionals (Ashford 1976). Today, OSHA employs approximately 1000 compliance officers, of whom approximately half are industrial hygienists.

The preamble to the 1972 asbestos standard, OSHA's first health standard, was only two pages long, while the preamble to the asbestos standard published in 1986 totaled 144 pages and the 1994 standard was 93 pages. It took only six months from the publication of the NPRM to publication of the final standard in 1972, but it was over four years from notice to final for the current asbestos standard.

The complexity of today's health standards, coupled with additional requirements imposed by the courts and various administrations, have led many to conclude that OSHA needs a more streamlined, standard-setting process. OSHA's own advisory committee, the National Committee on Occupational Safety and Health (NACOSH 2000) said in a 2000 report: ". . . the standards setting process is not working as intended in the Occupational Safety and Health Act of 1970."

NACOSH recommended a better system for managing the standards-setting process, more use of advisory committees and negotiated rulemaking, better partnerships with standards-setting bodies and professional associations, and specific actions by Congress and the Executive Branch. NACOSH suggested that Congress should give the Secretary authority to update the PELs without requiring Section 6 rulemaking and making it possible to issue and maintain Emergency Temporary Standards. NACOSH concluded that the Office of Management and Budget's role in reviewing OSHA standards should be limited to economic impact and paperwork burdens, not risk assessment, health effects, or means of control.

OSHA, in spite of its shortcomings and the roadblocks placed before it, has been instrumental in improving working conditions in this country and in educating the public on the importance of health and safety. Fatality and injury rates have dropped markedly. Although accurate statistics were not kept at the time, it is estimated that in 1970 around 14,000 workers were killed on the job. That number fell to approximately 4340 in 2009. At the same time, U.S. employment has almost doubled and now includes over 130 million workers at more than 7.2 million worksites. Since the passage of the OSH Act, the rate of reported serious workplace injuries and illnesses has declined from 11 per 100 workers in 1972 to 3.6 per 100 workers in 2009 (BLS 2010).

While OSHA does not deserve all the credit for these reductions, its standards and enforcement activities, as well as the growth in the safety and health profession that resulted after passage of the OSH Act, clearly have contributed to safer workplaces.

Endnotes

[1]Alice Hamilton is widely considered to be the founder of industrial medicine and industrial hygiene in the United States. She would later write her autobiography, which she began by saying, "Thirty-two years ago, in 1910, I went as a pioneer into a new, unexplored field of American medicine, the field of industrial disease" (Hamilton, 1995).

[2]Perkins served for 12 years and 3 months (longer than any other Secretary of Labor) and went on to serve as a member

of the Civil Service Commission. The Department of Labor headquarters was named for her in 1980 and she was inducted into the Labor Hall of Fame in 1988 (USDOL 2007a).

[3]OSHA PELs are found in the Z-tables (Z1, Z2, and Z3) within 29 CFR 1910.1000. In addition to an 8-hour PEL, some materials also have a short term exposure limit or ceiling limit.

[4]ACGIH® established the Threshold Limit Values for Chemical Substances (TLV®-CS) Committee in 1941. This group was charged with investigating, recommending, and annually reviewing exposure limits for chemical substances. It became a standing committee in 1944. Two years later, the organization adopted its first list of 148 exposure limits, then referred to as Maximum Allowable Concentrations. The term "Threshold Limit Values (TLVs®)" was introduced in 1956 (ACGIH 2007).

[5]The definition of "feasible" to a professional generally means engineering controls are available to reduce exposures below the PEL. However, its legal definition has been argued before the Occupational Safety and Health Review Commission (OSHRC) and the courts. There are two components of feasibility – technological and economic. It is OSHA's burden to establish that a control is both technologically and economically feasible. Once OSHA has shown a control is technologically feasible, the burden of producing evidence shifts to the employer, who may raise issues of economic feasibility. It is then up to OSHA to establish that the benefit of the engineering controls justifies their cost relative to other methods (OSHRC 1989).

[6]"The Secretary, in promulgating standards dealing with toxic materials or harmful physical agents under this subsection, shall set the standard which most adequately assures, to the extent feasible, on the basis of the best available evidence, that no employee will suffer material impairment of health or functional capacity even if such employee has regular exposure to the hazard dealt with by such standard for the period of his working life. Development of standards under this subsection shall be based upon research, demonstrations, experiments, and such other information as may be appropriate. In addition to the attainment of the highest degree of health and safety protection for the employee, other considerations shall be the latest available scientific data in the field, the feasibility of the standards, and experience gained under this and other health and safety laws. Whenever practicable, the standard promulgated shall be expressed in terms of objective criteria and of the performance desired."

[7]Morton Corn was the first industrial hygienist to head OSHA. He was professor of occupational health and chemical engineering at the University of Pittsburgh at the time of his appointment. Dr. Corn was appointed in 1975 by President Gerald Ford and served until 1977.

[8]"The term 'occupational safety and health standard' means a standard which requires conditions, or the adoption or use of one or more practices, means, methods, operations, or processes, reasonably necessary or appropriate to provide safe or healthful employment and places of employment."

[9]United Rubber, Cork, Linoleum and Plastic Workers of America (URW), the Oil, Chemical and Atomic Workers (OCAW), the International Chemical Workers Union (ICWU), and the American Federation of Labor and Congress of Industrial Organizations (AFL-CIO).

[10]The letter transmitting the agreement was signed by J.L. McGraw for the International Institute of Synthetic Rubber Producers (IISRP), Michael J. Wright for the United Steelworkers of America (USWA), and Michael Sprinker (CWU). The committee that worked on the issues also included Joseph Holtshouser of the Goodyear Tire and Rubber Company, Carolyn Phillips of the Shell Chemical Company, representing the Chemical Manufacturers Association, Robert Richmond of the Firestone Synthetic Rubber and Latex Company, and Louis Beliczky (formerly of the URW) and James L. Frederick of the SWA.

[11]OSHA has issued Hazard Alerts in the form of compliance directives and/or as guidance to employers. For an example, see http://www.osha.gov/pls/oshaweb/owadisp.show_document?p_table=DIRECTIVES&p_id=1799

[12]The benefits under this standard are, for each removal, an employer must maintain for up to six months the earnings, seniority, and other employment rights and benefits of the employee as though the employee had not been removed from MC exposure or transferred to a comparable job.

[13]The "objective data" must demonstrate that, under "the work conditions having the greatest potential for releasing asbestos," an activity coupled with a specific material, simply cannot result in excessive concentrations (OSHA, 1994b).

[14]Objective data is information which clearly demonstrates that employees cannot be exposed to asbestos at levels above the asbestos PELs. The employer is responsible for determining if and how this type of information can be developed for the particular conditions and work performed (OSHA 1999).

[15]John Pendergrass was the second industrial hygienist to serve as Assistant Secretary of Labor for OSHA. He was nominated by Ronald Reagan and served from 1986 to 1989. Mr. Pendergrass also served as President of the American Industrial Hygiene Association from 1974 to 1975. Prior to being appointed to OSHA, Mr. Pendergrass was employed by 3M Company.

[16]*AFL-CIO v. OSHA*, 965 F.2d 962 (11th Cir. 1992) (accessed August 21, 2011). http://bulk.resource.org/courts.gov/c/F2/965/965.F2d.962.89-7256.89-7274.89-7355.89-7430.89-7253.html

[17]Excursion limits and ceiling limits are short-term exposure limits which shall not be exceeded. They are averaged over a 15 to 30-minute time frame.

[18]John Henshaw is the third industrial hygienist to serve as Assistant Secretary of OSHA. He was appointed by President George W. Bush in 2001 and served until 2004. Prior to his appointment he had been employed at Monsanto and Solutia. Henshaw was president of the American Industrial Hygiene Association in 1990-1991.

REFERENCES

Advisory Committee on Construction Safety and Health (ACCSH). 2010. "Minutes of Dec 1-10 meeting." (accessed October 24, 2011) www.osha.gov/doc/accsh/meetingminutes/dec2010.html

American Conference of Governmental Industrial Hygienists (ACGIH) and American Industrial Hygiene Association (AIHA). 1963. *Respiratory Protection Devices Manual*. Michigan: Ann Arbor Publishers.

American Conference of Governmental Industrial Hygienists (ACGIH). 2007. *History* (retrieved April 11, 2011). www.acgih.org/about/history.htm

American National Standards Institute (ANSI). 1959. *American Standard Safety Code for Head, Eye, and Respiratory Protection*, Z88.2. Washington, D.C: ANSI.

Ashford, Nicholas. 1976. *Crisis in the Workplace*. Cambridge, Massachusetts: The MIT Press.

Brown, Ernest. 1940. "Industrial Hygiene and the Navy in National Defense." Presented at the Fifth Annual Meeting of the Air Hygiene Foundation of America, Inc., Pittsburgh, November 13, 1940.

Bureau of Labor Statistics (BLS). 2010. *Workplace Injuries and Illnesses* (accessed April 20, 2011) www.bls.gov/news.release/archives/osh_10212010.htm

California OSHA (Cal-OSHA), Division of Occupational Safety and Health (DOSH). 2011. "Policy and Procedure for the Advisory Committee Process for Permissible Exposure Limit (PEL); Updates to Title 8, Section 5155, Airborne Contaminants" (accessed April 16, 2011). www.dir.ca.gov/oshsb/aircontaminantsISOR.pdf

Corn, Jacqueline. 1992. *Response to Occupational Health Hazards, A Historical Perspective*. New York: John Wiley & Sons, Inc.

Corn, Jacqueline, and Jenifer Starr. 1987. "Historical Perspective on Asbestos: Polices and Protective Measures in World War II Shipbuilding." *American Journal of Industrial Medicine*, 11.

De la Cruz, Peter, and David Sarvadi. 1994. "OSHA PELs: Where Do We Go From Here?" *American Industrial Hygiene Association Journal* (October) 55:894–900.

Environmental Protection Agency (EPA). 2011. "Nonconfidential List of TSCA Section 5(e) New Chemical Exposure Limits" (accessed March 31, 2011) www.epa.gov/oppt/newchems/pubs/nceltbl.htm

Federal Register. 1978. "Occupational Exposure to Cotton Dust." 27379.

Federal Register. 1986. "Occupational Exposure to Asbestos, Tremolite, Anthophyllite, and Actinolite." 22612.

Foulke, Edwin. 2006. *OSHA: The Resource* (accessed April 11, 2011). www.osha.gov/pls/oshaweb/owadisp.show_document?p_table=SPEECHES&p_id=924

Hamilton, Alice. 1995. *Exploring the Dangerous Trades*. Beverly, Massachusetts: OEM Press.

MacLaury, Judson. 1981. *The Job Safety Law of 1970: Its Passage Was Perilous* (retrieved April 11, 2011). www.dol.gov/asp/programs/history/osha.htm

______. n.d. *Dunlop/Corn Administration, 1975–1977: Reform and Professionalization* (retrieved April 11, 2011). www.dol.gov/oasam/programs/history/osha13corn.htm

Martonik, John, Edith Nash, and Elizabeth Grossman. 2001. "The History of OSHA's Asbestos Rulemakings and Some Distinctive Approaches that They Introduced for Regulating Occupational Exposure to Toxic Substances." *American Industrial Hygiene Association Journal* (62):208–217.

Michaels, David. 2010. *OSHA at Forty: New Challenges and New Directions* (accessed April 16, 2011) orc-dc.com/files/2010/3649/osha_at_forty_new_challenges_and_new_directions__94762.pdf

Mine Safety and Health Administration. 2007. *Title 30 Code of Federal Regulations* (retrieved April 11, 2011). www.msha.gov/30cfr/0.0.htm

Mine Safety Appliances Company. 2007. *Catalog* (retrieved April 11, 2011). www.msanorthamerica.com/catalog/

National Advisory Committee on Occupational Safety and Health. 2000. *Report and Recommendations Related to OSHA's Standards Development Process*. www.osha.gov/dop/nacosh/nreport.html#ISSUES

National Institute of Occupational Safety and Health (NIOSH). 1973. *The Industrial Environment—Its Evaluation and Control*. Washington, D.C.: U.S. Government Printing Office.

______. 2006. *Alice Hamilton History* (retrieved April 11, 2011). www.cdc.gov/niosh/hamilton/HamHist.html

______. 2010. *NIOSH Pocket Guide to Chemical Hazards* (accessed March 31, 2011) www.cdc.gov/niosh/npg/

Nuclear Regulatory Commission. 1991. Occupational *Dose Limits for Adults*. Part 20.1201 (retrieved April 11, 2011). www.nrc.gov/reading-rm/doc-collections/cfr/part020/part020-1201.html

Occupational Safety and Health Administration (OSHA). 1971. *Air Contaminants* (retrieved April 11, 2011). www.osha.gov/pls/oshaweb/owadisp.show_document?p_table=STANDARDS&p_id=9991

______. 1974a. *Ventilation* (retrieved April 11, 2011). www.osha.gov/pls/oshaweb/owadisp.show_document?p_table=STANDARDS&p_id=9734

______. 1974b. 29 CFR 1910.1096, *Ionizing Radiation* (retrieved April 11, 2011). www.osha.gov/pls/oshaweb/owadisp.show_document?p_table=STANDARDS&p_id=10098

______. 1974c. 29 CFR 1910.95, *Occupational Noise Exposure* (retrieved April 11, 2011). www.osha.gov/pls/oshaweb/owadisp.show_document?p_table=STANDARDS&p_id=9735

______. 1983. *Hazardous Exposures to Pesticides May Be Cited Under the General Duty Clause* (retrieved April 11, 2011). www.osha.gov/pls/oshaweb/owadisp.show_document?p_table=INTERPRETATIONS&p_id=19104

______. 1989. *CPL 02-00-086 - CPL 2.86 - Memorandum of Understanding Between the OSHA and the U.S. Nuclear Regulatory Commission* (retrieved April 11,2011). www.osha.gov/pls/oshaweb/owadisp.show_document?p_table=DIRECTIVES&p_id=1658

______. 1991. *Hearing Report on OSHA Reform Senate Labor and Human Resources Committee, October 29, 1991* (retrieved April 11, 2011). www.osha.gov/pls/oshaweb/owadisp.show_document?p_table=INTERPRETATIONS&p_id=20443

______. 1993. *Compliance and Enforcement Activities Affected by the PELs Decision* (retrieved April 11, 2011). www.osha.gov/pls/oshaweb/owadisp.show_document?p_table=INTERPRETATIONS&p_id=21220

______. 2009. *Field Operations Manual.* (accessed April 16, 2011) www.osha.gov/OshDoc/Directive_pdf/CPL_02-00-148.pdf

______. 1994. *Occupational Exposure to Asbestos* (retrieved April 11, 2011). www.osha.gov/pls/oshaweb/owasrch.search_form?p_doc_type=PREAMBLES&p_toc_level=1&p_keyvalue=Asbestos~(1994~~~Amended)

______. 1997a. *Occupational Exposure to Methylene Chloride* (retrieved April 11, 2011). www.osha.gov/pls/oshaweb/owasrch.search_form?p_doc_type=PREAMBLES&p_toc_level=1&p_keyvalue=Methylene~Chloride

______. 1997b. *1,3–Butadiene* (retrieved April 11, 2011). www.osha.gov/pls/oshaweb/owadisp.show_document?p_table=STANDARDS&p_id=10087

______. 1998a. *Methylene Chloride; Final Rule* (retrieved April 11, 2011). www.osha.gov/pls/oshaweb/owadisp.show_document?p_table=FEDERAL_REGISTER&p_id=13852

______. 1998b. *Respiratory Protection* (retrieved April 11, 2011). www.osha.gov/pls/oshaweb/owadisp.show_document?p_table=STANDARDS&p_id=12716

______. 1999. *Asbestos: Notification Requirements and Exposure Monitoring* (retrieved April 11, 2011). www.osha.gov/pls/oshaweb/owadisp.show_document?p_table=INTERPRETATIONS&p_id=22740

______. 2000. *Ergonomics Program* (retrieved April 11, 2011). www.osha.gov/pls/oshaweb/owadisp.show_document?p_table=FEDERAL_REGISTER&p_id=16305

______. 2001. *Ergonomics Program* (retrieved April 11, 2011). www.osha.gov/pls/oshaweb/owadisp.show_document?p_table=FEDERAL_REGISTER&p_id=16515

______. 2004. *OSHA's Budget Request for Fiscal Year 2005* (retrieved April 11, 2011). www.osha.gov/pls/oshaweb/owadisp.show_document?p_table=TESTIMONIES&p_id=348

______. 2005. *Chemical Sampling Information* (retrieved April 11, 2011). www.osha.gov/dts/chemicalsampling/toc/toc_chemsamp.html

______. 2006. *OSHA Enforcement: Effective, Focused, and Consistent* (retrieved April 11, 2011). www.osha.gov/

______. 2007. *Health Standards* (retrieved April 11, 2011). www.osha.gov/comp-links.html

______. 2007. *OSHA—A History of its First Thirteen Years, 1971-1984, U.S. Department of Labor Office of the Assistant Secretary for Policy* (retrieved April 11, 2011). www.dol.gov/asp/programs/history/mono-osha13introtoc.htm

______. 2008. *Technical Manual* (accessed March 31, 2011) www.osha.gov/dts/osta/otm/otm_ii/otm_ii_1.html

______. 2010a. "Input received through Web Forum for identifying hazardous chemicals for which OSHA should develop exposure reduction strategies" (accessed April 16, 2011). www.osha.gov/dsg/PEL-forum-comments2010.html

______. 2010b. "Injury and Illness Prevention Program." *Federal Register*, Volume 75, Number 85, May 4, 2010.

______. 2010c. "Interpretation of OSHA's Provisions for Feasible Administrative of Engineering Controls of Occupational Noise." *Federal Register*, Volume 75, Number 201, October 19, 2010. http://frwebgate1.access.gpo.gov/cgi-bin/TEXTgate.cgi?WAISdocID=VWmECb/0/1/0&WAISaction=retrieve

______. 2011a. "U.S. Department of Labor's OSHA withdraws proposed interpretation on occupational noise" (accessed April 20, 2011) www.osha.gov/pls/oshaweb/owadisp.show_document?p_table=NEWS_RELEASES&p_id=19119

______. 2011b. "Sampling and Analytical Methods" (accessed on March 31, 2011) www.osha.gov/dts/sltc/methods/index.html

Showlater, David. 1972. *How to Make the OSHA–1970 Work for You.* Ann Arbor, Michigan: Ann Arbor Science Publishers.

SKC, Inc. 2011. *Sampling and Analytical Methods* (accessed March 31, 2011) www.skcinc.com/OSHA-NIOSH/default.asp

Speer, Rebecca. 1999. *Industry Proposes PELs Revision.* (accessed October 24, 2011). www.ehstoday.com/news/ehs_imp_32806

U.S. Congress, Office of Technical Assessment. 1985. *Preventing Illness and Injury in the Workplace*, OTA–H-256. Washington, D.C.: U.S. Government Printing Office.

U.S. Congress. 1970. Occupational Safety and Health Act of 1970, Public Law 91-596.

______. 1977. Federal Mine Safety & Health Act of 1977, Public Law 91-173.

U.S. Department of Labor. 2007a. *Frances Perkins* (retrieved April 11, 2011). www.dol.gov/oasam/programs/history/perkins.htm

______. 2007b. *George Guenther Administration, 1971–1973: A Closely Watched Start-up* (retrieved April 11, 2011). www.dol.gov/oasam/programs/history/osha13guenther.htm

______. 2007c. *OSHA 35-Year Milestones* (retrieved April 11, 2011). www.osha.gov/as/opa/osha30yearmilestones.html

______. 2007d. *State Occupational Safety and Health Plans* (retrieved April 11, 2011). www.osha.gov/dcsp/osp/index.html

White, Frank. 2002. "Statement of Frank A. White, Vice-President, Organization Resources Counselors, Inc. before the Subcommittee of Workforce Protections Committee on Education and the Workforce." Testimony before the U. S. House of Representatives, July 16, 2001 (accessed April 16, 2011) http://archives.republicans.edlabor.house.gov/archive/hearings/107th/wp/oshapel71602/white.htm

2

GENERAL PRINCIPLES

Susan Arnold, Deborah Imel Nelson,
and Sheryl A. Milz

LEARNING OBJECTIVES

- Define and contrast risk, risk assessment, risk management, and risk communication.
- Be able to describe in general terms how a risk assessment is conducted.
- Learn how to determine the need for risk management.
- Compare the risk assessment/risk management model with the "anticipation, recognition, evaluation, and control" model for industrial hygiene.
- Define exposure assessment, and describe its role in the occupational and environmental health and safety (OEHS) program.
- Recognize the difference between compliance exposure assessment and comprehensive exposure assessment, and explain why comprehensive exposure assessment is preferred.
- Learn basic methodologies for determining concentrations of airborne contaminants.

THE DEFINING ROLES of workplace safety and health professionals can be described in terms of risk: assessing the risks posed by workplace hazards, evaluating the acceptability of the risks, and managing the risks, while engaging in constant risk communication with affected parties (see Figure 1). Hazards—whether chemical, physical, biological, or mechanical—are the sources of risk. *Risk* can be defined as the probability and magnitude of harm resulting from exposure to hazards. *Risk assessment* is a matter of characterizing—qualitatively, semiquantitatively, or quantitatively[1]—the probability and magnitude of harm. We often speak of the risk of exposure to a chemical hazard as a function of the magnitude, duration, and frequency of exposure, and of the toxicity of the chemical. If there is no exposure to the chemical, then technically there is no risk (although one must always keep the *potential* of exposure in mind).

Risk assessment is followed by a judgment of the acceptability of the risk. Many scientific and nonscientific factors influence the perceived acceptability of a risk and resulting risk-management decisions, including:

- toxicological profile of a chemical (Are the effects acute and minimal? Is it an irritant or are the effects dreaded and insidious? Does it cause a reproductive health effect?)
- magnitude of estimated risk, dimensions of the risk (see Table 1), and potential public reactions
- availability of human, technical, and financial resources to conduct risk assessment/management (e.g., it might be less expensive to initiate risk management than to conduct a detailed risk assessment)
- estimated uncertainty/error of risk-assessment methods (a high degree of uncertainty would argue for more conservative risk-management methods)

FIGURE 1. Relationship of risk functions (Nelson 2008)

- social/cultural/moral/ethical/political factors (e.g., acceptable risk levels may be lower for children than for adults)
- risk perception of stakeholders/special interest groups
- time available for analysis (if time is limited, analysts may recommend proceeding directly to risk management)
- efficacy of risk-management methods (e.g., if a simple, inexpensive, and effective control method is available, it might be instituted immediately)
- policy decisions (e.g., acceptance of the Precautionary Principle in Europe may lead to more risk-management efforts) (Bales 2006)
- applicable laws or regulations (if an exposure level is below regulated levels, it might be deemed acceptable)

Determining how much risk is acceptable is a very difficult question to answer, because it cannot be determined scientifically. It has been stated that the "best level of risk is zero, if it is free, but it never is" (Caplan and Lynch 1996). Every stakeholder may have a different answer, and nobody is wrong. For example, consider a hazardous chemical used in a manufacturing plant upwind from an elementary school. As the exposure to this chemical (which is a function of both concentration and length of exposure) increases, the risk of experiencing adverse health effects goes up. A small amount of the chemical is routinely released from the facility; however, the downwind ambient concentration is orders of magnitude lower than the concentration inside the facility. What is the acceptable concentration in the plant, and in the elementary school? The dimensions of risk shown in Table 1 suggest that the acceptable concentration in the workplace is higher, because of the following:

- voluntariness (theoretically, the workers could quit their jobs)
- controllability (workers could use respirators)
- benefits and equity (workers are eligible to receive compensation)
- institutional trust (workers know and have a higher level of trust in the employer)
- understanding (workers routinely handle this chemical)
- characteristics of the potential victims (workers are adults and are typically healthier than the average population) (McMichael 1976)

The plant workers are thus more likely to tolerate higher concentrations of the chemical than would be

TABLE 1

Selected Factors Affecting Risk Perception in the Workplace

Factor	Conditions Associated with Lower Risk Perception	Conditions Associated with Higher Risk Perception
Voluntariness	Voluntary	Involuntary
Controllability	Controllable	Uncontrollable
Benefits	Clear benefits	Little or no benefit
Equity	Fair distribution of risks	Unfair distribution of risks
Origin	Natural	Man-made
Institutional trust	Trusted source	Untrusted source
Catastrophic potential	Limited	Widespread
Understanding	Familiar	Not understood
Victims	Adults	Children

(Adapted from Fischoff et al. 1981; Covello et al. 1988)

considered acceptable in the school. The children's exposure is not voluntary or controllable; they receive no benefits; biologically, children are a more sensitive population; they are children rather than adults; they (or their parents) may not trust the manufacturer or understand the chemical; and they (or their parents) may have learned of catastrophic chemical releases through the media. The worker has a higher level of understanding and is generally more aware of when the exposure is taking place and thus is able to take appropriate protection measures. A member of the community is less likely to know when exposure occurs and is, therefore, less likely to find the exposure acceptable.

As illustrated by this example, the level of acceptable risk varies in environmental and occupational settings. Because of such factors as voluntariness and equity, workers tend to accept higher levels of risk in the workplace, ranging from 1 incident per 10,000 workers exposed up to 1 incident per 1000 workers exposed (often expressed as 10^{-4} to 10^{-3}). In contrast, in environmental settings, acceptable risks range from 1 incident per 1,000,000 people exposed up to 1 incident per 100,000 people exposed (often expressed as 10^{-6} to 10^{-5}). In other words, the acceptable risk in an occupational setting ranges from 10 to 1000 times higher than for the general public.

These levels of acceptable risk may be used by the Environmental Protection Agency (EPA) and the Occupational Safety and Health Administration (OSHA) in establishing acceptable concentrations—for residual soil concentrations of contaminants at hazardous waste site clean ups, for example. National Ambient Air Quality Standards (NAAQS) are established by the EPA to protect the public health, including sensitive populations such as asthmatics, children, and the elderly (EPA 2006a). The OSHA law was written "to assure so far as possible every working man and woman in the Nation safe and healthful working conditions" (OSH Act 1970). The permissible exposure limits (PELs) were adopted from several sources, including the 1968 American Congress of Governmental Industrial Hygienists (ACGIH) Threshold Limit Values® (OSHA 1989). TLVs® represent "conditions under which it is believed that nearly all workers may be repeatedly exposed day after day without adverse health effects" (ACGIH 2005). Contrasting selected NAAQS with OSHA PELs indicates this trend of establishing acceptable occupational concentrations at higher values than acceptable environmental values (see Table 2).

TABLE 2

Comparison of OSHA PELs and EPA NAAQS

Contaminant	OSHA PEL*	EPA NAAQS
CO (carbon monoxide)	50 ppm, 8-hour time-weighted average	9 ppm, 8-hour time-weighted average
O_3 (ozone)	0.1 ppm, 8-hour time-weighted average	0.08 ppm, 8-hour time-weighted average
PM_{10} (particulate matter less than 10 μg in diameter)	5 mg/m^3 (respirable nuisance dust)	150 μg/mg^3, 24-hour time-weighted average
SO_x (sulfur oxides)	SO_2: 5 ppm, 8-hour time-weighted average	0.03 ppm, annual arithmetic average
Pb (lead)	50 μg/m^3, 8-hour time-weighted average	1.5 μg/m^3, quarterly average

*ppm = parts per million parts; 1 ppm = 0.0001% concentration by volume. mg/m^3 = 1 milligram contaminant per cubic meter of air. 1000 μg/m^3 = 1000 micrograms per cubic meter = 1 mg/m^3.

(*Sources:* EPA 2006a; OSHA 1971)

Based on the acceptability of a risk, a decision may be made to do nothing, to conduct further risk assessment, or to implement risk-management measures. *Risk management* is prevention or reduction of risk in a scientifically sound, cost-effective, acceptable manner.

Risk communication completes the risk-assessment and risk-management functions. At its simplest, *risk communication* is a two-way dialogue between risk managers and those who are potentially affected by a risk. Other stakeholders, such as the general public, workers' families, risk assessors, and other experts may also be involved. Risk communication is a necessary and powerful component of the risk function, because people are much more likely to *buy in* to a decision in which they have participated.

Making Risk Decisions

These four risk functions—assessment, evaluation, management, and communication—can be neatly separated on paper. The risk assessor, guided primarily by scientific factors and influenced by values, identifies and defines the risk in qualitative or quantitative terms; the risk evaluator, strongly influenced by values, determines how acceptable the risk is; the risk manager, guided primarily by values and influenced by science, does what is necessary to eliminate or reduce that risk to the acceptable level; and the risk communicator maintains a constant dialogue among all stakeholders. However, in reality, the OEHS professional may be wearing all four hats at once. How does he/she balance the potentially conflicting values guiding the different aspects of occupational health risk decision making?[2] Fortunately, there are several risk decision-making models available to OEHS professionals.

The traditional approach in the United States for controlling worker exposure to hazardous airborne chemicals has been to compare the results of an exposure assessment to the occupational exposure limits (OELs).[3] The U.S. Department of Labor PELs are mandatory concentration limits, mostly in the form of 8-hour time-weighted average concentrations (OSHA 1971). The ACGIH® annually publishes lists of recommended OELs, including the threshold limit values (TLVs®) (ACGIH® 2005). Other sources of OELs include the American Industrial Hygiene Association (AIHA) Emergency Response Planning Guidelines Series (ERPGs) and the Workplace Environmental Exposure Level Guide Series (WEELS) (AIHA 2002), the National Institute for Occupational Safety and Health (NIOSH) recommended exposure limits (RELs) (NIOSH 2005), EPA acute exposure guideline levels (AEGLs) [EPA undated(a)], and OELs established by corporations and organizations for their own internal use.

Risk decision makers usually do not have the data, time, or resources to conduct a full quantitative or even semiquantitative risk assessment for all scenarios, and they often rely on experience and professional judgment. For example, he or she might observe a well-ventilated workroom where a small quantity of a nonvolatile, low toxicity chemical is occasionally used, and conclude that the risk level is very low. Simple matrices can be used to rank dissimilar risks, and to document the decision-making process. These are qualitative risk-assessment processes that do not necessarily use numbers, but nonetheless can provide valuable information to risk decision makers.

Figure 2 is based on a matrix developed by a major multinational corporation. The matrix is based on severity of impact and probability of event occurrence. The matrix is easy to use and communicate to stakeholders, and it has the advantage of allowing different types of impacts to be considered. To illustrate the use of this matrix, consider the removal of leaking underground storage tanks from service stations, a common occurrence in the 1990s. These tanks were often too large to remove from the site in one piece, and were cut with welding torches into several pieces prior to removal. In several instances, the welding torches sparked explosions of residual fuel in the tanks. From mid-1984 to mid-1990, at least nine deaths and seven injuries requiring hospitalization directly resulting from underground tank-removal operations were reported to OSHA. An additional 38 deaths and 32 injuries requiring hospitalization resulted from activities around tanks not specified to be underground were also reported (Nelson 1991). How can the hypothetical tank-removal service, Yankee Tank Yank, Inc. (YTY), use this information to determine the appropriate level of risk management for explosion of fuel tanks during the removal process?

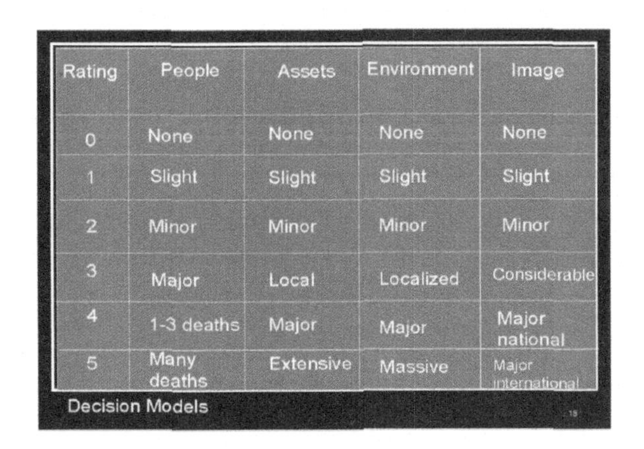

Rating	People	Assets	Environment	Image
0	None	None	None	None
1	Slight	Slight	Slight	Slight
2	Minor	Minor	Minor	Minor
3	Major	Local	Localized	Considerable
4	1-3 deaths	Major	Major	Major national
5	Many deaths	Extensive	Massive	Major international

Decision Models

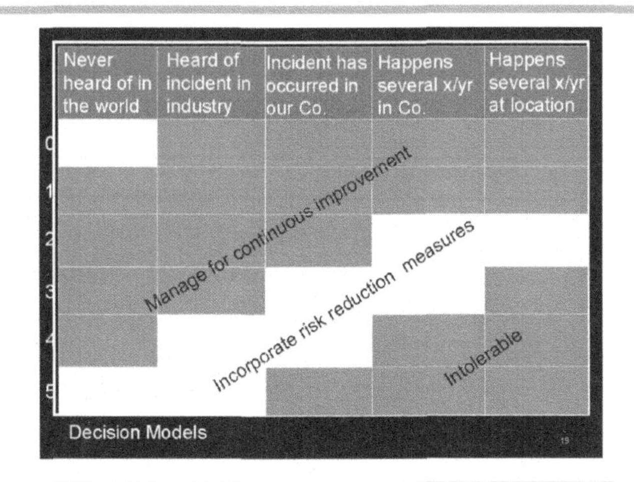

FIGURE 2. A simple risk decision-making matrix (Adapted from Nelson et al. 2003)

The rating on severity of impact will be examined first, followed by the rating of probability. The impact ratings of an explosion with respect to people, assets, the environment, and image range from 0 to 5. An explosion could kill one or more people, resulting in a rating of 4. The impact on assets and the environment would be local, for a rating of 3. YTY's image would potentially suffer at the national level, for a rating of 4. The highest impact rating is 4, resulting from impact on people and on image. To consider probability, move across the matrix to the right. Deaths resulting from tank explosions have occurred in the industry, but not at YTY. Crossing the row and the column leads to a white box labeled "Incorporate risk reduction measures." YTY should therefore make timely and significant efforts to protect their people, their assets, the environment, and their image, but not on the urgent basis implied by an "Intolerable" rating.

Control banding is a semiquantitative, matrix-based approach. The best developed and tested version was developed by the UK Health and Safety Executive (HSE) to help small and medium enterprises (SME) comply with the Control of Substances Hazardous to Health (COSHH) regulations, which require that a risk assessment be conducted in all workplaces (see Health and Safety Executive undated).

COSHH Essentials has roots in earlier efforts of the pharmaceutical and chemical industries to improve workplace health and safety, particularly when workers were handling little-known chemicals. These earlier approaches based control strategies on the toxicity of a chemical. The HSE added the dimension of exposure assessment, using the quantity of the chemical in use, along with "dustiness" or volatility, as surrogates of employee exposure. Please note that COSHH Essentials is not synonymous with *control banding;* other versions of control banding have been designed by other countries and by private companies.

The first step of the analysis is to obtain the information that will be used to determine the necessary level of control for a specific activity with a chemical:

a. a measure of its toxicity
b. an indication of its volatility (for liquids) or dustiness (for solids)
c. the amount of the chemical in use

In the COSHH Essentials system, the European risk phrases, or R-phrases, for human health effects are used as a surrogate for toxicity. These phrases, such as *harmful by inhalation* or *toxic by inhalation,* have been grouped in Category A (irritants) up to Category D (very toxic). (Category E consists of carcinogens, mutagens, and reproductive hazards, and is reserved for use only by occupational health experts.) The volatility of liquids, or the dustiness of solids, indicates the potential of the compound to become airborne. The amount of the material in use (e.g., material being transferred from one container to another) is related to the quantity that could become airborne.

This information is entered into a matrix that yields the appropriate level of control (see Figure 3). Each of the four matrices is keyed to a category, ranging from A–D. Columns in each table relate to volatility or dustiness, and rows refer to the amount in use. The numbers in each cell of the matrix refer the analyst to the following control levels:

1. good industrial hygiene practice
2. engineering control (e.g., ventilation)
3. containment, with small breaches[4] only
4. refer to expert advice

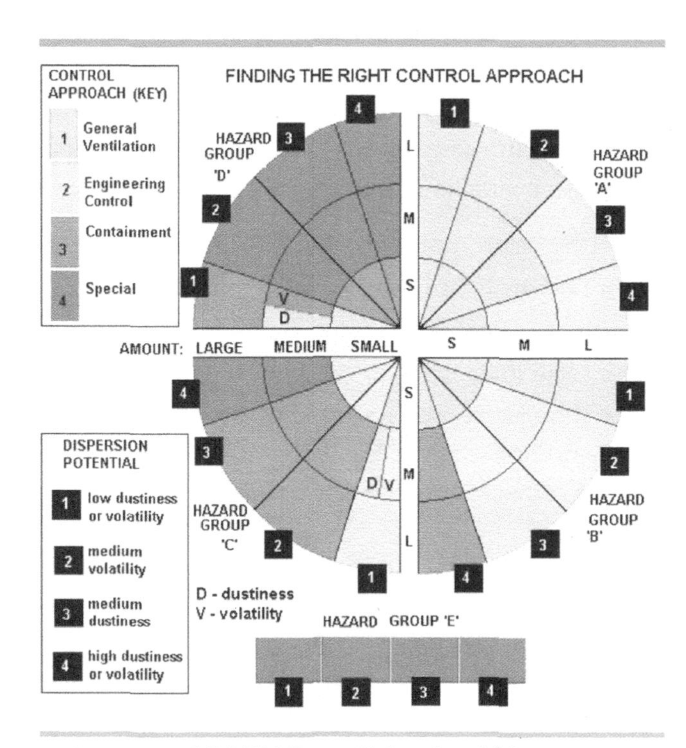

FIGURE 3. COSHH Essentials wheel (Crown Copyright: UK HSE)

After obtaining the recommended control level, the user is then directed to the control guidance sheets (CGS). Available for many, though not all, workplace tasks, CGS follow a standard template: control level 1 is green, 2 is blue, 3 is lavender, and 4 is hot pink. Each of these sheets contains information on access, design of control equipment (with illustration), maintenance, examination and testing, cleaning, personal protective equipment (PPE), training, supervision, and an employee checklist. This information is always located in the same place on every CGS. Thus, by providing minimum information, employees and employers can receive direct, appropriate guidance for reducing any exposure to chemical hazards.

Control banding is receiving much attention worldwide; for example, by the World Health Organization (WHO) and the International Labour Organization (ILO). An electronic workbook is available on the HSE Web site.

The Risk-Assessment Paradigm

The EPA has published the most extensively on risk assessment mainly because of its role in Superfund hazardous waste site management.[5] The EPA paradigm was based on the National Research Council "Red Book" (NRC 1983) and includes the following:

- hazard identification (which EPA implements as data collection and evaluation)
- dose-response (toxicity) assessment
- exposure assessment
- risk characterization

These four components have been memorably rephrased as the following (Barnes 1994):

- Is this stuff toxic?
- How toxic is it?
- Who is exposed to this stuff, for how long, and how often?
- So what?

Risk Assessment Paradigm and Practices: Twenty-five Years Later

Since the publication of the Red Book (NRC 1983), approaches to risk assessment have become increasingly more robust and technologically advanced (NRC 2009), while still conforming to the paradigmatic approach presented in 1983. Issues surrounding the limitations and appropriate use of default assumptions, incomplete data sets, and associated uncertainty, issues and approaches to accounting for population variability, low-dose extrapolation, and vulnerability have been explored in specific guidance documents: guidance on risk assessment for cancer (EPA 2005b) and noncancer endpoints, such as developmental (EPA 1991), mutagenic (EPA 1986), reproductive toxins (EPA 1996), and neurotoxins (EPA 1998). The framework presented in the Red Book was also adopted and integrated into ecological risk assessment (EPA 1988). Most recently, guidance documents on assessing susceptibility from early-life exposures to carcinogens (EPA 2005a), health risks to children, (EPA 2006), metals (EPA 2007), and cumulative health risk assessment of multiple chemicals, exposures, and effects (EPA 2008) have been made available.

The Red Book's framework has been widely adopted by other agencies (Barnes 1993), as well as public health organizations outside the United States, including the World Health Organization (WHO) (NRC 2009). The four core steps are evident in the globally harmonized framework on risk assessment (Meek 2011).

Despite these advances, critical data gaps, leading to uncertainty in assessments, competing priorities, resource limitations, and controversy surrounding the science has led to challenges to the process. Increasingly complex assessments mean more and more diverse data to analyze, and conflicting results from multiple studies complicate the assessment. Long delays in completing EPA risk assessments—dioxin, formaldehyde, and trichloroethylene have taken ten to twenty years to complete—have resulted in state and federal risk management and policy decisions being made without risk assessments taken into consideration. Such practices could cause the value of risk assessments to erode (NRC 2009). Furthermore, despite having clean-up responsibilities, other agencies and stakeholders have expressed concern that they have not been adequately involved in EPA processes.

In 2009, the Committee on Improving Risk Analysis Approaches Used by the U.S. EPA published its report, which recommended two additional steps. The first is a preliminary planning and scoping of the problem to provide clear guidance to influence why and how the risk assessment will be conducted. Assessments conducted within a well-articulated problem statement are more likely to produce usable information to aid the decision maker/risk manager and provide meaningful data. Furthermore, a clear problem statement would clarify the necessary level of complexity needed from the assessment to meet the decision makers' needs (NRC 2009). The committee also recommended an additional risk-management step that identifies *a priori*, risk-management options with the intent of using the risk assessment to evaluate the relative benefits of these options. This step reinforces the concept of risk assessment as a tool to aid decision making rather than as an end in and of itself. Both steps are included in the harmonized framework (Meek 2011).

Using Risk Assessment in Industrial Hygiene Practice

Industrial hygiene has been defined as the science and art of "anticipation, recognition, evaluation, and control of environmental factors arising in or from the workplace that may result in injury, illness, impairment, or affect the well-being of workers and members of the community" (Olishifski and Plog 1988). Anticipation and recognition can be difficult to distinguish, but anticipation can be thought of as an activity that occurs prior to an actual site visit, while recognition, evaluation, and control all occur at the workplace. Risk assessment and management can be roughly compared to anticipation, recognition, evaluation, and control, as seen in Table 3.

The remainder of this chapter will focus on the exposure-assessment aspects of industrial hygiene. While risk assessment requires both exposure assessment and toxicity assessment, the OEHS professional is far more likely to be involved in exposure assessment than in toxicity assessment. Exposure assessment is a highly site-specific scenario, while toxicity values are usually obtained from standard reference sources, such as AIHA WEELS, ACGIH® TLVs®, OSHA PELs, and EPA AEGLs.

TABLE 3

Comparison of Risk Assessment/Management to Anticipation/Recognition/Evaluation/Control

Risk Assessment/Management	Anticipation, Recognition, Evaluation, and Control
Hazard identification	Anticipation, recognition
Exposure assessment, toxicity assessment, risk characterization	Evaluation
Risk management	Control
Risk communication	Hazard communication

(Adapted from Jayjock, Lynch, and Nelson 2000)

Defining Exposure Assessment

Exposure assessment answers the questions posed by Barnes (1994): "Who is exposed to this stuff, for how long, and how often?" The trend in conducting exposure assessments has been shifting from collecting samples of airborne contaminants for the purpose of determining compliance with OSHA regulations (compliance strategy) to a more comprehensive approach to conducting exposure assessments. According to Mulhausen and Damiano (2003), this comprehensive approach can be described as the "systematic review of the processes, practices, materials, and division of labor present in a workplace that is used to define and judge all exposures for all workers on all days." Other reasons for performing exposure assessments include addressing employee complaints, for medical and epidemiological studies, and for determining the effectiveness of engineering and administrative controls. It is important to understand that the results of the exposure-assessment process must account for today's as well as tomorrow's regulations (Mulhausen and Damiano 2003).

Exposure-Assessment Strategies

Comprehensive exposure assessment is an iterative or cyclical process. The early efforts can be aimed at the "low-hanging fruit," that is, information that is fairly easy to obtain. As information is collected, it can be used to focus further efforts to assess and control exposures. Mulhausen and Damiano (2003) have outlined seven steps in an exposure-assessment strategy:

1. ***Start:*** Establish an exposure-assessment strategy that includes determining the goals of the strategy (i.e., compliance, comprehensive, etc.) and developing a written program.
2. ***Basic characterization:*** Collection of the information needed to characterize the workplace, the workforce, and the environmental agents.

3. ***Exposure assessment:*** Analysis of the information collected during the basic characterization to establish similar exposure groups (SEGs), to define the exposure profile of each SEG, and to determine exposure acceptability within each SEG.
4. ***Further information gathering:*** When exposures cannot be determined to be acceptable or unacceptable (i.e., undetermined), additional information such as additional workplace monitoring, modeling of exposures, biological monitoring, toxicological data, or epidemiological data can be collected to aid in the decision-making process.
5. ***Health-hazard control:*** When exposures are determined to be unacceptable, prioritized control strategies are implemented. Priority depends on the number of employees exposed, the risk of those exposures, frequency, and uncertainty.
6. ***Reassessment:*** The iterative process of the exposure-assessment strategy requires that the assessment be performed on a regular basis. The frequency of reassessment generally depends upon the severity of the hazard. Common reassessment frequencies are annual for highly hazardous operations or operations with many workers, and up to once every four years for administrative spaces.
7. ***Communication and documentation:*** All results and decisions, both qualitative and quantitative, need to be recorded and reported to the employees.

Quantitative Exposure-Assessment Methodologies

When selecting appropriate quantitative exposure-assessment methodologies, the OEHS professional has to consider many factors. These can be summarized as the "who, what, when, where, why, and how" of exposure assessment. Of these, "why are we sampling" and "what are we sampling for" have the greatest impact on selection of monitoring methodologies. Workplace monitoring may be conducted for a variety of reasons; for example, to determine compliance with regulations, to locate contaminant source(s), to measure the effectiveness of controls, and so on, each of which calls for a slightly different approach. Determining regulatory compliance, for instance, usually requires calculation of 8-hour time-weighted average exposures; evaluating the effectiveness of engineering controls may be best accomplished either by sampling before and after a control has been instituted or by sampling with and without the control operating (Mulhausen and Damiano 2003).

The next most important factor to consider in selecting a quantitative exposure-assessment methodology is the nature of the hazard being evaluated, that is, "what are we sampling for." If the concern is for airborne contaminants, it is important to consider all chemicals, including raw materials, intermediates,

FIGURE 4. Personal dust monitor (Courtesy of SKC, Inc.)

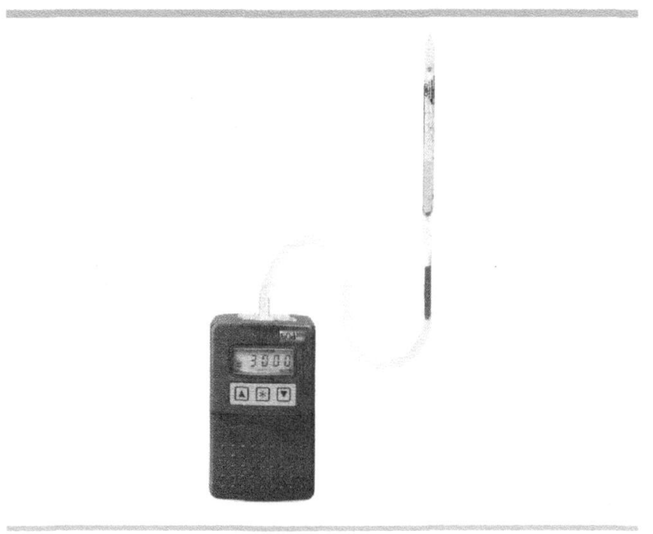

FIGURE 5. AirChek2000 low-flow pump (Courtesy of SKC, Inc.)

TABLE 4

Comparison of Air-Monitoring Methods

Method	Mechanism	Airborne Contaminant	Analytical Technique
Direct-reading instruments	Varies	Gases, vapors, particulates, noise, radiation	N/A
Colorimetric detector tubes	Chemical reaction on fixed media	Gases, vapors	N/A
Passive dosimeters	Adsorption	Gases, vapors	GC/FID, etc.
Air sampling pumps and media (e.g., filters, charcoal tubes, impinger solutions)			
Filters	Filtration	Particulates	Gravimetric, chemical analysis
Charcoal tubes	Adsorption	Vapors	GC/FID, etc.
Impinger solutions	Absorption, chemical reaction	Gases	Chemical analysis

(Adapted from Jayjock, Lynch, and Nelson 2000)

by-products, waste products, and final products. However, it is usually too expensive and time-consuming to collect samples of all airborne contaminants, so OEHS professionals often prioritize their sampling and analytical approach based on the quantity of the chemical in use, its volatility/dustiness, relationship to OEL, and so on. The list of hazards (i.e., the hazard inventory) to determine the sampling priority is generally developed during the basic-characterization step. The hazard inventory should include the chemical hazards, often found on the material safety data sheets (MSDSs), the physical hazards (noise, radiation, etc.), as well as the biological hazards. Evaluating the potential for exposure in comparison to the toxicity of the contaminant can be thought of as qualitative or perhaps even semiquantitative exposure assessment (Bisesi 2004).

Together, the *why* and the *what* determine the how, who, when, and where of exposure assessment.

How? Quantitative exposure assessment can be performed in many ways. Workplace monitoring may be done at a screening level or a comprehensive level. Samples may be collected in the workers' breathing zone or in that general area. Semiquantitative assessment can be performed using mathematical models to estimate exposures. Each type of monitoring can be performed with a variety of equipment, which can include direct-reading instruments, colorimetric detector tubes, passive monitors, sampling pumps and media, and so on (see Figures 4 and 5, and Table 4). Unfortunately, no universal sampler exists. Therefore, several factors may need to be considered in the selection of instrumentation, such as the efficiency of the instrument, the reliability of the instrument in real-world situations, as well as the preference of the investigator (Bisesi, 2004).

Quantitative exposure assessment is just one part of a comprehensive exposure-assessment strategy. The quantitative approach encompasses workplace monitoring and may be performed to answer many questions, such as the level of personal employee exposures and the effectiveness of engineering controls. The methods utilized for workplace monitoring are varied; they depend on the reason the monitoring is being conducted. The summary below discusses a few of the considerations when selecting a sampling strategy. A more comprehensive discussion of sampling equipment and methods can be found in Bisesi (2004), Plog and Quinlan (2002), and DiNardi (2003). Advice on specific sampling and analytical techniques is well beyond the scope of this chapter, but it is available from OSHA (undated), NIOSH (1994), ASTM (2003), and ACGIH (2001, 2004). Various manufacturers, such as SKC, Inc. (undated) or Mine Safety Appliances (undated), provide a wealth of information on their Web sites.

Instantaneous, or Real-Time, Monitoring

Instantaneous, or real-time, monitoring is generally used for short-term sampling lasting from a few seconds up to fifteen minutes. However, instantaneous monitoring can also be performed over longer periods of time, such as eight hours or longer, in the data-logging mode. Instantaneous monitors provide results immediately but are best used as screening tools to determine what concentrations of contaminants are present in order to plan future assessment needs. Instantaneous monitoring is also useful during short-term operations or in determining peak concentrations (Bisesi 2004). Instantaneous monitors include direct-reading instruments and colorimetric detector tubes.

Integrated Monitoring

Integrated monitoring generally occurs over a period of several hours. Work shifts often last eight hours, and therefore integrated monitoring lasts eight hours, or a full shift. OELs used for comparison purposes are usually based on an 8-hour time period. Integrated monitoring for a full shift can be performed by collecting one sample for the entire 8-hour shift. Additionally, multiple consecutive samples can be collected over the shift. A common approach is to collect two samples—one before the lunch break and one after. The individual samples are then combined to determine the 8-hour time-weighted average (8HR TWA) concentration, in which C is the measured concentration of each and T is the sample time of that sample given in hours.

$$\text{8HR TWA} = \frac{C_1T_1 + C_2T_2 + \cdots + C_nT_n}{\text{8 hours}} \quad (1)$$

With integrated sampling, samples must be sent to a laboratory for analysis, resulting in a delay between the sampling event and the reporting of results (Bisesi 2004).

Nontraditional work shifts, such as 10-hour or 12-hour shifts, are becoming more common in today's workplaces. Sampling strategies should be designed not only for comparison to applicable OELs, but also to assess the workers' full-shift exposures. OSHA compliance officers are directed to either sample during the estimated "worst continuous 8-hour work period of the entire extended work shift," or to collect multiple samples over the entire work shift (OSHA 1999). In this way, time-weighted average exposures can be calculated for comparison to any 8-hour OELs, as well as for the entire work shift. Alternatively, OELs can be modified for application to unusual work shifts. For more information on the evaluation of these extended exposures, consult Paustenbach (2000), Brief and Scala (1975), the ACGIH *TLV Guide* (2007), Klonne (2003), or OSHA (1999).

Personal Monitoring

Personal monitoring can be performed with both instantaneous samplers and integrated samplers. Personal samples are collected on the worker, in the breathing zone for an inhalation hazard or in the hearing zone for a noise hazard. Breathing-zone samples are generally collected by integrated monitoring. Hearing-zone samples are generally collected by instantaneous sampling. The breathing zone refers to the area within a 1-foot radius of a worker's nose and mouth. Breathing-zone samples are often attached to a worker's collar near the collar bone. The hearing zone refers to the area within a 1-foot radius of the ear (Bisesi 2004).

Area Monitoring

Area monitoring takes place at a location, often at a source of contamination, and not on a person. Workers are often quite mobile and are usually at some varying distance from the source; thus, area-monitoring results are not representative of personal exposures. For this reason, area monitoring should not be compared to OELs. Area monitoring is, however, a good tool for evaluating background concentrations or the effectiveness of engineering controls, or for checking for leaks.

Both instantaneous monitors and integrated monitors can be used during area monitoring. Samples can be collected at multiple locations throughout a facility (Bisesi 2004).

Mathematical Modeling

Exposure monitoring provides valuable information about worker exposures but it is time-consuming and expensive to collect these measurements. Often, sampling methods do not exist or are not feasible for a given situation; in such cases alternative exposure-assessment approaches are needed. Historical exposures for which exposure data are scarce or not available, processes that are not yet in production, and downstream user exposures are just a few examples of situations that preclude conventional quantitative assessment methods. In these situations, semiquantitative methods, such as mathematical exposure modeling, are very useful.

Models range from the very simple to the very complex and are generally applied in a tiered approach, beginning with simple models and progressing through more complicated ones. The simple models often overestimate exposures. However, if the exposure can be categorized as acceptable using a conservative estimate, no further action needs to be taken. If the exposure cannot be judged acceptable, a higher-tier model may be needed. The more complex models are more resource-intensive in terms of time, effort, and money but provide more realistic exposure estimates. The tiered approach may begin with the tier-one, saturation vapor pressure model, proceed to a general ventilation model, and end with a tier-two, two-box or dispersion model.

A comprehensive description of the model theory and application is provided elsewhere (Keil et al. 2009). An overview is provided here to describe generally how modeling exposures may be helpful to the risk assessor.

The saturation vapor pressure model is often used as a first-tier estimate. All that is needed for this estimate is the vapor pressure of the contaminant of interest and the atmospheric pressure, using the following equation:

$$C_{sat} = \frac{(10^6)(\text{vapor pressure})}{(\text{atmospheric pressure})} \qquad (2)$$

For example, if a drum of toluene is left uncovered in a workspace, the saturation vapor pressure model determines the maximum concentration that could exist in the workspace. If this maximum concentration is less than the OEL of the contaminant, then the exposure can be deemed acceptable. For toluene, the vapor pressure is 21 mm Hg (NIOSH 2005). Therefore, the saturation concentration when atmospheric pressure is 760 mm Hg (1 atmoshere) is 27,631 ppm. Since this concentration is greater than both the PEL (200 ppm) and the TLV (50 ppm), the exposure cannot be judged acceptable, and a higher-tier model may be necessary.

More information is needed about the work environment and the job tasks before a more complex model can be applied. It can be obtained through direct observation and interviews with site personnel, EHS professionals, and management. The Internet is also a valuable resource in gathering general reference and use-pattern information. In this scenario, a worker manually transfers toluene from a 55-gallon drum into a smaller container to clean parts in another area of the facility. This task takes approximately ten minutes to complete and is performed six times per shift. The emission rate can be estimated conservatively, assuming that toluene headspace vapors escape from the drum bung hole while the transfer is taking place. This yields an estimated emission rate of 2164 mg/min. There is mechanical ventilation in the facility, but there is relatively little local airflow (approximately 20 m/min) around the drum storage area where the transfer takes place. The estimated general airflow is four air changes per hour (ACH) and the room volume is approximately 1000 m^3.

A tier-two model, the two-box or near-field/far-field model, can now be used to estimate the worker's exposure. This box-within-a-box model assumes air within each box is well mixed; the local airflow data from the facility comports with this assumption. The area encompassing the worker's breathing zone is used to define the inner box or near field. The rate at which air moves from one box into the other, and vice versa, is called the *interzonal airflow rate*, denoted by the symbol β. It is influenced by the geometry around and presence of the worker, and the local air velocity(s). When this interzonal airflow rate is small, the concentration in the inner box is much higher than in the outer box, since contaminant buildup in this smaller space is not able to disburse easily. When β is large, the concentration disparity between the inner and outer box is much smaller. The model estimates airborne concentrations within the inner or near-field (NF) and outer or far-field (FF) boxes:

$$C_{FF}(t) = \frac{G}{Q} + \frac{G}{\beta} + G\left(\frac{\beta\sqrt{Q} + \lambda_2\sqrt{V_{NF}}\,(\beta + Q)}{\beta\sqrt{Q}\sqrt{V_{NF}}\,(\lambda_1 - \lambda_2)}\right)\exp\left(\lambda_1\sqrt{t}\right) - G\left(\frac{\beta\sqrt{Q} + \lambda_1\sqrt{V_{NF}}\,(\beta + Q)}{\beta\sqrt{Q}\sqrt{V_{NF}}\,(\lambda_1 - \lambda_2)}\right)\exp\left(\lambda_2\sqrt{t}\right) \qquad (3)$$

$$C_{NF}(t) = \frac{\beta(C_{FF,0} - C_{NF,0}) - \lambda_2\sqrt{V_{NF}}\sqrt{C_{NF,0}}}{V_{NF}\,(\lambda_1 - \lambda_2)}\exp\left(\lambda_1\sqrt{t}\right) + \frac{\beta(C_{NF,0} - C_{FF,0}) + \lambda_1\sqrt{V_{NF}}\sqrt{C_{NF,0}}}{V_{NF}\,(\lambda_1 - \lambda_2)}\exp\left(\lambda_2\sqrt{t}\right) \qquad (4)$$

A freeware Excel spreadsheet tool, from their AIHA Model Exposure Assessment Strategies Committee, called AIHA MOD (AIHA 2009), is used to calculate these values. Remember that the models calculate airborne concentrations, so the time spent in each box or field must be reconciled to calculate a time-weighted average (TWA) exposure. In this scenario, the worker spends approximately 10 min × 6 times per shift in the inner box and the rest of his shift in the outer box. The TWA airborne concentration at ten minutes is approximately 124 mg/m³. He is in this environment for a total of one hour per shift. The rest of the time he is in the outer box or far field, where the steady-state concentration is 32 mg/m³. His estimated TWA exposure is

$$\frac{124\ \mathrm{mg/m^3} \times 60\ \mathrm{min} + 32\ \mathrm{mg/m^3} \times 380\ \mathrm{min}}{480\ \mathrm{min}} \quad (5)$$

TWA exposure = 40.8 mg/m³

The PEL for toluene is 200 ppm or 754 mg/m³. The refined exposure estimate suggests this exposure is acceptable. Validation of the model for this application is recommended to complete the assessment.

Looking beyond individual exposure scenarios, the need to quickly and efficiently assess thousands of chemicals for regulatory purposes (e.g., the European Chemicals legislation, REACH) necessitates the use of modeling tools. Unlike monitoring data, models permit the user to assess past, present, and future scenarios. Conservative, default assumptions are used in place of real-world data to inform the models. In concordance with the precautionary approach, conservatism is traded for data, and more sophisticated models can be used until the necessary level of refinement is achieved. Physical-chemical models, such as the saturation vapor concentration and box models and expert models, including EASE and Risk of Derm, can be employed for assessing single chemical scenarios. Other models are available for assessing and screening hundreds or thousands of chemicals, such as the (freeware) complex exposure tool (CEPST) (Lifeline Group 2007).

In all cases, the models are premised on a set of assumptions with which the user must be comfortable; since these are simplifying assumptions, they may not be completely accurate, but the user must be conscious of and comfortable with them to be confident in the model's output. The models operate from either a single or set of mathematical algorithms. The inputs to the algorithms represent the determinants of exposure and the output represents the predicted exposure. Models can be deterministic, providing a single-point estimate of exposure, based on point estimates of the determinants, or they can be probabilistic, providing a distribution of exposure estimates based on ranges or distributions of input parameters. The latter enables the user to quantitate his or her level of confidence in the exposure estimate.

The models facilitate "what if" questions about a given scenario; for example:

- What if the ventilation is doubled?
- What if the production rate is tripled while the ventilation rate is doubled?
- What if the emission source is stopped after 30 minutes?

Collecting information about the determinants of exposure allows the assessor to resolve these questions where exposure measurement data alone does not. Ideally, both kinds of data will be available to the assessor so they can be used collaboratively. A more detailed discussion of this is presented under the "Professional Judgment" section.

Use of Exposure-Assessment Results

Sampling and analytical results are interpreted/evaluated/judged for acceptability using accepted statistical techniques (the science) and experience/knowledge/expertise (the art) of the OEHS professional. If results are below the OEL by an adequate margin, then exposures are considered acceptable, and the only follow-up activity might be to document and communicate the results. An adequate margin is generally user defined at a company level and may or may not be statistically based. An adequate margin could be defined so that the sample average with its confidence interval does not overlap the confidence interval of the appropriate PEL. If the results are above the OEL, then exposures are considered unacceptable, and appropriate control measures (e.g., engineering controls, administrative controls, or PPE) should be selected, implemented, and maintained. Exposures between acceptable and unacceptable are the undetermined exposures. For these SEGs, additional information needs

CASE STUDY

Quantitative Exposure Assessment

Quantitative exposure assessment can be demonstrated in the following hypothetical evaluation of the staff supporting a firing range. The range is staffed daily by two range safety officers and one range master. The range staff can be exposed to lead up to eight hours per day. To assess exposures to this group, the staff can be divided into two separate SEGs based on their different exposure potential from the different tasks performed. One SEG would include the range master, and the second SEG would include the range safety officers. Therefore, monitoring of both the range master and the range safety officers is warranted. Because only three persons work the range, all three should be monitored, if possible. At a minimum, the range master and one range safety officer need to be monitored.

The selection of the sampling day should be as random as possible. In other words, each day of operation should have an equal opportunity of being selected for sampling. For this hypothetical operation, lead exposure needs to be assessed at least twice each year. Each day the range is operating during each six-month period could be assigned a number in order from 1 to 130 (5 days per week for 26 weeks). A random number table could then be used to determine which day to sample. Suppose Day 73 is selected. If the numbering began at Monday, January 1, Day 73 would be Wednesday, April 11. Sampling would then be performed on Wednesday, April 11.

Now that the date has been picked, sampling preparation can begin. First the sampling method must be determined. The *NIOSH Manual of Analytical Methods* (NIOSH 1994) is a good source of sampling methods. Analytical laboratories are also good sources for determining the method. Both the laboratories and the *Manual of Analytical Methods* can then provide the details necessary to complete the sampling. For lead, NIOSH Method 7082 is used to determine the amount of lead by flame atomic absorption spectrophotometry. The method calls for the sample to be collected on a 0.8-micrometer cellulose ester membrane filter. The sample must be collected at a flow rate of 1–4 liters per minute (lpm) for a total collected volume between 200 and 1500 liters.

The OEL for lead is reported as an 8-hour time-weighted average. Therefore, the sampling should be performed for a full 8-hour shift. As stated above, collecting multiple samples is better than collecting just one 8-hour sample. For this hypothetical firing range, the air is not very dusty and therefore two 4-hour samples can be collected without overloading the filters. At a flow rate of 2 lpm, each 4-hour sample would have had a sampling volume of 480 liters pulled through the filters. This sampling volume meets the requirements of NIOSH Method 7082, and the samples can therefore be collected at a flow rate of 2 lpm.

Prior to the sampling event, the sampling media (in this case the filters preloaded into cassettes) must be ordered from the analytical laboratory. To ensure accuracy of the results, it is best to make sure the laboratory is accredited by the AIHA.[7] The cost of the media is generally included in the cost of the analytical method. Before the media arrive, the integrated sampling pumps and calibrator must be fully charged.

On the day of sampling, Wednesday, April 11, the fully charged integrated sampling pumps must be pre-calibrated with a filter in place in the sampling train to set the pumps at an operating flow rate of 2 lpm. This pre-calibration can be done either in the office or on site, but must be done on the day of sampling. Then upon arriving at the site, the pumps should be placed on the two range safety officers and the range master before the workers enter the firing range for the morning session. The pumps need to be turned on to begin collecting the sample, and the flow rate should be checked to ensure the pump is still operating at 2 lpm. The pump is generally attached to the belt and worn on the side or the back of the person so that it does not interfere with work procedures. The filter is attached to the collar in the breathing zone, generally within 12 inches of the nose and mouth (Bisesi 2004). After sampling has begun, the flow rate should be checked multiple times during the 4-hour sampling event; suggested times could be at 30 minutes, 1 hour, 2 hours, and 3 hours into the sampling event. At the end of the morning session, the sampling pump is removed from the worker, the flow rate checked one final time, and the sample stopped. After the workers return from lunch, the same procedure is used for the 4-hour afternoon session. Post-calibration can then be performed in the field or back in the office. With a calibrated rotameter, the post-calibration can be done as the final flow rate check in the field prior to the pump's being turned off. The stopped sampling pumps can also be returned to the office with the sampling media still in place for the post-calibration.

After the sampling event has been completed, all six filters (two for each of the three workers) along with two field blanks[8] are sent back to the AIHA-accredited laboratory for analysis.[9] The field blanks are required per NIOSH Method 7082 and are taken to the site and treated in the same manner as the samples except that no air is pulled through them (Jordan 2003).

to be collected to further refine the assessment in order to better determine acceptability. To make statistically based decisions, six to ten samples need to be collected in each SEG, in order to minimize uncertainty without the cost of each sample outweighing the amount of uncertainty improvement (diminishing returns). These six to ten samples do not all need to be collected during one sampling event; they can be collected over time as long as the SEG remains stable. These samples should be randomly spaced and cover all shifts and seasons in which the work is done. If a truly statistically random sampling strategy is utilized, then each and every person in each and every shift of the SEG will have an equal chance of being monitored. This could be accomplished by assigning numbers to each person in every shift every day during one year. A random-number generator can then be used to determine which person on which day working which shift will be sampled. In the real world, a more *representative* sampling approach is generally used. This representative approach may entail selecting a convenient sampling date, but without regard to process operations, then rolling a die to determine which shift on that date, and finally drawing numbers to determine who will be sampled (Ignacio and Bullock 2006).

The data collected can then be statistically analyzed to aid in the decision-making process. A first step is to determine whether the data are log-normally distributed, as are most sampling data. This determination can be done with such tests as the Shapiro and Wilk W test or with probability plotting. After determining that the data is log-normally distributed, other calculations can be made, including the arithmetic mean, geometric mean, 95th percentile, exceedance fraction, and the upper tolerance limit. Depending on the policy of each company, any one or all of these statistics can be used to determine acceptability. Examples of acceptability cutpoints include an exceedance fraction less than 5 percent or an upper tolerance limit less than the OEL. The exceedance fraction is the proportion of all possible exposures in a SEG that could exceed the OEL and the upper tolerance limit is the 95 percent upper confidence limit of the 95th percentile. (Typical benchmarks include an exceedance fraction of less than 5–10 percent, or when the 95 percent upper confidence limit of exposures is less than the OEL.) An extensive discussion on these statistics, along with step-by-step instructions and a spreadsheet program, is available in Ignacio and Bullock (2006).

Impacts of Uncertainty and Data Quality

Two additional concepts—uncertainty and data quality—need to be addressed relative to acceptability of occupational exposures and subsequent decisions to conduct risk management. Uncertainty stems from two sources: natural variability and ignorance (lack of knowledge). Variability can be measured either directly or indirectly. Generally, the contribution of variability-driven uncertainty is small relative to lack-of-knowledge uncertainty. Nevertheless, adequately quantifying human variability is a critical step in assessing variability in human susceptibility (Burke 2011).

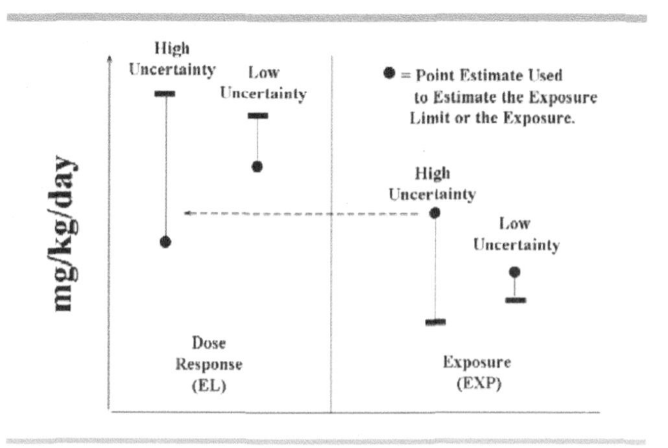

FIGURE 6. Levels of confidence in exposure and dose-response assessments (*Source:* Jayjock, Lynch, and Nelson 2000)

This lack of knowledge impacts the risk assessment-management-communication chain because an assessment cannot be conducted without any information on the agent or scenario. Large gaps drive conservative assumptions in lieu of data. Critical data gaps can prevent completion of an assessment altogether. Likewise, it is difficult, if not impossible, to effectively communicate a message without facts and data. Because of this difficulty, risk assessment tends to be iterative, with data traded for conservatism until satisfactory answers and actions are defined.

Conclusions regarding the acceptability of risk are impacted by the quality of data for both the exposure limit (EL) and the exposure (EXP). If EXP is below the EL, any combination of high-quality (low-uncertainty) estimates for either the EL or EXP will result in the conclusion of acceptability, because the upper-bound estimate of exposure will be less than the lower-bound estimate of the EL (Jayjock, Lynch, and Nelson 2000).

Figure 6 illustrates this concept, showing the point estimate and range of values for both the EL and EXP. In this illustration, the upper-bound exposure estimate with high uncertainty overlaps with the lower-bound estimate of the EL with high uncertainty; the exposure and risk would be deemed unacceptable. As either or both estimates are refined and the uncertainty is reduced, the two do not overlap and one would conclude that the exposure and risk are acceptable (Jayjock et al. 2000).

PROFESSIONAL JUDGMENT

Risk assessment is an inherently subjective process; it necessarily involves professional judgment as part of the assessment of risk. When the assessor must render a judgment for a scenario in which not all the facts are known, he or she must bridge the gap using professional judgment. If the risk assessor's judgment is faulty, there is a potential for faulty risk management and, ultimately, faulty risk-management policy. Thus, risk assessors need to ensure their judgments are calibrated. Decisions made in the face of uncertainty can introduce biases when based on intuitive tools. Decisions made using quantitative and semiquantitative tools, such as statistical tools, mathematical modeling, and Bayesian tools, may lead to more accurate and calibrated judgments.

There are many occasions when judgments must be rendered without availability of all the facts; indeed, this is true for most scenarios. The assessor must compensate for this knowledge gap by using professional judgment, thus introducing uncertainty into the judgment. Recent studies investigating agreement between rendered exposure and risk judgments versus "true" exposure and risk have unveiled a lesser degree of concordance between rendered versus true exposure and risk than expected (Logan et al. 2009). There was also considerable judgment variability between risk assessors judging the same scenarios. Both findings suggest the need for improvement in the risk assessors' judgments (Logan et al. 2009).

As a first step in improving professional judgment, it is important to understand how individuals make decisions when faced with uncertainty. When rendering decisions based on an incomplete data set, individuals use heuristics, or simple rules of thumb, to form a judgment. These heuristics are the "guiding principles for transforming information to solve a problem or to form a judgment" (Kahemann, and Tversky 1982a). Unfortunately, they are subject to biases that can result in poorly calibrated exposure and risk judgments. Some examples of heuristics are *representativeness, availability,* and *anchoring and adjustment* (O'Hagan et al. 2006).

Representativeness

People evaluate the probability of events by the degree to which the scenarios or events are representative of one with which they are familiar (Kahemann and Tversky 1982b). For example, in making a judgment about a particular work task, the assessor may compare the task and process with one he or she has previously assessed quantitatively. The degree to which the two tasks and processes are truly similar will impact the accuracy of this judgment.

Availability

One strategy for assessing the likelihood of an event or scenario is the *availability* heuristic. The assumption is that events or scenarios that occur more frequently are more likely to occur. This cue can be appropriate in many cases, but availability is also influenced by one's ability to recall instances of an event or scenario, and this can be influenced by factors such as the dread factor, media coverage, and personal experiences. For example, a risk assessor may overestimate the risk of crushed limbs resulting from mishaps with presses if such an injury occurred at his facility. This heuristic is also influenced by the recentness with which it has occurred; perceived risks of events tend to be higher immediately after such an event has just occurred. If the assessor has recently experienced or been made aware of a relatively rare but catastrophic failure, he or she may rate the probability of such an event reoccurring higher than the true likelihood of reoccurrence. Conversely, if it has been many years since a failure has occurred, the risk is often underestimated (Kahemann and Tversky 1982b). Thus, judgments based on availability may be skewed high or low, depending on the situation.

Adjustment and Anchoring

Another common heuristic is adjustment and anchoring (O'Hagan et al. 2006). People tend to anchor their first estimates to the initial value of a data set. Further adjustments to the estimate tend to be insufficient to compensate for this phenomenon. For example, an assessor considers a data set of personal monitoring results for which the OEL is 10 ppm. The data are presented in the following order: 0.6, 2.1, 5.4, 2.1, 7.3 ppm. Her initial judgment of the 95th percentile is anchored by the first value, and she concludes the exposure is most likely a category two exposure (95th percentile between 0.1 and 0.5 times OEL), when it is in fact a category four exposure (95th percentile > OEL). While it is a common belief that the risk assessor's exposure judgments tend to be health conservative, one can see how using this heuristic can (and does) bias the outcome to underestimate, rather than overestimate, the exposure.

The use of heuristics may mask sources of uncertainty, giving the assessor more confidence in the results than is otherwise justified. Studies have shown that decision makers tend to be overconfident with heuristic-based judgments; even experts tend to be overconfident in judgments that go beyond the bounds of their data (thereby invoking heuristics). One reason for this overconfidence may be that, in simplifying, one ignores alternative outcomes. Lack of or misinterpreting feedback can also contribute to overconfidence. For example, as an assessor becomes increasingly seasoned in making exposure judgments—but without feedback to suggest the judgments are frequently wrong—he or she may become increasingly confident, but still be wrong. Whether it is the representativeness, availability, adjustment and anchoring, or some other heuristic upon which a decision is based, the outcome may be faulty, potentially driving inappropriate risk-management decisions.

Knowing this, it is important to rely on rules and tools that minimize these biases and lead to more accurate judgments. Tools that provide timely, accurate feedback, such as statistical tools, mathematical modeling, and Bayesian decision strategies and tools, should be used instead of intuitive professional judgment. These strategies provide more objective analyses upon which to make better judgments because they can integrate complex information more accurately than people. Individuals are good at selecting predictor variables for these models and coding them so that the right questions are asked but are not good at integrating information from diverse and incompatible sources (Dawes 1982). For example, risk assessors tend to know who, when, and where to sample to characterize exposures. They are good at identifying the important determinants of exposure to include in a mathematical model but are less adept at computing complex equations without the aid of computers. These strategies may also moderate overconfidence by allowing assessors to quantify their confidence in their professional judgment, taking into account the uncertainty associated with the judgment.

Several freeware tools have been developed to facilitate incorporation of the statistical and mathematical models and Bayesian decision analysis into the assessor's cadre of tools. Their use is supported by several AIHA publications (Ignacio and Bullock 2006) and professional development courses (PDCs), as well as other professional development venues, such as distance education. They can be downloaded from the AIHA Exposure Assessment Strategies Web site.

The application of these strategies and tools will be discussed within an exposure-assessment context in further detail.

Focus on Exposure Assessment

Collecting personal exposure measurements is commonly considered the gold standard in industrial hygiene, despite the fact that obtaining the recommended 6–10 samples per similar exposure group is the exception rather than the rule. The most common number of samples collected for exposure judgments is zero, then one, then two, and so on (Ignacio and Bullock 2006). When there are sufficient data, the conventional statistical tools should always be used; they will most likely provide sufficient information to accurately characterize an exposure. Where sampling data are scarce or unavailable, however, a different approach is needed, one that uses the tools in a collaborative framework.

This collaborative approach allows the assessor to make use of all the information available, culminating in a more robust assessment than would be realized by using the tools individually. Working within a Bayesian decision framework, subjective inputs and objective data are integrated to produce a posterior judgment. This framework provides a mechanism by which decisions can be refined and updated as new information becomes available. This setup also provides the critical feedback loop required to calibrate and improve professional judgment.

Bayes' theorem (Equation 6) formally acknowledges the influence of subjective inputs to our judgment and the associated uncertainty, and weights them appropriately against our objective likelihood inputs. The subjective prior is represented by our qualitative and semiqualitative assessments, such as direct-reading instrument output, mathematical models, and other screening-level assessments. The likelihood estimate is represented by objective data, such as personal or area monitoring data. More robust likelihood estimates are weighted more heavily against their priors to yield an updated posterior judgment. The prior, likelihood, and posterior estimates are expressed as probability density functions. In this way, confidence in a particular judgment can be quantified.

$$P(\text{Exposure}_i/\text{data}) = \frac{P(\text{data}/\text{Exposure}_i) \times P(\text{Exposure}_i)}{\Sigma[P(\text{data}/\text{Exposure}_i) \times P(\text{Exposure}_i)]} \quad (6)$$

Defining the Prior

Heuristics, also referred to as subliminal or subconscious models, mask assumptions associated with exposure judgments. Using an approach for rendering an initial judgment that defines assumptions explicitly, allowing those assumptions to be evaluated and refined, facilitates validation and calibration of the judgment. A suite of simple tier-one and -two mathematical models for which the assumptions are clearly defined is available in spreadsheet format freeware called IH MOD. This tool can be downloaded from the AIHA Exposure Assessment Strategies Web site (AIHA 2009).

Applying these models requires the assessor to provide values for the model's input parameters; in other words, the *determinants of exposure*. While this approach does not eliminate the subjective element in decision making, it may help focus the assessor on the specific workplace or task parameters and thereby reduce bias associated with a heuristics approach (Vadali et al. 2009).

The models use physical and chemical principles to predict behavior of chemical, and to a lesser degree, physical agents. Parameter uncertainty is more visible when defining values for the determinants (model inputs) than it is with a heuristic, especially when a probabilistic approach is used. The explicit definition of assumptions upon which the model is based highlights the possibility of alternative outcomes that may help mitigate overconfidence in our decision making. Of course, if there is insufficient information available to apply even a simple model, the prior can be defined as uniform or flat, in which case the probability of an exposure belonging in any one of the four defined exposure categories is defined as equally likely.

Defining the Likelihood

The likelihood estimate is defined by the objective sampling data. Freeware Bayesian analysis tools are available that can accommodate sample sizes as small as N = 1. Likelihood data can be added iteratively as needed until the desired level of confidence in the posterior judgment is reached. As with all very small data sets, the assessor must be careful to ensure the uncertainty is taken into account when rendering a judgment. A more robust likelihood estimate has greater influence on the posterior judgment.

The Posterior Judgment

When the prior and likelihood estimates have been entered, an updated posterior judgment is calculated. This is the normalized outcome of the integrated subjective and objective inputs. The posterior expresses the probability of the exposure belonging in any one of the four AIHA exposure decision categories (see Figure 7). This can also be interpreted as defining the

Exposure Decision Category	Recommended Control
1 (< 10% of OEL)	General HazCom
2 (10–50% of OEL)	+ chemical-specific HazCom
3 (50–100% of OEL)	+ exposure surveillance, medical surveillance, work practices
4 (> 100% of OEL)	+ respirators, engineering controls, work-practice controls

FIGURE 7. Exposure decision categories
(*Source:* Ignacio and Bullock 2006)

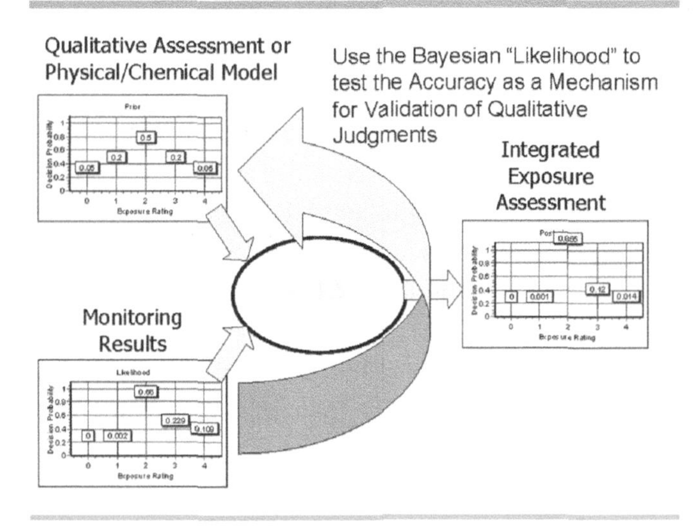

FIGURE 8. Bayesian decision analysis feedback loop (*Source:* Logan 2011)

confidence level in the exposure belonging to a particular category. In this way, the assessor can quantify his or her confidence in the exposure judgment.

The Feedback Loop

It is the posterior judgment that provides critical feedback to calibrate one's professional judgment. The posterior judgment is compared with the initial assessment to determine how well calibrated the decisions are. Ideally, several scenarios across all four categories will be evaluated. Judgments for which robust likelihood estimates are available are recommended to ensure accurate calibration. These data sets also provide an opportunity to validate the models (and other semi-quantitative assessments). A model is considered a good

CASE STUDY

Iron Foundry Phenol Exposures

(EASC Foundry Workshop Project Team 2009)

Basic Characterization

Workers at a small custom iron foundry make and fill molds with molten metal to meet customers' specifications. In one operation, shell-core operators use a resin-coated sand matrix to produce a mold which then shapes the metal part. Phenol is added to the matrix as a binder. According to section 2 of the MSDS, phenol is present at 1–5%. The OSHA PEL for phenol is listed as 5 ppm (19 mg/m^3).

There are three shell-core workstations located together in an area approximately 5 m x 5 m x 5m. At each workstation, there is a mold press into which the sand matrix is gravity fed, a worktable on which the mold is removed from the core, a cart for stacking the finished molds, and a recycle bin for rejected molds. Each press is situated under a canopy hood, and local airflow is augmented by a radial fan located just past the third workstation.

The operator spends the entire work shift at his workstation. He sequentially fills the mold with the sand matrix, triggers the press to apply heat and pressure, then removes the mold from the press by hand. The mold is still hot so the operator wears a thermally insulating glove on one hand to hold the mold and applies a file to remove any imperfections with the other. The mold is then placed on the cart, and the process is repeated. The operator periodically cleans the surface area surrounding the press and his worktable using an air hose.

In many cases, this is the extent of information upon which the exposure assessor would be expected to render a judgment regarding exposure. Based on previous experience with foundry operations, the assessor makes an initial judgment and concludes the exposure is most likely a category 3 or 4. He decides to gather additional data and information to refine this judgment.

The assessor decides to collect two personal samples and while on site takes some basic measurements around the operator's work area. Using an anemometer, he documents local airflow readings, s, and determines that the air movement is random, not directional. He also measures the work area and confirms it is 25 m^2 with ceilings that are approximately 5 m high.

The facility has mechanical ventilation, but the assessor was not able to obtain exact airflow data from building records, nor was it feasible to take airflow readings directly. He estimated based on the general feel of air movement in the area that the airflow, Q, was probably moving at 4–5 air changes per hour (ACH).

Finally, the assessor collects more information on the emission rate of phenol from the molds over an 8-hour shift. Using production information and knowledge gathered from the operators, he estimates the emission rate, G, to be 16 mg/min.

The assessor now has enough information to apply The two-box or near-field/far-field model (see Figure 9), which accounts for the contaminant source being located close to the worker. A detailed description of this and other tier 1 and 2 models is presented elsewhere (Keil et al. 2009). This model was previously evaluated and shown to be a good fit for this kind of scenario.

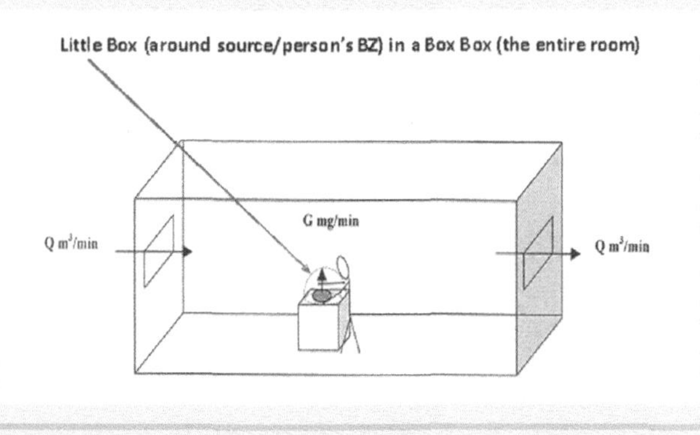

FIGURE 9. Two-box or near-field/far-field model (*Source:* Nicas 2005)

Near-Field Concentration

$$C_N(t) = \frac{G}{(\beta/\beta + Q)Q} + G\left(\frac{\beta\sqrt{Q} + \lambda_2\sqrt{V_N}\,(\beta + Q)}{\beta\sqrt{Q}\sqrt{V_N}\,(\lambda_1 - \lambda_2)}\right)\exp(\lambda_1\, t) - G\left(\frac{\beta\sqrt{Q} + \lambda_1\sqrt{V_N}\,(\beta + Q)}{\beta\sqrt{Q}\sqrt{V_N}\,(\lambda_1 - \lambda_2)}\right)\exp(\lambda_2\, t) \qquad (7)$$

Far-Field Concentration

$$C_F(t) = \frac{G}{Q} + G\left(\frac{\lambda_1\sqrt{V_N} + \beta}{\beta}\right)\left(\frac{\beta\sqrt{Q} + \lambda_2\sqrt{V_N}\,(\beta + Q)}{\beta\sqrt{Q}\sqrt{V_N}\,(\lambda_1 - \lambda_2)}\right)\exp(\lambda_1\, t) - G\left(\frac{\lambda_2\sqrt{V_N} + \beta}{\beta}\right)\left(\frac{\beta\sqrt{Q} + \lambda_1\sqrt{V_N}\,(\beta + Q)}{\beta\sqrt{Q}\sqrt{V_N}\,(\lambda_1 - \lambda_2)}\right)\exp(\lambda_2\, t) \qquad (8)$$

where $\lambda_1 = 0.5\left[-\left(\frac{\beta\sqrt{V_F} + V_N(\beta + Q)}{V_N\sqrt{V_F}}\right) + \sqrt{\left(\frac{\beta\sqrt{V_F} + V_N(\beta + Q)}{V_N\sqrt{V_F}}\right)^2 - 4\left(\frac{\beta\sqrt{Q}}{V_N\sqrt{V_F}}\right)}\,\right]$

and $\lambda_2 = 0.5\left[-\left(\frac{\beta\sqrt{V_F} + V_N(\beta + Q)}{V_N\sqrt{V_F}}\right) - \sqrt{\left(\frac{\beta\sqrt{V_F} + V_N(\beta + Q)}{V_N\sqrt{V_F}}\right)^2 - 4\left(\frac{\beta\sqrt{Q}}{\sqrt{V_N}\,V_F}\right)}\,\right]$

With time, if steady-state conditions are reached, the equations are simplified:

Near-Field Concentration (Steady State)

$$C_{N,SS} = \frac{G}{Q} + \frac{G}{\beta} \qquad (9)$$

Far-Field Concentration (Steady State)

$$C_{F,SS} = \frac{G}{Q} \qquad (10)$$

Using the defined parameter values, the model predicts an inner box or near-field 8-hour exposure of 0.19 mg/m^3. This point estimate represents an average daily exposure. To be consistent with the AIHA categorical framework, the assessor must reconcile this estimate with the 95th percentile exposure. Recognizing that the average exposure value is two orders of magnitude below the PEL, he concludes the upper tail is probably not more than an order of magnitude greater than the average exposure estimate. Based on this assumption, the assessor adjusts his judgment downward to a category 1 exposure.

The assessor could have used a more complex method to estimate a 95th percentile exposure from the model by using a probabilistic approach. Several add-in tools are available commercially or as freeware. In this case, instead of using point estimates to define the model inputs, he would use ranges or distributions, and running through the calculations iteratively, say, 1000 times, would yield a distribution of 1000 outputs. The mean and 95th percentile of predicted exposures would then be quantified.

After the normal turnaround time, the assessor receives from the lab the results for the two personal samples that were collected. The results (0.06, 1.6 mg/m^3) represent 8-hour TWA exposures. An $N = 2$ does not allow for a conventional statistical analysis, but these data can be used to define the Bayesian likelihood estimate in the Bayesian decision analysis framework. The likelihood estimate can also be compared with the model-prior to evaluate the model's fit for this kind of scenario.

Inputting the values for the model-prior and likelihood estimates, Bayes' theorem is used to calculate the updated posterior judgment (see Figure 10).

The exposure is most likely a category 1. In fact, we can say that, based upon the model and sampling data, there is a 65% probability the exposure is a category 1. This is the refined exposure judgment. Note that the initial judgment was a category 3 or 4.

In addition to refining the exposure judgment, using the semiquantitative modeling estimate and monitoring data collaboratively yields a more robust assessment and provides the assessor with valuable feedback about the true exposure category. This allows him to calibrate his exposure judgment. Well-calibrated exposure judgments are more likely to support appropriate risk-management decisions and policy.

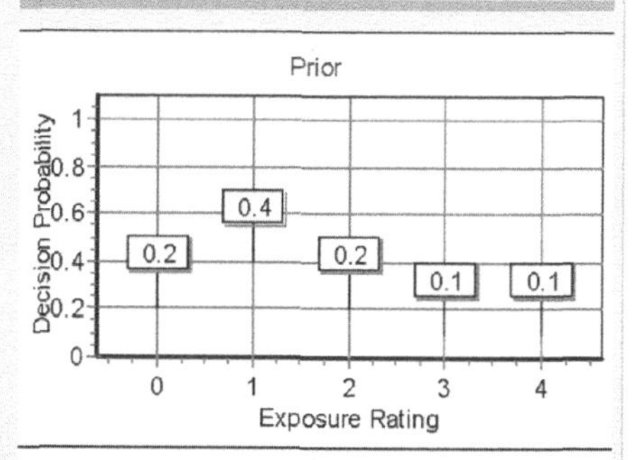

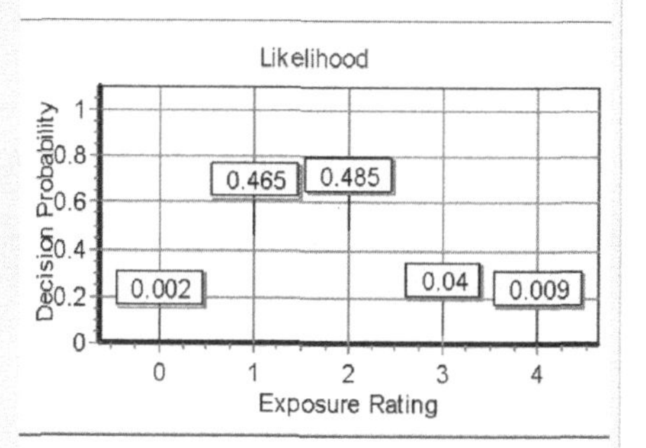

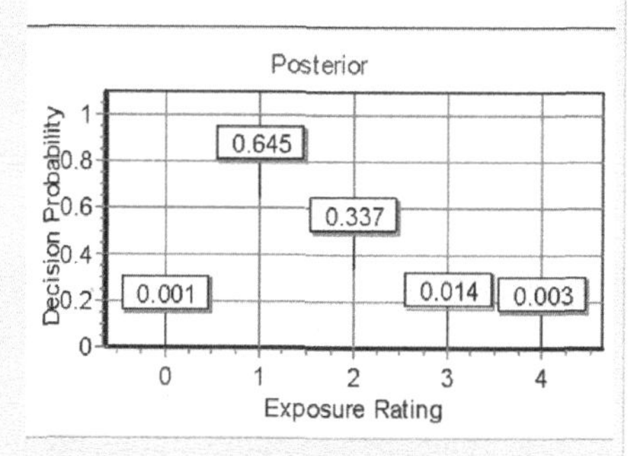

FIGURE 10. The final Bayesian decision analysis
(*Source:* EASC Foundry Workshop Team 2009)

fit when the prior exposure category predicted as most probable for a specific scenario is consistent with the likelihood exposure category.

Using the Bayesian decision framework provides a systematic, transparent framework for integrating both subjective and objective professional judgment inputs. It also provides a valuable feedback loop for calibrating and improving professional judgments (see Figure 8). Initial assessments based on heuristics provide efficient but often inaccurate judgments. Semiquantitative tools such as mathematical modeling can provide a more robust and balanced basis on which to make prior judgments, especially when the assessor is required to render a decision based on an incomplete data set.

Role Within OSH Programs

Exposure assessment has matured from the compliance mode (e.g., is the highest exposure less than the OEL?) to comprehensive assessment (e.g., characterization of all exposures on all days to all workers). The comprehensive approach allows the OEHS professional to focus resources on areas of high priority and, therefore, operate in a more efficient manner than the compliance approach. Additionally, the iterative nature of the comprehensive approach forces the OEHS professional to update information for each SEG on a regular cycle. Therefore, the OEHS professional is better able to manage risks to protect workers at the present time, and to anticipate and avoid future risks.

Conclusion

OEHS professionals have increasingly incorporated the concepts of risk assessment and management into their practice. Conducting a risk assessment requires knowledge of the toxicity or hazard of environmental agents and of worker exposure to these environmental agents. Toxicity measures are typically obtained from standard reference sources, but exposure assessment is a site-specific activity. Risk is characterized by comparing the results from the exposure assessment with the toxicity measures. Risk-management activities are initiated by a finding of unacceptable risk resulting from exposure to occupational hazards. Risk communication is a continual, two-way dialogue involving all relevant stakeholders. A comprehensive understanding of the toxicity and other hazardous properties of an environmental agent, exposures to that agent, and the resulting risk leads to better management of OEHS programs.

Endnotes

[1]A qualitative risk characterization would utilize verbal descriptors, such as low, medium, or high risk. A quantitative process might express the risk of exposure to a toxicant under a particular scenario as 1 case per 1000 persons exposed, or 1×10^{-3}. A semiquantitative risk description would have both verbal and numeric descriptors—for example, a high probability of 15–20 percent of a work force absent with pandemic flu during a 2–3-week period.

[2]Unlike "pure" risk assessment, in which the assessment is conducted entirely by scientists with little or no field experience, occupational risk assessment and management tend to be more integrated. The familiarity of the risk profile and more realistic expectations of control measure options promote a more grounded approach to risk management. That is, the OEHS professional tends to better appreciate the practical limitations of engineering controls, PPE, and administrative controls and can make risk management recommendations accordingly.

[3]In some situations, more in-depth methods—including wipe samples, biomonitoring, dermal absorption, and/or evaluation of environmental exposure—are needed to manage exposures to occupational airborne hazards.

[4]A *breach* is a rupture or break in containment—for example, for sampling (intentional) or a leak (unintentional).

[5]OSHA's introduction to risk assessment was the July 1980 U.S. Supreme Court decision striking down the benzene standard. The court found that OSHA failed to show that the benzene standard would prevent a "significant risk in the workplace," suggesting that 10–3 is a significant risk and 10–7 is not. OSHA has thus incorporated risk assessment into the standard-setting process (e.g., ethylene oxide, formaldehyde, and methylene chloride).

[6]In random sampling, each worker has an equal probability of being selected for personal monitoring. This is a basic premise of common statistical tests used in exposure evaluation and should be the goal of any sample selection method. Much sampling intended to be "random" is actually "representative." For a comprehensive discussion of the designation of similar exposure groups, and the selection, number, and duration of samples, refer to Ignacio and Bullock (2006).

[7]For more than 30 years, the AIHA's Industrial Hygiene Laboratory Accreditation Program (IHLAP) has been accrediting labs that analyze samples collected in the workplace. Labs that have been accredited through IHLAP must meet defined standards for performance based on a variety of criteria,

resulting in a high level of professional performance. Criteria evaluated include personnel qualifications, results from participation in the Proficiency Analytical Testing (PAT) program, facilities, quality control procedures, laboratory records, methods of analysis, and the results of site visits to the laboratories. The AIHA IHLAP is the largest program of its kind in the world and has been in operation since 1974.

[8]Blanks are the same sampling media used to collect the personal samples. The blanks are generally opened in the area where samples are taken and immediately resealed. They are analyzed along with the personal samples to ensure that the sampling media are not contaminated.

[8]The limit of detection (LoD) must be distinguished from the limit of quantitation (LoQ). LoD is the smallest quantity or concentration required by a method to reliably determine presence or absence of a compound. LoQ is the smallest quantity or concentration required by a method to reliably determine the amount present. The LoD is lower than the LoQ.

References

American Conference of Governmental Industrial Hygienists (ACGIH). 2001. *Air Sampling Instrumentation*. 9th ed. Cincinnati: ACGIH.

______. 2004. *Air Monitoring for Toxic Exposures*. 2d ed. Cincinnati: ACGIH.

______. 2007. *TLVs® and BEIs®. Threshold Limit Values for Chemical Substances and Physical Agents: Biological Exposure Indices*. Updated annually. Cincinnati: ACGIH.

American Industrial Hygiene Association (AIHA). 2002. *Emergency Response Planning Guidelines and Workplace Environmental Exposure Level Guides Handbook*. Fairfax, VA: AIHA Press.

American Society for Testing and Materials (ASTM). 2003 (May 10). ASTM D6196-03. *Standard Practice for Selection of Sorbents, Sampling, and Thermal Desorption Analysis Procedures for Volatile Organic Compounds in Air* (retrieved July 21, 2007). West Conshohocken, PA: ASTM. www.techstreet.com/cgi-bin/detail?product_id1094393

Bales, J. 2006. "Health Fears Lead Schools to Dismantle Wireless Networks: Radiation Levels Blamed for Illnesses." *Times Online* (retrieved July 21, 2007). www.timesonline.co.uk/tol/life_and_style/education/article642575.ece

Barnes, D. G. 1993. Conference on the Risk Assessment Paradigm After Ten Years: Policy and Practice Then, Now and in the Future. Washington, D.C.: EPA.

______. 1994. "Times Are Tough—Brother, Can You Paradigm?" *Risk Analysis* 14:219–223.

Bisesi, M. S. 2004. *Bisesi and Kohn's Industrial Hygiene Evaluation Methods*. 2d ed. Boca Raton, FL: Lewis Publishers.

Brief, R. S., and R. A. Scala. 1975. "Occupational Exposure Limits for Novel Work Schedules." *American Industrial Hygiene Association Journal* 36:467–469.

Burke, Thomas A. 2011. "Improving Risk Assessment Approaches and Ensuring Consistency in Risk Assessment." Presented at the 2nd International Conference on Risk Assessment, Brussels, Belgium.

Caplan, K. J., and J. Lynch. 1996. "A Need and an Opportunity. AIHA Should Assume a Leadership Role in Reforming Risk Assessment." *American Industrial Hygiene Association Journal* 57:231–237.

Covello, V. T., P. M. Sandman, and P. Slovic. 1988. *Risk Communication, Risk Statistics, and Risk Comparisons: A Manual for Plant Managers*. Appendix C, p. 54 (retrieved January 15, 2007). Washington, DC: Chemical Manufacturers Association. www.psandman.com/articles/cma-appc.htm

DiNardi, S. R., ed. 2003. *The Occupational Environment: Its Evaluation, Control, and Management*. Fairfax, VA: AIHA Press.

Environmental Protection Agency. (EPA) n.d.a. *The Development of Acute Exposure Guideline Levels (AEGLs)* (retrieved July 21, 2007). www.epa.gov/opptintr/aegl/

______. n.d.b. *Human Health* (retrieved July 21, 2007). www.epa.gov/ebtpages/humanhealth.html

______. 1986. *Guidelines for Mutagenicity Risk Assessment*. Washington, D.C.: EPA.

______. 1988. *Guidelines for Ecological Risk Assessment*. Washington, D.C.: EPA.

______. 1991. *Guidelines for Developmental Toxicity Assessment*. Washington, D.C.: EPA.

______. 1996. *Guidelines for Reproductive Toxicity Risk Assessment*. Washington, D.C.: EPA.

______. 1998. *Guidelines for Neurotoxicity Risk Assessment*. Washington, D.C.: EPA.

______. 2005a. *Supplemental Guidance for Assessing Susceptibility from Early-Life Exposure to Carcinogens*. Washington, D.C.: EPA.

______. 2005b. *U.S. EPA Guidelines on Carcinogen Risk Assessment*. Washington, D.C.: EPA.

______. 2006a. *National Ambient Air Quality Standards (NAAQS)* (retrieved February 25, 2007). www.epa.gov/air/criteria.html

______. 2006b. *Framework for Assessing Health Risks of Environmental Exposures to Children*. Washington, D.C.: EPA.

______. 2007. *Framework for Metals Risk Assessment*. Washington, D.C.: EPA.

______. 2008. *Cumulative Health Risk Assessment of Multiple Chemical Exposures*. Washington, D.C.: EPA.

Environment Canada. 1999. "Canadian Environmental Protection Act, Environmental Registry." Gatineau, Quebec, Canada (retrieved March 18, 2007). www.ec.gc.ca/CEPARegistry/the_act

European Commission. 2006. "Registration, Evaluation, Authorisation, and Restriction of Chemicals" (retrieved March 18, 2007). Brussels, Belgium: European Commission, Joint Research Centre. ec.europa.eu/enterprise/reach/index_en.htm

Exposure Assessment Strategies Committee (EASC) Foundry Workshop Team. 2009. "Iron Foundry Phenol Exposures." Presented at Advancements in Exposure Assessment: Decision Making in a Changing World. Vancouver, B.C.

Fischhoff, B., S. Lichtenstein, P. Slovic, and D. Keeney. 1981. *Acceptable Risk*. Cambridge: Cambridge University Press.

Government Accounting Office (GAO). 2006. GAO-06-1032T. *Chemical Regulation: Actions Are Needed to Improve the Effectiveness of EPA's Chemical Review Program*. Washington, D.C.: U.S. Government Printing Office.

Health and Safety Executive (HSE) (Great Britain). n.d. "COSHH Essentials Wheel." www.coshh-essentials.org.uk/

Ignacio, J. S., and W. H. Bullock. 2006. *A Strategy for Assessing and Managing Occupational Exposures*. 3d ed. Fairfax, VA: AIHA Press.

Jayjock, M. A. 2003. Chapter 8, "Modeling Inhalation Exposure." In S. R. DiNardi, ed. *The Occupational Environment: Its Evaluation, Control, and Management*. 2d ed. Fairfax, VA: AIHA Press.

Jayjock, M. A., J. R. Lynch, and D. I. Nelson. 2000. *Fundamentals of Risk Assessment for the Industrial Hygienist*. Fairfax, VA: AIHA Press.

Jordan, R. C. 2003. Chapter 42, "Quality Control for Sampling and Laboratory Analysis." In S. R. DiNardi, ed. *The Occupational Environment: Its Evaluation, Control, and Management*. 2d ed. Fairfax, VA: AIHA Press.

Keil, C. B., ed. 2000. *Mathematical Models for Estimating Occupational Exposure to Chemicals*. Fairfax, VA: AIHA Press.

Keil, C. B., C. E. Simmons, and T. R. Anthony. 2009. *Mathematical Models for Estimating Occupational Exposures to Chemicals*. 2d ed. Fairfax, VA: AIHA Press.

Klonne, D. R. 2003. Chapter 3, "Occupational Exposure Limits." In S. R. DiNardi, ed. *The Occupational Environment: Its Evaluation, Control, and Management*. 2d ed. Fairfax, VA: AIHA Press.

Logan, Perry, Ramachandran Gurumurthy, John Mulhausen, and Paul Hewett. 2009. "Occupational Exposure Decisions: Can Limited Data Interpretation Training Help Improve Accuracy?" *Ann. Occup. Hyg.*, Vol. 53, No. 4, pp. 311–324.

Logan, Perry. 2011. "Professional Judgment in Exposure Assessment Decision Making." Proceedings of the American Industrial Hygiene Conference and Exhibition, Portland, Oregon.

McMichael, A J. 1976. "Standardized Mortality Ratios and the 'Healthy Worker Effect': Scratching Beneath the Surface." *J Occup Med*. 18(3):165–8.

Meek, M. 2011. "Risk Assessment of Combined Exposure to Multiple Chemicals: A WHO/IPCS Framework." *Regulatory Toxicology and Pharmacology* 60(2):S1-S14.

Mine Safety Appliances (MSA). n.d. Catalog. Pittsburgh, PA (retrieved July 21, 2007). www.msanorthamerica.com/catalog/

Mulhausen, J. R., and J. Damiano. 2003. Chapter 6, "Comprehensive Exposure Assessment." In S. R. DiNardi, ed. *The Occupational Environment: Its Evaluation, Control, and Management*. 2d ed. Fairfax, VA: AIHA Press.

National Institute for Occupational Safety and Health (NIOSH). 1994. Schlecht, P. C., and P. F. O'Connor, eds. DHHS-NIOSH Publication 94-113, *NIOSH Manual of Analytical Methods (NMAM®)*. 4th ed. (August, 1994). 1st Supplement Publication 96-135 (1996). 2d Supplement Publication 98-119 (1998). 3d Supplement 2003-154 (2003) (retrieved July 21, 2007). www.cdc.gov/niosh/nmam/

______. 2005. DHHS-NIOSH Publication No. 2005-149, *NIOSH Pocket Guide to Chemical Hazards* (retrieved July 21, 2007). www.cdc.gov/niosh/npg/default.html

National Research Council (NRC), Committee on the Institutional Means for Assessment of Risks to Public Health, Commission on Life Sciences. 1983. *Risk Assessment in the Federal Government: Managing the Process*. Washington, D.C.: National Academy Press. (Also known as the "Red Book.")

______. Committee on Improving Risk Analysis Approaches Used by the U.S. EPA. 2009. *Science and Decisions: Advancing Risk Assessment*. Washington, D.C.: National Academy Press.

Nelson, D. I. 1991. "Health and Safety Training for Removal of Underground Storage Tanks." *Applied Occupational and Environmental Hygiene* 6(12):1015–1019.

Nelson, D. I., F. Mirer, G. Bratt, and D. O. Anderson. 2003. Chapter 9, "Risk Assessment in the Workplace." In S. R. DiNardi, ed. *The Occupational Environment: Its Evaluation, Control, and Management*. 2d ed. Fairfax, VA: AIHA Press.

Nicas, M. 2005. "Mathematical Models for Assessing Exposure to Indoor Air Contaminants." Proceedings of the American Industrial Hygiene Conference and Exhibition, Anaheim, CA.

______. 2006. Appendix I, "Estimating Airborne Exposure by Mathematical Modeling." In J. L. Ignacio and W. H. Bullock, eds. *A Strategy for Assessing and Managing Occupational Exposures*. 3d ed. Fairfax, VA: AIHA Press.

Occupational Safety and Health Act (OSH Act). 1970. Public Law 91-596, 84 STAT. 1590, 91st Congress, S.2193, December 29, 1970, as amended through January 1, 2004 (retrieved February 25, 2007). www.osha.gov/pls/oshaweb/owadisp.show_document?p_table=OSHACT&p_id=3356

Occupational Safety and Health Administration (OSHA). 1971. "Limits for Air Contaminants." *Code of Federal Regulations*, Title 29, Section 1910.1000.

______. 1989. *Air Contaminants (Amended Final Rule, January 1989). Preamble to Final Rule. Section 6—VI. Health Effects Discussion and Determination of Final PEL* (retrieved July 21, 2007). www.osha.gov/pls/oshaweb/owadisp.show_document?p_table=PREAMBLES&p_id=770

______. 1999. OSHA Policy Regarding PEL Adjustments for Extended Work Shifts, 11/10/1999 (retrieved September 3, 2006). www.osha.gov/pls/oshaweb/owadisp.show_document?p_table=INTERPRETATIONS&p_id=22818

______. Undated. *Safety and Health Topics: Sampling and Analysis* (retrieved July 21, 2007). www.osha.gov/SLTC/samplinganalysis/index.html

O'Hagan, Anthony, Caitlin E. Buck, Alirez Daneshkhah, J. Richard Eiser, Paul H. Garthwaite, David J. Jenkinson, Jeremy, E. Oakley, and Tim Rakow. 2006. Chapter 3, "The Psychology of Judgement Under Uncertainty." In *Uncertain Judgments Eliciting Experts' Probabilities*. West Sussex, England: John Wiley & Sons, Ltd.

Olishifski, J. B., and B. A. Plog. 1988. Chapter 1, "Overview of Industrial Hygiene." In B. A. Plog, G. S. Benjamin, and M. A. Kerwin, eds. *Fundamentals of Industrial Hygiene*. 3d ed. Itasca, IL: National Safety Council.

Paustenbach, D. J. 2000. "Pharmacokinetics and Unusual Work Schedules." In R. L. Harris, ed. *Patty's Industrial Hygiene*. 5th ed., vol. 3, pp 1787–1901. New York: John Wiley & Sons.

Plog, B. A., and P. J. Quinlan. 2002. *Fundamentals of Industrial Hygiene*. 5th ed. Itasca, IL: National Safety Council.

SKC, Inc. n.d. "Help with Air Sampling" (retrieved July 21, 2007). www.skcinc.com/help.asp

The Lifeline Group. 2007. *Complex Exposure Tool (CEPST)* (retrieved March 18, 2007). www.thelifelinegroup.org

Toxic Substances Control Act (TSCA). 1976. Title 15, Chapter 53, 15 USC s/s 2601 et seq. www.access.gpo.gov/uscode/title15/chapter53_.html

Vadali, Monika, Gurumurthy Ramachandran, and John Mulhausen. 2009. "Exposure Modeling in Occupational Hygiene Decison Making." *Journal of Occupational and Environmental Hygiene* 6:6:353–362.

Appendix: Recommended Reading

Milz, S. A., R. G. Conrad, and R. D. Soule. 2003. Chapter 7, "Principles of Evaluating Worker Exposure." In S. R. DiNardi, ed. *The Occupational Environment: Its Evaluation, Control, and Management*. 2d ed. Fairfax, VA: AIHA Press.

Ramachandran, G. 2005. *Occupational Exposure Assessment for Air Contaminants*. Boca Raton, FL: Taylor & Francis Group.

3

CHEMICAL HAZARDS

William Piispanen

LEARNING OBJECTIVES

- Understand chemical terminology as it applies to workplace safety.
- Possess a basic understanding of industrial hygiene chemical sampling techniques and the limitations of the methods.
- Be familiar with safe workplace practices for working with chemicals.

CHEMISTRY IS one of the oldest and most basic of the sciences. Early chemists were concerned with the basic essential elements—the air we breathe, the water we drink, and fire as the source of energy. The quest for many scientists was identifying the basic elements that constituted our world. Further experimentation turned to the transforming of materials from lesser value to richer value through alchemy. Early experiments by the English physicist and chemist John Dalton led to the concept that basic elemental materials were constituents of everything that made up the living world. Finally, in 1869 the idea of a periodic table of the elements was developed to explain similarities in material character (Pauling 1970, 144–145). Additional research based on this ordering of chemical substances led to the theory of elements combining to form new chemical compounds. With this growing understanding of chemical properties came the use of new chemical compounds and materials in industrial applications. The world was changing as new products were introduced into the marketplace and new jobs were developed to create those products.

We have come a long way from these early discoveries, but new elements are still being added to the periodic table as complex experiments continue to probe the very nature of matter. From a safety and health perspective, we know that some combinations of elements are not only safe to use but are also essential to life, whereas the same elements combined in a different formula can be poisonous or can introduce hazardous chemicals to the workplace. Sodium chloride, or table salt, is a good example. Considered by many people to be absolutely necessary for the enjoyment of some foods, this compound can be disassociated to the elements of sodium and chlorine. The element sodium (Na) is an extremely hazardous material in the workplace because of its ability to generate explosive hydrogen gas when it contacts water. Chlorine (Cl) gas is poisonous to any life form and is also corrosive and reactive in nature. But where would we be without common table salt, NaCl? This chapter discusses the role of chemistry in the practice of safety, identifies sources for chemical safety information, and provides a basis for understanding how the professional practice of industrial hygiene protects worker health.

Chemicals in the Workplace

Although the understanding that some workplace materials can contribute to illnesses and disease is hardly a new revelation—the published studies of Ramazzini in 1713 (Ramazzini 1964) showed correlations between disease and certain occupations—the study of occupational diseases associated with worker exposure to specific chemicals, either as raw materials or as unwanted waste products, is relatively recent. Early correlations of workplace exposure to hazardous chemicals is usually traced to the late eighteenth and early nineteenth centuries when studies showed the correlation between London chimney sweeps and incidences of scrotal cancer. In the twentieth century, studies of mortality from lung and bladder cancer in steel workers identified coal tar pitch as a hazardous workplace chemical. Later studies by the U.S. Public Health Services looked at incidence rates of lung cancer in asbestos workers and other lung disease in granite quarry workers exposed to crystalline silica dust.

The Occupational Safety and Health Act was passed in 1970, and with it was created the Occupational Safety and Health Administration (OSHA). This agency of the federal government was charged with setting workplace exposure limits for select hazardous chemicals and materials. The initial permissible exposure limits (PELS) were based on existing occupational exposure limits published by the American Conference of Industrial Hygienists (ACGIH) or the American National Standards Institute (ANSI). In the United States there are published occupational exposure limits for well over 400 substances considered hazardous to human health.

Occupational exposure limits are defined for acceptable limits of worker exposure to potentially hazardous materials. It is important to understand that these limits are defined for healthy workers with an assumption of lifetime exposure based on 8 hours per day and 40 hours per week exposure. Some chemicals may pose a potential risk of cancer in either animals or humans, and these chemicals, mixtures of chemicals, or exposure circumstances associated with technological processes are identified in technical literature; see U.S. Department of Health and Human Services (DHHS), *Report on Carcinogens*, published as a biennial report per Section 262 of Public Law 95-622 (CDC 2004). In the case of substances that are known to be or reasonably anticipated to be human carcinogens, worker exposure should be minimized to the lowest feasible concentration (LFC) unless there are quantitative occupational recommended exposure limits (RELs) based on human and/or animal data as well as on technological feasibility (U.S. DHHS 2005, Appendix A).

The definitions included at the end of this chapter are those used in regulations and technical literature to describe chemical hazards and the methods used to measure or monitor these materials in the workplace (Washington Group International 2005, 4.2–4.4). Other terminology and units of measure may be found in technical literature concerning community health regulations (such as Title X of Housing Urban Development, which describes acceptable levels of contamination in public and family housing) or environmental regulations promulgated by Environmental Protection Agency (EPA) regulations, or the transportation of a hazardous material and soluble compounds on public means of transit, as described in the Department of Transportation regulations (49 CFR 172.101).

Recognizing Common Occupational Health Hazards

An occupational illness is any abnormal condition or disorder, other than an occupational injury, that is caused by exposure to environmental factors associated with the work environment.

There are six major categories of occupational illnesses (ANSI 1977, A2.8):

1. ***Occupational skin diseases or disorders.*** Examples: dermatitis (the most common occupational illness), eczema, or rash caused by irritants such as cement or poisonous plants; chemical burns from contact with strong acids or bases; chloracne, which may be a symptom of skin contact with chlorinated chemicals such as PCBs; or generalized inflammation or allergic response from exposure to chemicals such as isocyanates in paint formulations.
2. ***Dust diseases of the lungs.*** Examples: silicosis, asbestosis, coal workers' pneumoconiosis, and other pneumoconiosis.
3. ***Respiratory conditions caused by toxic agents.*** Examples: pneumonitis, pharyngitis, rhinitis, or acute congestion. This may be the result of allergic reactions in some cases.
4. ***Poisoning.*** Examples: poisoning by lead, mercury, arsenic, or other metals; carbon monoxide or other gases; organic solvents; insecticide sprays; and chemicals such as resins.
5. ***Disorders caused by physical agents.*** Examples: heatstroke, sunstroke, heat exhaustion, freezing, frostbite, caisson disease, hearing loss, effects of radiation and X-rays, sunburn, and flash burn. Although not directly attributable to chemical exposure, some physical injuries do result from contact with chemical products, such as direct skin contact with liquefied nitrogen causing freezing of the skin.
6. ***Disorders caused by repeated trauma.*** Examples: hearing loss, swelling of the joints, and other conditions due to repeated motion, vibration, or pressure. These disorders are not generally considered related to chemical exposure.

When considering possible occupational diseases that may be related to chemical exposures in the workplace, it is necessary to examine the chemicals in their physical forms that would exist in typical work environments. In many cases, it is possible for chemicals to exist in more than one physical form, so the following discussion is not to be considered exclusive, and the safety professional should review the MSDS and other technical information regarding the safety of any industrial chemical in use on the job site or in the work environment. More recently, chemical hazards considered to be reproductive or development toxicants are considered important in addressing chemical safety (see Quigley et al 2010 for an overview of reproductive toxicants).

Gases, Vapors, Mists, and Fumes

Industrial Sources

Gases, vapors, mists, and fumes in the workplace originate from many sources. These sources are normally controlled to limit the release of the materials into the workplace. In the case of flammable storage areas, volatile vapors are captured by air-handling systems, and containment of the solvents in containers or storage units limits the release of vapors. In chemical processes, generated vapors and gases may be captured by air-handling systems such as covers and air shrouds over the process, as in the case of dip or pickling tanks. In operations such as spray painting, the over-spray and excess paint spray is captured in spray booths or with water curtains to limit the spread of paint-spray materials. Fumes that can be generated in hot torch-cutting or welding operations are more difficult to contain, but point-of-use air capture is available to limit worker exposure to the airborne metal fumes. An unplanned or uncontrolled release, such as spills of solvents or breaks in process lines, have the potential for high exposure levels in the immediate work area and for dissipation to other work areas and the environment. In all cases, it is critical to understand both the degree of toxicity to the worker and the physical parameters that affect the degree of dispersal.

Potential Routes of Occupational Exposure

Toxic or irritant gases, vapors, fumes, or mists can enter the human body in four ways (Schaper and Bisesi 1998, 67):

1. Inhalation—breathing in through the nose or mouth.

2. Ingestion—generally considered hand-to-mouth transfer of material.
3. Absorption—typically considered direct skin contact and transfer through the pore structure.
4. Injection—mechanical penetration of material through the outer skin layer.

The most common form of exposure is through inhalation, which is the focus of this section. The degree of hazard associated with mist and fume inhalation depends on the toxicity, concentration, size, and solubility of the aerosol particles. Gases and vapors are subject to molecular diffusion characteristics, and the degree of hazard is more dependent on the chemical toxicity of the compound or the degree of irritation or chemical reactive damage caused by chemical reaction with throat and lung tissues. Important parameters that affect inhalation hazards include the following:

- Particles larger than 10 microns in size are usually trapped in the nasal passages, throat, larynx, trachea (windpipe), and bronchi (tubes from windpipe leading into lungs), causing local irritation or more permanent tissue damage.
- Particles smaller than 10 microns in size may be deposited deeply within the lungs. These particles may then affect large areas of the body, producing systemic effects that are typical of heavy metals such as lead, or they may damage the lung tissue locally as with silica or asbestos.
- Certain inert gases and vapors have the capability of displacing oxygen and causing simple asphyxiation. Some typical examples are nitrogen, propane, helium, methane, argon, carbon monoxide, and hydrogen sulfide. Simple asphyxiants (e.g., argon and nitrogen) displace oxygen in the surrounding air, and chemical asphyxiants (e.g., carbon monoxide and hydrogen sulfide) displace oxygen in the body.
- The acceptable standards for the maximum exposure to regulated hazardous substances are listed in 29 CFR, in Part 1910.1000, Subpart Z, of the OSHA general industry standards and in Part 1926.55 of the construction standards.
- The acceptable standards for the maximum allowable exposure to unregulated hazardous substances are NIOSH's recommended exposure limits (RELs), ACGIH threshold limit values, and/or AIHA workplace exposure limits (see definitions for ACGIH, AIHA, and NIOSH in the definition section for assistance in sourcing these publications).

The principal route of occupational exposure to gases, vapors, mists, and fumes is inhalation (Stokinger 1977, 11). Ingestion could be a route if the material were to condense or accumulate on a surface or on a worker's hand and then be transferred to the mouth. Skin contact also could occur through a condensation or deposition mode. Injection would be unlikely except for an incident such as high-pressure gas-stream impact on exposed skin. Gases, vapors, mist, and fumes are typically associated with industrial and workplace exposures where these materials are commonly in use and the air distribution of the material is uncontrolled.

Particulates and Fibers

Industrial Sources

Industrial sources of particulates and fibers are widespread. Fibrous materials such as asbestos and fiberglass are used in insulation, gaskets, valve packings, siding, roofing materials, and other applications where both thermal and acoustic insulation properties are important.

Particulates are found both as raw materials, such as cement, coal dust, and blasting grit, and as raw chemical products. Particulates result from mechanical operations on solid materials, such as grinding on painted or metal surfaces, cutting or drilling operations, milling and machining of solid materials, and even windblown dust or direct application of air pressure to particulate material. Particulate material, therefore, represents distinct chemical properties of the original material, but the size distribution is a function of the mechanical process that distributes the particulate into the air. For a graphic depiction of the particle characteristics and particle dispersoids, see Figure 12.1 in *The Occupational Environment* (AIHA 1998), which is a reproduction of the classic SRI diagram from an article by C. E. Lappler in the *SRI Journal*, published in 1961.

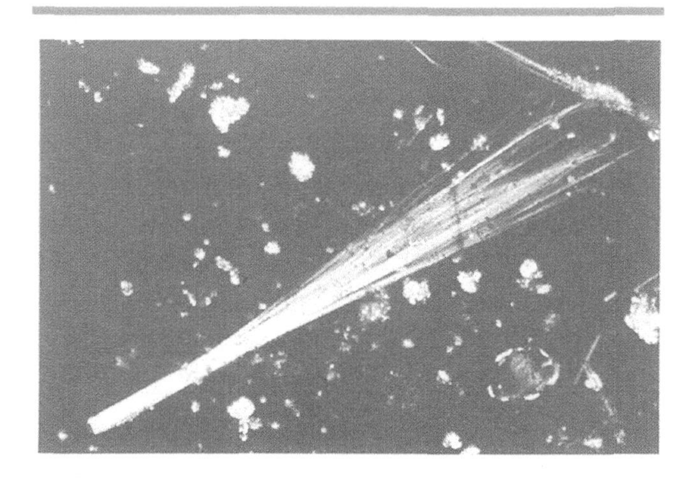

FIGURE 1. Asbestos fiber viewed using scanning electron microscope (Photo courtesy Industrial Hygiene Resources, Boise, Idaho.)

Potential Routes of Occupational Exposure

Fibers are principally an inhalation hazard. Some fibers, such as fiberglass, can cause skin irritation but without significant health consequences. Fibers in the workplace can represent chronic or acute health hazards. But in most cases, the concern is chronic exposure, and the fiber of major concern is asbestos. A photomicrograph of an asbestos fiber is shown in Figure 1.

Asbestos is a mineral material composed primarily of silicates. A number of silicate minerals exist as fibers, but according to the U.S. Bureau of Mines, to be asbestos, the material must have crystal growth along two planes and must have sufficient fiber growth so that the fibers can be identified, separated, and processed (Campbell et al. 1977). For a comprehensive definition of asbestos, see 29 CFR 1910.1001, Appendix J, 3.5. The use of asbestos in the workplace has been widespread, and worker exposure is found in many industries and trades (DHHS 2004, III-23). The effects of occupational exposure to asbestos fibers are not dependent on the chemical reaction of the fiber; in fact, the material is chemically very inert. Instead, the mode of action is primarily mechanical injury. Asbestos is considered a human carcinogen. The U.S. Department of Health and Human Services' *Report on Carcinogens* first listed asbestos in its 1980 edition (DHHS 1980). It is characterized by a *marker* type of cancer usually associated with pleural and peritoneal mesotheliomas (see the Agency for Toxic Substance and Disease Registry publication ATSDR-WB 1093 (available online) or ATSDR 2001 for information on asbestos diseases). The primary route of occupational exposure to asbestos is inhalation of fibers and deposition of these fibers within the lung.

Particulate material is also inhaled into the lung and can be deposited in the lung tissue, can be absorbed or digested, or can leach or otherwise release adsorbed chemicals into the lung tissues and fluids. Thus, the toxicology of inhaled particulate material is complex and depends on particle size, aerodynamic characteristics, chemical composition, and sometimes crystallography, as in the case of some silica minerals.

In many industrial and work conditions, the primary concern of worker exposure is particulate from heavy metals. Of particular concern are lead (found in paints and coatings), cadmium (also found in paints and coatings), and chromium (particularly the hexavalent form, which is listed as a known human carcinogen). In 2004 the Centers for Disease Control and Prevention (CDC) reported data on workplace injuries and illnesses that showed the 4-year mean prevalence rate for adult workers with blood lead levels (BLLs) above 40 micrograms per deciliter of blood was 2.9 per 100,000 workers. This value is a decline from the value of 3.9 reported for the years 1994–1997 (CDC 2004, 55), which indicates that worker uptake of lead is declining because of better controls, a reduction of lead materials in the workplace, and environmental protection regulations like the Clean Air Act Amendments of 1990, which outlawed leaded gasoline in the United States beginning in 1965 (CAA 1990).

Lead and similar chemicals can be found in a particulate form when surface coatings are cut or abraded. These chemicals can also form aerosol sprays if applied in a paint formulation and can form a fume if heated above the boiling point of the metal or compound. In the case of heavy metals, the form is often dependent on the source and type of worker exposure. The most important step for eliminating worker exposure is reviewing the material safety data sheet for potential sources of heavy metal constituents and then limiting worker exposure to these materials through appropriate engineering controls and respiratory protection. More recently, exposure to some metals has been associated with allergic reactions, making them a consideration when reviewing potential susceptibility of workers to metals in the workplace (Thyssen and Menn 2009).

Solvents, Acids, and Bases

Industrial Sources

Solvents, acids, and bases are commonly encountered in the work environment, and not all exposures represent occupational health risks. Solvents are frequently used in cleaning operations for paints, grease, oils, and other organic-based materials. Acids such as muriatic acid (HCl) may be used to clean concrete, and phosphoric acid (H_3PO_4) and nitric acid (HNO_3) are used to clean metal surfaces before painting them. Caustic-based materials are found in soaps and cleaning agents used to remove dirt and other surface contamination. Acids and bases are also found in many raw materials used in industrial processes.

Some of these materials can represent potential hazards. For example, benzene as a solvent is recognized as a known human carcinogen, and yet in 1987 OSHA estimated that about 237,000 workers in the United States were potentially exposed to benzene (OSHA 1987). It is not known if this number has changed since that time (ACS 2006). Benzene can constitute, by volume, between 1 and 5 percent of petroleum products (commercial gasoline usually contains between 1 and 2 percent benzene) and is considered both an inhalation health hazard and a possible skin hazard. The NIOSH short-term exposure limit (15-minute maximum level per workday) is 1 ppm (NIOSH 2005, 26). Repeated skin exposure to benzene can cause sensitization and skin lesions and should be avoided.

Acids and bases represent less of a chronic or carcinogenic risk, but in exposures resulting from spills and splashes, there can be severe skin, eye, and throat irritation due to the corrosive nature of these chemicals on body tissues. Hydrofluoric acid (HF) is a particularly dangerous industrial material in that skin exposure to even dilute solutions may not cause immediate pain but can develop later into painful ulcers. HF in contact with skin results in the fluoride ion easily passing through the skin pores, after which it rapidly binds with calcium and magnesium in the body tissues and bone material. The result is a significant alteration of calcium and magnesium levels in the body tissues (Gosselin, Smith, and Hodge 1984, 188–190). Treatment for HF exposure requires immediate flushing with water and medical treatment of the exposed and underlying subcutaneous layers. Salts of acids are also potential hazards, and many are considered poisonous, both chronically and acutely.

Potential Routes of Occupational Exposure

Organic solvents, such as naphtha, mineral spirits, gasoline, turpentine, and alcohol, can be hazardous for two reasons:

1. They affect the central nervous system to some extent, acting as depressants and anesthetics. Effects can range from mild unnoticed irritation to narcosis and death from respiratory arrest.
2. All solvents that contact and wet the skin can cause dermatitis (inflammation, rashes) and allergic reactions. Solvents contacting the eyes can cause slight irritation and, in some cases, permanent blindness. Many chlorinated solvents, for example carbon tetrachloride, can also penetrate the intact skin and cause systemic effects in other organ systems, such as the liver. Certain solvents are also carcinogenic, and some are considered potentially life threatening or lethal following skin exposure; for a discussion on skin notations for chemical hazards, see DHHS *Current Bulletin 61* (DHHS 2009a).

Protective measures that can be used to control solvent exposure include the following:

- Substitution of a less toxic alternative. An example is the use of Stoddard solvent, a petroleum spirit, for parts-degreasing operations instead of methylene chloride solvent, which is a possible human carcinogen (DHHS 2004, 91).
- Engineering controls installed at the point of vapor generation. An example is installation of an air-moving ventilation system over a

parts-cleaning operation to remove solvent vapors from the workers' breathing zone.
- Adequate ventilation of the work area. An example is paint-spray containment and a ventilation system to remove excess paint aerosol from the painting process.
- Proper work practices. An example is using tongs to remove parts from an acid cleaning bath to prevent direct skin contact with the acid solution.
- Personal protective clothing. PPE would include suitable eye protection, face splash shields, chemically impervious aprons, chemical gloves, and impervious boots specified to reduce the skin exposure to hazardous chemicals.
- Barrier skin creams. These provide only limited protection. Some skin barriers contain silicone and other suspended metals in oil- or lanolin-based materials and may not be effective for all chemical exposures. In most applications, barrier creams are limited to certain water-based solutions (i.e., coolants), alcohol-based solvents, and some mild alkaline solutions. The intent of barrier creams is the prevention of mild chemical dermatitis, not permeation of the skin by a toxic chemical.

Acids are liquids or solids with a pH value below 7. A strong acid has a pH below 4. The EPA defines a corrosive acid as less than pH 2.0 (EPA 2005, 34561). Table 1 is a tabular depiction of the pH scale of relative acid and base strengths. Note that pH measurements are actually logarithmic powers of hydrogen ion activity in solution and are used as representations of relative strength of activity. However, as in the case of the EPA, pH measurements may be used to classify liquids as potentially corrosive with the ability to cause serious skin and tissue injury.

Acids cause localized injury at the area of contact, causing burns. Acid mist can irritate the eyes and the lungs if inhaled. Pulmonary edema or fluid buildup in the lungs can also occur. Examples of common acids include sulfuric acid, hydrochloric acid, and nitric acid. Potential routes of exposure include contact with liquids in dip-cleaning tanks, entry into storage vessels containing acids, spraying or applying acids during surface cleaning, transfer operations of bulk liquids, and line breaks or leaks of industrial sources. While performing any of these operations, it is important to provide proper skin, eye, and respiratory protection against acid liquids and mists.

Bases are liquids or solids with a pH above 7. A strong base has a pH above 10. The EPA defines a corrosive base as one with a pH greater than 12.5 (EPA 2005, 34561). Bases are irritants to the skin, eyes, and lungs if inhaled. Common bases such as ammonia, sodium hydroxide, cement, and lye can cause tissue damage, which may initially go unnoticed. Preventing eye exposure is critical when handling bases. Skin contact may produce delayed effects, so it is essential that any potential areas of skin or eye contact be washed with water and treated as a potential chemical burn or irritation.

Acceptable Risks and Occupational Limits

The three modes of action by toxicological substances in the body are physical, chemical, and physiological. Of these, the physiological is the most common. The physiological role of toxic substances in the body may be simply classified as either Reaction I or Reaction II (Stokinger 1977, 25). With Reaction I the toxic agent acts on the body—for example, carbon

TABLE 1

Scale Representation of pH based on 40 CFR 261.22

14	12.5	10	8	7	6	4	2.0	0
Very strong base	Corrosive base	Strong base	Weak base	Neutral solution	Weak acid	Strong acid	Corrosive acid	Very strong acid

(Source: EPA 2005)

monoxide can rapidly bind with the iron (hemoglobin) in the blood, thus reducing the ability of the red blood to take up oxygen in the respiration process. With Reaction II, the body acts on the toxic agent, as with liver detoxification of pesticides and chlorinated solvents, such as methylene chloride, which is metabolized to carbon monoxide in the body (Torkelson and Rowe 1981, 3450). In both cases, carbon monoxide is involved in the physiological effects, but the rate of reaction is significantly different for the two chemicals, and the acute and chronic effects of exposure can be significantly different for these two chemicals.

Toxins may also be classified according to toxic mode of actions in the following categories: (1) irritants, (2) asphyxiants, (3) anesthetics, (4) systemic poisons, (5) sensitizers, and (6) particulate matter other than systemic poisons (Dinman 1978, 137–140). Chemicals may act in multitoxic modes, and the mode may be dependent on concentration, exposure time, and method of entry into the body. Thus, occupational exposure limits consider acceptable levels of exposure based on chemical species and physical characteristics, as well as physiological responses of the body to the chemical toxin.

In some toxic modes, the toxin is metabolized in the body and excreted as a waste product. In other cases, the toxin may be absorbed into body tissues as the toxin, a metabolite of the toxin, or a conjugate of the toxin. In many cases the metabolites or conjugates of the toxin are less toxic than the original material and, therefore, allow the body to cope with the potential injury. This ability to cope with the toxin provides the baseline for acceptance of a "no toxic effect" dose limit. This no-toxic-effect limit provides the basis for occupational exposure limits that set the workplace limits for exposure to chemicals where the body has the ability to tolerate and repair damage or eliminate the toxin through physiological responses.

Occupational exposure levels (OELs) have been established for workers that reflect the body's natural capacity to protect against injury and illness from exposure to hazardous chemicals and materials. Often, these exposure levels are based on a daily exposure for 8 hours a day, 40 hours a week, and a lifetime of 40 years of work activity. In many cases these exposure models assume a recovery period between exposures for detoxification and elimination of the toxin and also assume a standard 5-day workweek. For nonstandard work schedules, the OEL may need to be adjusted.

In some chemicals and products the effects of exposure are much more immediate (Reaction I type), and the occupational exposure levels reflect short-term effects and damage of the chemical. These levels are typically set to reflect a 15-minute exposure, although other time limits are also established.

Additionally, there are short-term exposures that should never be exceeded in the workplace at any time because of the potential for immediate injury or health effects. Ceiling limits are established for these materials.

There are other OELs that apply to skin exposure and potential carcinogenic or teratogenic materials. In these instances, the goal is to minimize or eliminate to the extent possible any worker exposure.

Finally, it should be recognized that there are additional OELs that recognize the toxin metabolites and conjugates as markers of human exposures. These biological exposure indices (BEIs), published by ACGIH, establish levels of indicators in the blood, urine, and fecal material that would be indicative of a potential chemical exposure or other physiological condition. The use of BEIs can assist the occupational health professional to assess body burden of a contaminant, reconstruct past exposures in the absence of other exposure measurements, detect any nonoccupational exposures, test the efficacy of control methods, and monitor all work practices (ACGIH 2010, 95). Other studies have also examined exhaled breath as an indicator of exposure. Even hair samples that indicate arsenic exposure and saliva tests showing ethyl alcohol consumption are recognized biological indicators of exposure.

In all exposure-level models there is an element of acceptable risk. There is a level that is presumed safe for humans for most chemicals (excluding carcinogenic and other chemicals that cause irreparable or very rapid damage). Returning to our earlier example of the chemical sodium chloride—table salt—there is a presumption that most levels of exposure are safe (this is excluding synergistic effects on other system functions such as blood pressure, heart function, and kidney). But actually, salt water can be quite irritating to the eyes—try opening your eyes while swimming in the ocean—and even toxic in large quantities: toxicity is estimated as between 0.5 and 1.0 grams of NaCl per kilogram of body weight (MEDITEXT 2010).

Methods for Determining Exposure Levels

Personal Sampling

Monitoring vapors, gases, particulates, and fibers in the workplace is generally conducted using two methods:

1. By using extractive sampling techniques where the material of interest is trapped on a filter media or adsorbent.
2. By a direct-reading instrumental method in which the concentration of material of concern is correlated to a concentration through a detection media and signal amplification.

Both exhibit advantages and limitations in their approach to assessing workplace exposure to chemical hazards.

Direct-reading instruments generally are used to monitor organic vapors, inorganic gases, aerosols, and particulates and fibers suspended in the air. There are a variety of detection methods. The detection system for gases and vapors often uses infrared, ultraviolet, photo ionization, thermal conductivity, electron capture, colorimetric, or electrochemical means of discriminating the physical characteristics of a target analyte. Aerosols, particles, and fibers generally rely on light-scattering properties or mass attenuation of the material of interest and may be detected by photometric detectors, beta attenuation monitors, and condensation nuclei counting devices. There are also direct-reading instruments for surface contamination, such as X-ray fluorescence for lead in paint. Levels of detection for portable direct-reading gas and vapor analyzers range from the subparts per million up to percent levels (see Table 9.1 in *The Occupational Environment—Its Evaluation and Control*, AIHA 1998). Accuracy of the detection method varies with the instrumental method, and some methods for vapors and gases are subject to interferences (a quenching or masking of the signal) from other chemicals as well as false positive data from similarly responding chemicals (leading to erroneously high readings).

Portable aerosol and particle monitors generally can measure particle concentrations in the range of 0.01 to 200 or more milligrams per cubic meter. The problem with aerosol and particulate monitoring instruments is that they provide only a quantitative measure of particle concentration—no information on composition is provided. Also, many particle monitors do not provide discrimination of the particle size, which is often critical in assessing the potential health hazard of particulate material in the breathing zone (though some of the new monitoring systems use size-range channels to provide size-distribution frequency data). For a complete discussion of aerosol photometers, see Section G of the *NIOSH Manual of Analytical Methods*, "Aerosol Photometers for Respirable Dust Measurements" (DHHS 2003).

As a result of potential inaccuracies, integrated sampling may be needed to provide samples that can be analyzed outside of the monitoring system and under more controlled laboratory systems. This integrated sampling may include media such as charcoal, selective polymer resins (XAD and others), silica gel, and polyurethane foam as a collection media for organic vapors and gases. Inorganic gases may be collected on chemically treated sorbents; sometimes liquid adsorbent media are used for acid gases. In all integrated sampling it is critical that the flow rate and time of sampling be noted accurately because this is included in the calculation. Therefore, sampling systems normally include some type of air mover and calibrated flow control or measuring system.

When collecting particulate and fibers, it is important to determine if the material being sampled is representative of the material that is being inhaled into the lung (i.e., respirable size with potential to travel into the airway passages or total particulate that the worker is exposed to in the breathing zone without regard to particle size). Generally, this is accomplished using a sampling cyclone in conjunction

FIGURE 2. Parallel particle impactor (Photo courtesy of SKC, Inc.)

with the filter, but other methods include impactors, elutriators, and even direct-reading instruments that use light-scattering methods. An example of a personal sampler impactor is shown in Figure 2.

In most cases, the sizing of the particle or fiber is dependent on the shape, size, and density of the particle, which are generally unknown parameters, and, as a result, particle size is generally correlated to the aerodynamic equivalent diameter (a.e.d.) which is the diameter of a unit-density sphere that would exhibit the same aerodynamic-characteristic settling velocity (Johnson and Swift 1998, 248). Other factors, such as particle shape and density, together with slip factors and sampling turbulence, may impact the sizing of the particles. In most cases, particle-sizing instrument flow rates correlate well to particle aerodynamic diameters for the purposes of determining the percentage or proportion of particles that could potentially travel into the lungs and the lower air-exchange areas of the lungs.

An example of this application is the method for determining the respirable fraction of crystalline silica in dust (NIOSH Method 7500). This method recommends sampling using a cyclone separator operated at a flow rate of 2.5 liters per minute (l/min) with a polyvinyl chloride (PVC) filter media. At a flow rate of approximately 2.5 l/min, using an aluminum (SKC) cyclone, the "cut point" of the cyclone will produce a sample of approximately 50 percent of 4-micron a.e.d. or less. In this case, the 50 percent cut point (d50) represents the particle size captured with 50 percent efficiency.

For crystalline silica, the PVC filter sample is analyzed using X-ray diffraction microscopy. In asbestos sampling, the fibers are trapped on a mixed cellulose ester (MCE) filter, but the analysis of the fibers (including size information) is determined directly by microscopic methods. Figure 3 shows an elemental analysis of a typical dust particle from a filter media, but this information shows the presence of Si, the chemical symbol for silicon; as in some chemical compounds, it does not identify the material as crystalline silica. Therefore, additional analysis would be required to assess the health risk of crystalline silica.

There are also sampling methods that do not involve either direct-reading instruments or integrated sampling using air-collection techniques. These methods can be referred to as passive sampling—sampling by simple grab or wipes or by diffusive-type air samplers. Passive sampling offers a simple and nonintrusive method to provide a quantitative assessment of potential chemical exposure hazards. Passive sampling methods have been developed and validated for a number of chemicals. See "Chlorinated and Organonitrogen Pesticides," NIOSH Method 9201, for an example of dermal patch, passive sampling method, or "Nitrogen Dioxide," NIOSH Method 6700, for a treated sampling badge technique (DHHS 2003). These types of sampling systems may be subject to error when used in lower atmospheric pressures (high altitudes) or in high-dust work locations, but their ease of use makes them ideal for controlled workplace exposure monitoring. The ANSI/ISEA 104-1998 (R2009) Standard (ANSI/ISEA 2009) provides guidance to manufacturers

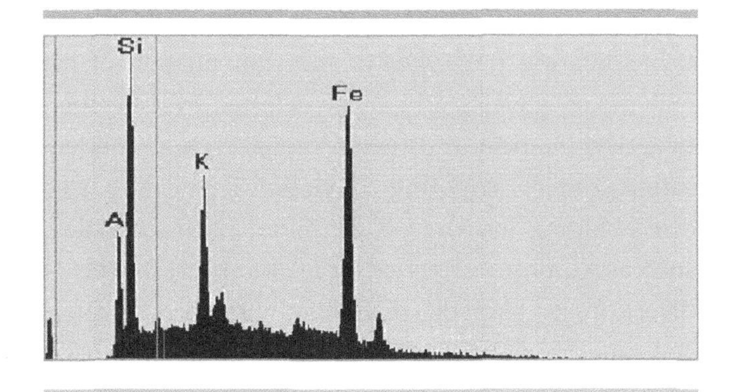

FIGURE 3. Elemental analysis of a typical dust particle (*Source:* Piispanen 2001)

and users on the methods to evaluate passive sampling devices for a variety of chemicals and conditions.

Passive samplers are also useful in fixed locations to monitor general work-area concentrations; for example, diffusive charcoal tubes suspended in the work area monitor potential benzene levels. By adjusting the length of time the samplers are exposed, very low levels can be detected. Results are used to approximate potential area concentrations of contaminants in the work area.

Area Sampling

Area sampling is often used in conjunction with or in support of personal sampling in assessing chemical hazards in the workplace. Area sampling may include direct-reading instruments used in a survey mode, where the work area is surveyed for potential contamination level. Handheld photoionization detectors and chemical cell devices are readily available for this application. The direct-reading data can be collected by an instrument data logger and later downloaded or managed to provide maximum, minimum, and average concentrations. In data-logging mode, multiple instantaneous readings over time are recorded on a built-in data system. Data summary may be displayed directly on the instrument meter or downloaded to a computer data-management program.

This data is useful when assessing a work zone for potential chemical hazards from organic solvent vapors and specific inorganic species such as ammonia, chlorine, carbon monoxide, hydrogen sulfide, nitric oxides, sulfur dioxide, hydrogen cyanide, phosphine, and other compounds and gases. In most cases where direct-reading instruments are used in a survey mode, there is usually some *a priori* knowledge of the potential contaminant so that the appropriate instrument is selected. The error of the method is that additional materials may be present or that other materials present may mask the response signal or result in a false positive signal.

Therefore, area sampling also includes samples that are collected and analyzed at an off-site laboratory using instrumental methods as shown in Figure 4.

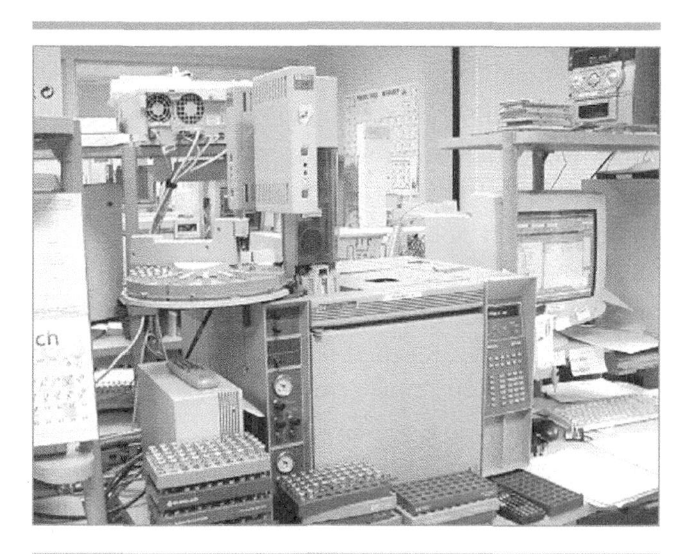

FIGURE 4. Analytical instruments for semivolatile organic analysis (Courtesy Washington Group International)

FIGURE 5. SUMMA® evacuated canister sampler (Courtesy Washington Group International)

In this application, samples are collected in a manner that preserves the sample, protecting it from degradation or chemical alteration. A common collection media is the SUMMA® canister, or equivalent product, shown in Figure 5. These are preevacuated, specially polished, spherical stainless steel canisters that are used to collect volatile organic gases. The frequently referenced methods for the analysis of these SUMMA® samples are EPA TO-14A and EPA TO-15 (EPA 1999). These EPA analytical methods provide quantitative analysis of many volatile species at concentrations ranging from 1 ppb to 10,000 ppm, depending on the size of the container and the analytical detection limits. A list of organic compounds known to have been analyzed by the canister method can be found in ASTM Method D-5466-01, Table 1 (ASTM 2007). There are also new canisters with specially coated interior surfaces for active polar and low-sulfur-containing organic species. (See ASTM Standard Guide D-6345-98 for discussion of whole air sampling with canisters). These coated canisters are identical in appearance to standard pre-evacuated cylinders except for the addition of the interior surface coating, which may include silica or polymer materials. Silica-treated canisters may be referred to as SilcoCans.

The evacuated canisters are set out in preselected work locations, and then, through a control bleed orifice, air samples are collected in a controlled flow rate. The advantages of using evacuated canisters are that there is no requirement for power or a pump in the sampling location, and the results provide very detailed analysis of potential air contaminants. However, the results are limited in that they do not necessarily represent the direct worker exposure and can be influenced by environmental conditions, changes in operations, and local heating and ventilation systems.

It is critical, therefore, that air movement and environmental conditions be monitored and recorded during passive area sampling. Frequently, carbon dioxide (CO_2) is monitored both as an indicator of building occupancy and as a measure of ventilation dilution of the air. ASTM Method D-6245-98 (ASTM 2007) provides guidelines on using carbon dioxide concentrations to evaluate indoor air ventilation rates. In this method, the percent of outdoor air (OA) is calculated based on CO_2 concentrations as follows:

Calculation of Outdoor Air Dilution (ASTM 2007)

$$\% \text{ OA} = 100 \times (C_r - C_s) \;/\; (C_r - C_{out}) \qquad (1)$$

where

C_r is the concentration of CO_2 (ppmv) in the recirculation air stream.

C_s is the concentration of CO_2 (ppmv) in the ventilation supply stream

C_{out} is the concentration of CO_2 (ppmv) in the outside ambient air.

Many direct-reading indoor air-quality monitors are programmed to perform this calculation directly. The results can be used to determine the impact of outside air either as a dilution factor in a workspace or as source of contamination to the workspace.

Other factors that should be monitored include temperature and relative humidity because these are often reported as indicators of worker comfort levels. An inventory and use pattern of chemicals in the work area should be maintained during area sampling. Samplers should not be placed near known sources of chemicals unless the intent is to identify specific components of the source as a contributor to the overall area contamination.

Area-sampling data provide a picture of the potential air contaminants and constituents that could potentially impact worker health and comfort levels. Of course, the task now is to determine how to use the data collected and to identify and correct potential contamination or discomfort conditions. (*Note:* This discussion does not address biological contaminants or odors that also may contribute to worker health and comfort levels. Additional sampling and analysis may be required to assess these contributions as well.)

Modeling of Exposure

Modeling of exposures is an approach to determine the temporal and spatial variations and impacts of sources of air contaminants in the workplace. Models are also available to estimate potential impact of water or soil sources of contaminants in the workplace (see Marlowe 1994 for a developed model). Modeling is used to understand the factors in the work environment that may expose workers to hazardous chemicals. With this understanding, controls can be designed to reduce or eliminate the exposure potential.

Most models are based on the principle of mass conservation (i.e., the mass of materials in the system that is maintained, including factors such as the workspace and any ancillary air-handling system). Chemicals may undergo chemical or physical transformation due to thermodynamic reactions or mechanical displacement mechanisms. Uncertainty factors or safety factors (usually between 4 and 100) are often incorporated to provide an additional measure of protection to workers.

Models generally focus on a single material or a similar class of materials. Models of particulate material-based chemicals must account for physical factors that influence suspension, transport, removal, coagulation, and deposition. Gaseous and vapor-phase materials are subject to volatilization, sorption, and condensation factors. Most models provide some average flux measurement or emission rate for the material of interest based on input values for the source of the material. Ultimately, the value and accuracy of the model is dependent on the precision of measurement of the input values and the applicability of the physical laws that drive the model.

The true test of any model is its ability to predict the desired results with accuracy—for example, the average daily airborne exposure level to lead dust from a contaminated soil-removal operation or the short-term concentration to carbon monoxide from a combustion source. Additional data is usually collected during the operations using personal or area sampling techniques to validate the model results and to determine the amount of error in the prediction. Additionally, sensitivity analysis methods may be applied to the model to evaluate the relative impact of input parameters. With this information, the input values may be reexamined to determine the accuracy of the data, and, if necessary, the sample size of the input data may be increased to provide a better statistical chance of accuracy. For a discussion of methods for evaluating indoor air-quality models, refer to ASTM Method D-5157-97 (ASTM 2007).

General Methods of Controlling Potential Exposures

When chemical hazards in the workplace are predicted or discovered, steps must be taken to eliminate or control them. General methods of control might include the following (based on "General Methods of Controlling Environmental Factors," Procedure 1, of Washington Group International 2005, 11):

- Substituting less harmful materials for materials that are dangerous to health. For example, using a citrus-based degreaser product instead of a petroleum solvent product.
- Changing or altering the process or work operation to reduce the number of persons exposed. This might include scheduling dip tank change-out or cleaning operations to night-shift operations when fewer workers are in the area.
- Isolating or enclosing the process or work operation to reduce the number of persons exposed, such as containing the operation in a glove box or enclosure.
- Using wet methods, such as water spray or mist, to reduce dust in excavation and other construction activities. Water trucks are used on construction and demolition sites, and water mist sprays and water curtains are used to control chemical product use areas.
- Incorporating engineering control measures, such as point-of-use air suction/blowers, to remove or disperse contaminants at the source before they reach the worker, such as the slot-hood dust capture shown in Figure 6.
- Ventilating work areas and chemical storage areas with clean makeup air, thus reducing

FIGURE 6. Local exhaust ventilation, slot hood (Courtesy of Gayla McCluskey, 2007)

the concentration of the material below recommended workplace limits.

- Employing good hygiene work practices, including hand- and face-washing; prohibiting eating, smoking, or chewing in contaminated areas; and controlling spread of contamination on workers' clothing by maintaining decontamination procedures.
- Wearing personal protective equipment and devices such as chemical gloves and boots, spill aprons or chemical-resistant clothing, respirators, and eye and face protection, as exemplified by a worker wearing a powered air-purifying respirator in Figure 7.
- Maintaining good work-area housekeeping, including cleanliness in the work area, proper waste disposal, adequate washing facilities, clean lavatories and eating facilities, safe drinking water sources, and control of insects and rodents.
- Continuous or frequent personal and area sampling with monitoring devices, complemented by worker medical surveillance programs, when required, to detect potential intake of toxic materials. This may also include installing continuous chemical monitors on process lines to warn of chemical leaks in the process.
- Maintaining adequate training and educational programs to supplement engineering controls. Training should include hazard communication training as specified in 29 CFR 1910.1200, as well as task-specific hazard analysis of potential chemical hazards that may be encountered in the work area or from other sources of chemical hazards.

FIGURE 7. **Powered air-purifying respirator (PAPR)** (Courtesy of Gayla McCluskey, 2007)

Summary of Safe Work Practices

Chemicals in use in the workplace exhibit defined properties such as physical state, chemical composition, solubility, and flammability, as well as the potential ability to cause negative health effects and irreparable harm to humans and the environment if used incorrectly. Yet the ability to use chemicals in the creation of new materials, drugs, and other beneficial materials is what creates and sustains work in the world. The safe use of chemicals in the workplace is not in need of a "Philosopher's Stone" or an "Elixir of Life" as sought by the early alchemists; instead it relies on prudent safety practices based on chemical principles and good practices. With an understanding of these principles and an appreciation for safe practices, the risk of health impact and irreparable injury from exposure to workplace chemicals can be managed.

Safe practices for working with chemicals in laboratories are based on OSHA regulation 29 CFR 1910.1450 and in the general workplace on 29 CFR 1910.1200, but, in addition, they should include the following at a minimum:

- Review and understand the chemical material's composition and physical and chemical properties. This would include understanding physical and chemical transformation that may occur in any use, either planned or unplanned, such as an emergency condition, spill, or release to the environment.
- Within the planned use of a chemical material (including high-potential, unplanned releases), the points of potential exposure and the timeframe of potential exposure must be identified. This provides information needed to design sampling programs and a basis for identify-

ing protective measures when required to limit occupational exposures.

- Determine the potential exposure levels using both worst-case scenarios and average exposure scenarios. Sometimes a hazard-ranking model can be used to assess potential risk factors. It is important to consider additive and synergistic effects of certain chemicals. Consider including an assessment of the physical conditions in the workplace that could contribute to additional safety problems, such as open flames when flammable solvents are in use, incompatibility in material storage or containment facilities, and thermal and ventilations systems that could disperse or distribute the materials outside the immediate work area.
- Establish controls that reduce the potential exposures to below acceptable occupational exposure levels. Controls may include engineering controls such as ventilation, administrative controls such as establishing work-entry boundaries to hazardous areas, or the use of personal protective equipment such as respirators and protective clothing.
- Monitor the work area to assure that the controls are effective. It is critical to assure that changes to the materials in use and the process are not made without reassessing the potential hazards. It is also important that workers report any unusual conditions or problems immediately because these could be indicative of changing or unexpected conditions.
- Finally, it may be necessary or desirable to include medical monitoring or other surveillance programs of worker health to ensure that there are no detectable health impacts. Medical monitoring may require blood samples to determine potential lead exposure or urine samples to determine potential cadmium exposure. Exposure to a number of hazardous chemicals and tasks requires medical monitoring as specified in the OSHA standards. It is important to use the information gathered in the previously outlined steps to support the medical monitoring program.
- Worker training is a critical element of any chemical safety program. Information is presented to workers in a variety of media, but a thorough understanding of the potential for exposure and the need to follow safe work practices to minimize any potential risk is important.
- Finally, it should be noted that occupational exposure limits (OELs) for chemical hazards are limited because of the increasing number of new hazardous chemicals in the workplace and the ability of agencies to determine associated OELs (DHHS 2009b, 1). As a result, chemical hazard risk-management approaches that are under consideration include identifying chemicals according to hazard categories, or *control banding*. This approach greatly expands the ability to relate potential chemical hazards to a larger base of chemicals and provides a more uniform method for workers and users of chemicals to identify the potential hazards. Examples include the European Union REACH (EC 2006) or the United Nations Global Harmonization System (GHS) (UN 2005).

Chemistry is not a subject that is within the technical discipline of many workers, including many safety professionals. A wealth of technical information is available, and there are a number of professional industrial hygienists who can assist in the understanding of the material. With this available information and technical assistance, a safety program that incorporates good chemical safety practices is readily available. The history of chemistry in the workplace is a long history, often focused on the negative impact of chemicals on workers. Chemical substances exist in all facets of life both on and off the job. It is the responsibility of the safety professional to identify safe work practices for those substances with the potential to create any negative impacts.

Important Terms

American Conference of Governmental Industrial Hygienists (ACGIH): Technical Information Office, 6500 Glenway Avenue, Building D-7, Cincinnati,

OH, 45211-4438. Source for handbook on threshold limit values (TLVs) and other technical information.

Acid: An inorganic or organic compound that (1) reacts with metals to yield hydrogen, (2) has a pH of less than 7.0, (3) dissociates in water to yield hydrogen or hydronium (H_3O^+) ions, and (4) neutralizes bases or alkaline media. Many acids are corrosive to human tissue and must be handled with care. Acids are used in industrial pickling processes and also as raw material in chemical processes. Acids also constitute industrial waste streams.

American Industrial Hygiene Association (AIHA): 2700 Prosperity Avenue, Suite 250, Fairfax, VA, 22031, (703) 849-8888. Source for technical publications and laboratory accreditation information.

American National Standards Institute (ANSI): 23 West 43rd Street, New York, NY, 10036, (212) 642-4900. Source for many safety and engineering consensus standards (online search for standards at www.nssn.org).

Asbestos: A commercial term applied to a family of magnesium-silicate minerals in fibrous form. They have electrical and thermal insulating properties and can be woven into fabrics. These mineral forms have been used extensively in the construction industry and for other uses such as brake and clutch linings.

American Society for Testing and Materials (ASTM): 100 Barr Harbor Drive, West Conshohocken, PA, 19428, (610) 832-9693.

Base (caustic): An alkaline substance that (1) dissociates in water to liberate hydroxide (OH^-) anions, (2) has a pH greater than 7.0, and (3) can sometimes be used to neutralize acids. Bases can be corrosive to living tissue and must be handled with care. Caustics are often found in strong industrial cleaning products as well as in chemical processes as a raw material.

Biological exposure indices (BEIs): Guidance values, determined by the ACGIH, for assessing biological monitoring results based on determinants that are likely to be observed in biological samples collected from healthy workers who may be exposed to chemicals to the same extent as inhalation exposure.

Calibrate: To check, adjust, or systematically standardize a measuring instrument (e.g., an air-sampling pump or combustible gas indicator per the manufacturer's instructions and specifications).

CAS Registry and CAS Numbers: The CAS Number is a unique numeric identifier that can contain up to 10 digits divided into three parts by hyphens and is used to provide a definitive registry of known chemicals. Currently, the CAS Registry contains more than 52 million organic and inorganic substances.

Cassette: The filter holder used when sampling for particulates.

Centers for Disease Control and Prevention (CDC): An agency of the U.S. Department of Health and Human Services (DHHS). Its main office is located in Atlanta, Georgia. The CDC also includes the National Institute for Occupational Safety and Health (NIOSH) and the Agency for Toxic Substance and Disease Registry (ATSDR). (See www.cdc.gov for information and access to CDC information.)

Contaminant: An undesirable substance or constituent in an unwanted location.

Cyclone: An air-sampling device that is used for sampling respirable particulates. A cyclone *swirls* the incoming air stream and, through centrifugal action, causes the larger nonrespirable particles (less than 10 microns) to drop out. The respirable particles then travel with the air stream and are captured on a filter cassette. The nonrespirable particles accumulate in the bottom of the cyclone and are usually discarded.

Dust: Solid particulate matter suspended in air by mechanical means, such as handling, crushing, grinding, abrading, or blasting. Dusts can become an inhalation, fire, or explosive hazard.

Flammable: Any solid, liquid, or gas that ignites easily and burns rapidly. A flammable liquid is typically defined by OSHA as one with a flashpoint below 100°F (37.8°C). A vapor or gas is flammable when its concentration in air is higher than its lower explosive limit (LEL) or lower than its upper explosive limit (UEL). The flammable range for gas or vapors is between these values. The LEL and

UEL are expressed in percent of gas or vapor in air by volume.

Flow rate: The volume of air or other fluid that flows within a given period of time.

Fume: Minute, solid particles (generally less than one micron in diameter) dispersed in air from the heating of a solid. The heating is often accompanied by a chemical reaction when the particles react with oxygen to form an oxide. An example is metal fume production during welding or torch-cutting operations.

Gas: A formless fluid that occupies the space of its enclosure. Gases change to a liquid or solid state with increased pressure and decreased temperature. Gases have low densities and viscosities and can expand or contract greatly.

Global Harmonization System (GHS): An international system of identifying chemical and physical hazards of products using standardized symbols, signal words, and hazard statements on safety data sheets and container labels. This system is the result of a United Nations mandate that was adopted in 1992 as Agenda 21, para 19:27.

Hazard Communication Standard: An OSHA standard that requires chemical manufacturers and importers to assess the hazards associated with the materials they produce. Material safety data sheets, which are used to communicate hazard information to the user, are a result of this regulation (see OSHA 29 CFR 1910.1200 for general industry or 1926.59 for construction).

Heavy metals: Metallic elements with high atomic weights, such as iron, lead, arsenic, cadmium, vanadium, and uranium. Many heavy metals represent potential health hazards when inhaled or ingested in high concentrations.

International Agency for Research on Cancer (IARC): An agency of the World Health Organization (WHO) located in Lyons, France, IARC publishes the *IARC Monographs on the Evaluation of Carcinogenic Risks of Chemicals to Man*. (See www.iarc.fr for access to information.)

Immediately dangerous to life and health (IDLH): A level of exposure determined to ensure that a worker could escape without injury or irreversible health effects in the event of a failure of a respiratory protection system. These values are documented in "Documentation for Immediately Dangerous to Life and Health Concentrations" (DHHS, 1994).

Indicator tube: A glass tube containing a solid material that changes color when brought into contact with a specific chemical or class of chemicals. When a known volume of air is pulled through the tube, the length of the resulting stain is proportional to the concentration of the contaminant. These tubes are used primarily as screening tools to approximate the concentration of a contaminant in the workplace.

Inorganic: Designates compounds that generally do not contain carbon. Exceptions are carbon monoxide, carbon dioxide, carbides, and carbonates.

Mists: Suspended liquid droplets formed by condensation from the gaseous to the liquid state or by mechanically breaking up a liquid into a dispersed form by splashing, foaming, or atomizing.

Material safety data sheets (MSDS): Describe the safety precautions and components of a hazardous material. MSDSs are prepared by the product manufacturer, and the hazard information required on the MSDS is defined in the *Hazard Communication Standard* (29 CFR 1910.1200g).

National Institute for Occupational Safety and Health (NIOSH): 4676 Columbia Parkway, Cincinnati, OH, 45226 (513) 533-8287. Source for criteria documents and technical guidance.

Organic: Compounds or chemicals that contain carbon, hydrogen, and other elements in chain or ring structures. These may be solid, liquid, or gaseous.

Occupational Safety and Health Administration (OSHA): 200 Constitution Avenue NW, Washington, D. C. An agency of the U.S. Department of Labor established by the Williams-Steiger Occupational Safety and Health Act of 1970. OSHA provides sources of health and safety regulations as well as enforcement of published regulations. Regulations enacted by Congress under OSHA are codified under Title 29 of the Code of Federal Regulations (CFR). Part 1910 of 29 CFR applies to general industry rules, and Part 1926 applies to construction industry rules. Under Subpart A, states may also administer occupational safety and health regulations under state plan programs. (See www.osha.gov for information and access to material published by OSHA, or check state government Web sites for state programs.)

Polychlorinated biphenyls (PCBs): Very stable, organic materials of low flammability that contain 12 to 68 percent chlorine. They have been used as insulating materials in electrical capacitors and transformers, as plasticizers in waxes, in paper manufacturing, and for other industrial purposes, and are still encountered in the workplace today.

Permissible exposure limit (PEL): The allowable personal exposure level averaged over an 8-hour work shift. This is an OSHA legislative value (see 29 CFR 1910.1000 through 1910.1050 for general industry values).

Personal protective equipment (PPE): Includes clothing and equipment worn to shield or isolate individuals from chemical, physical, and biological hazards that may be encountered in the workplace. PPE is used to protect the respiratory system, skin, eyes, hands, face, head, body, and hearing.

Parts per million (ppm): A unit of measure, equal to 0.000001. When applied to a gas concentration in air, it is equal to 1 liter of gas or vapor per 1000 cubic meters of air and is frequently referred to as ppmv to denote that the units refer to volumes. The term is also used as a mass-based unit, such as for lead concentration in soil; in mass-based measurements, only ppm is used. In this case, 1 ppm is equal to 1 milligram per kilogram.

Recommended Exposure Limit (REL): Occupational exposure limits recommended by NIOSH (see DHHS 2005, xi).

Respirable: The respirable portion of the total particulate collected. Respirable particulates are usually those having an aerodynamic diameter of ten microns or less.

Silica: Silica (chemically silicon dioxide or SiO_2) is a mineral that, with prolonged exposure, can cause lung diseases. The OSHA standard for "crystalline silica" is currently based on the percentage of quartz in the respirable fraction.

Threshold limit value–Ceiling (TLV–C): The concentration of a contaminant that should not be exceeded during any part of the working exposure. For some substances, such as irritant gases, only one category—the TLV–C—may be relevant. For other substances, the TLV–STEL or TLV–TWA may be relevant, depending on the contaminant's physiologic action. If any one of these three TLVs is exceeded, a potential health hazard is presumed to exist. (*Note:* TLVs® are prudent industrial guidelines established by the American Conference of Governmental Industrial Hygienists and are not regulatory limits. The use of the term TLV in any of the forms in this chapter implies the use of the ACGIH registered name and disclaimer of liability with respect to the use of the guideline.)

Threshold limit value–Short-term exposure limit (TLV–STEL): The concentration to which workers can be exposed continuously to a substance for a short period of time without suffering from (1) irritation, (2) chronic or irreversible tissue damage, or (3) narcosis of a sufficient degree to increase the likelihood of accidental injury, impair self-rescue, or materially reduce work efficiency, and provided that the daily TLV–TWA (see next definition) is not exceeded. STEL is not a separate independent exposure limit; rather, it supplements the time-weighted average (TWA) where there are recognized acute effects from a substance whose toxic effects have been reported from high short-term exposures in either humans or animals. A STEL is defined as a 15-minute time-weighted average exposure, which should not be exceeded any time during a workday, even if the 8-hour time-weighted average is within the TLV. Exposures at the STEL should not be longer than 15 minutes and should not be repeated more than four times per day. There should be at least 60 minutes between successive exposures at the STEL. An average period other than 15 minutes may be recommended if observed biological effects warrant.

Threshold limit value–Time-weighted average (TLV–TWA): The time-weighted average concentration for a normal 8-hour workday and a 40-hour workweek, to which nearly all workers may be repeatedly exposed—day after day—without an adverse effect.

Total dust: The collection of all particulates, regardless of size, onto a filter or other measuring device.

Vapors: The gaseous state of a material suspended in air that would be a liquid under ordinary conditions.

References

Agency for Toxic Substances and Disease Registry (ATSDR). 1997 (rev. 2007). "Case Studies in Environmental Medicine, Asbestos Toxicity." Report ATSDR-WB 1093. www.atsdr.cdc.gov/csem/asbestos/docs/asbestos.pdf

______. 2001. *Toxicological Profile for Asbestos*. Atlanta, GA: U.S. Department of Health and Human Services, Public Health Service.

American Cancer Society (ACS). 2006 (rev. 02/02/2006). *Benzene*. www.cancer.org

American Conference of Governmental Industrial Hygienists (ACGIH). 2010. *Threshold Limit Values for Chemical Substances and Physical Agents and Biological Exposure Indices*. Cincinnati, OH: ACGIH.

American Industrial Hygiene Association (AIHA). 1998. *The Occupational Environment—Its Evaluation and Control*. Salvatore R. DiNard, ed. Fairfax, VA: AIHA Press.

American National Standards Institute (ANSI). 1977. *American National Standard for Uniform Recordkeeping for Occupational Injuries and Illnesses*. ANSI Z 16.4-1977. New York, NY: ANSI.

American National Standards Institute and International Safety Equipment Association. 2009. *American National Standard for Air Sampling Devices-Diffusive Type for Gases and Vapors in Working Environments*. ANSI/ISEA 104-1998 (R2009). Arlington, VA: International Safety Equipment Association.

American Society for Testing Materials (ASTM). 2007. *ASTM Standards on Indoor Air Quality*. ASTM No. IAQ07. West Conshohocken, PA: ASTM.

Campbell, W. J. et al. 1977. "Selected Silicate Minerals and Their Asbestiform Varieties." U.S. Department of Interior, Information Circular 8751. Washington, D.C.: U.S. Government Printing Office.

Centers for Disease Control and Prevention (CDC). 2004. *Worker Health Handbook*. U.S. Department of Health and Human Services publication DHHS 2004-146. Washington, D.C.: U.S. Government Printing Office.

Clean Air Act Amendments of 1990 (accessed October 24, 2011). thomas.loc.gov/cgi-bin/query/D?c101:5/temp/~c101/tbPJ9p

Dinman, B. D. 1978. "The Mode of Entry and Action of Toxic Materials." In G. D. Clayton and F. E. Clayton, eds., *Patty's Industrial Hygiene and Toxicology*, vol. 1. New York: Wiley.

European Community (EC). 2006. *Regulation EC No. 1907/2006 of the European Parliament and of the Council*. Official Journal of the European Union, December 30, 2006.

Gosselin, R. E., R. P. Smith, and H. C. Hodge. 1984. *Clinical Toxicology of Commercial Products*. Baltimore, MD: Williams and Wilkins.

Johnson, D. L., and D. L. Swift. 1998. "Sampling and Sizing Particles." In S. R. DiNardi, ed., *The Occupational Environment—Its Evaluation and Control*. Fairfax, VA: AIHA Press.

Marlowe, C. 1994. "Action Levels for Hazardous Waste Site Work." AIHA Seminar Publication. Fairfax, VA: AIHA Press.

MEDITEXT. 2010.Thompson Micromedex [online searchable database]. www.csi.micromedex.com

Occupational Safety and Health Administration (OSHA). 1987. Occupational exposure to benzene. Final Rule. Federal Register 52:34460-34578.

Pauling, L. 1970. *General Chemistry*. New York: Dover.

Piispanen, W. H. 2001. Unpublished data, collected in New York City.

Quigley, D., F. Simmons, H. Whyte, J. Robertson, and D. Freshwater. 2010. "Variations in Reproductive and Development Toxicant Identification." *Journal of Chemical Health and Safety*, 17(1) January 2010, pp. 29–53.

Ramazzini, B. 1964. *Diseases of Workers*. Translated from *De Morbis Artificum Diatriba*. New York: Hafner Publishing.

Schaper, M. M., and M. S. Bisesi. 1998. "Environmental and Occupational Toxicology." In S. R. DiNardi, ed., *The Occupational Environment—Its Evaluation and Control*. Fairfax, VA: AIHA Press.

Stokinger, H. E. 1977. "Routes of Entry and Modes of Action." In *Occupational Diseases: A Guide to their Recognition*. U.S. Department of Health Education and Welfare Publication DHEW 77-181. Washington, D.C.: U.S. Government Printing Office.

Thyssen, J. P., and T. Menn. 2009. "Metal Allergy—A Review on Exposures, Penetration, Genetics, Prevalence, and Clinical Implications." *Chem. Res. Toxicol.* 23(2) October 2009 (retrieved February 15, 2010). Chemical Research in Toxicology Article ASAP. www.acs.org

Torkelson, T. R., and V. K. Rowe. 1981. "Halogenated Aliphatic Hydrocarbons Containing Chlorine, Bromine, and Iodine." In G. D. Clayton and F. E. Clayton, eds., *Patty's Industrial Hygiene and Toxicology*, vol. 2B. New York: Wiley.

United Nations. 2005. *Globally Harmonized System of Classification and Labelling of Chemicals (GHS)*. Publication ST/SG/AC.10/30/Rev 1 (note: subsequent revisions 2 and 3 include corrections to rev 1). New York and Geneva: UN.

U.S. Department of Health and Human Services (DHHS), NIOSH. 1994. *Documentation for Immediately Dangerous to Life and Health Concentrations*. PB-94-195047. Springfield, VA: National Technical Information Service.

______. 2003. *NIOSH Manual of Analytical Methods*. 4th ed. NIOSH PB 2003-154, 3rd supplement. Springfield, VA: National Technical Information Service.

______. 2005. *NIOSH Pocket Guide to Chemical Hazards*. DHHS Publication 2005-149. Pittsburgh, PA: U.S. Government Printing Office.

______. 2009a. DHHS Publication 2009-147. *Current Intelligence Bulletin 61: A Strategy for Assigning New NIOSH Skin Notations*. Cincinnati, OH: DHHS.

______. 2009b. DHHS Pub 2009-152.*Qualitative Risk Characterization and Management of Occupational Hazards: Control Banding (CB)*. Cincinnati, OH: DHHS.

U.S. Department of Health and Human Services, Public Health Service. 1980. *1st Annual Report on Carcinogens*. Research Triangle Park, NC: National Institute of Environmental Health Sciences.

______. 2004. *11th Report on Carcinogens*. Research Triangle Park, NC: National Institute of Environmental Health Sciences.

U.S. Department of Labor, Occupational Safety and Health Administration (OSHA). 2009. 29 CFR 1926, *Safety and Health Regulations for Construction*, and 29 CFR 1910, *Occupational Safety and Health Standards for General Industry*. Washington, D.C.: U.S. Government Printing Office.

U.S. Environmental Protection Agency (EPA). 1999. *EPA Compendium of Methods for the Determination of Toxic Organic Compounds in Ambient Air*. 2d ed. EPA Pub. 625/R-96-010. Washington, D.C.: U.S. Government Printing Office.

______. 2005. "Part 261—Identification and Listing of Hazardous Waste." In 70FR, June 14, 2005. Washington, D.C.: U.S. Government Printing Office.

Washington Group International. 2005. *Industrial Hygiene Procedures Manual*. W. H. Piispanen, ed. Boise, ID: Standard Register Publishers.

4

Physical Hazards

James C. Rock

LEARNING OBJECTIVES

- Describe the characteristics that distinguish chemical from physical agents in workplaces.
- Summarize the bases for permissible exposure limits (OSHA PEL) and threshold limit values (ACGIH TLV).
- Be able to list the four types of electromagnetic radiation.
- Summarize the key principles of wave propagation and their application when selecting commercially available engineering controls.
- Describe how the principle of conservation of energy allows the evaluation of the performance of engineering controls
- Recognize how time, shielding, and distance are the keys to the safe use of physical agents.
- Learn the criteria for the proper selection of welding goggles and the dangers of short-wavelength light sources to the eye.

THE POTENCIES OF physical agents in the workplace arise from the rate and quantity of energy delivered to tissue by mechanical, electrical, and magnetic forces.[1] In contrast, the potencies of chemical hazards are based on chemical reactivity with molecules of tissues. This distinction is clouded, in practice, because many modalities of physical agents deliver energy in ways that either create reactive chemicals in tissue or facilitate damaging metabolic chemical reactions by thermal heating that increases molecular rotation or bends, twists, and vibrates molecules. This chapter emphasizes engineering design that prevents absorption of damaging quantities of energy at damaging power levels from physical agents.

Physical Agents

A Chemical Reaction Is Not a Physical Agent

A chemical reaction is said to occur when one or more valence electrons from one molecule are spontaneously donated to another molecule (ionic bond) or are shared with another molecule (covalent bond). Chemical reactions are either exothermic, releasing energy as the electron transfer occurs, or endothermic, absorbing energy from the immediate environs to complete the electron transfer. When energy is taken from or deposited in the wrong place, a toxic event occurs, sometimes in the form of a cascade of chemical reactions. At low doses, most of this damage is quickly repaired by homeostatic processes. When the repair mechanism is overwhelmed, damage accumulates, and a poisoning, or toxic, event is said to have occurred.

Physical Agents and Their Interactions

In a physical reaction, energy is delivered to molecules by means other than electron sharing between atoms in molecules. Several such phenomena are discussed in this chapter: noise, vibration, thermal stress, static or quasistatic electromagnetic fields, nonionizing radiation, and ionizing radiation. These occupational stressors, known collectively as physical agents, have potencies characterized by intensity and frequency. The typical physical agent standard involves specifications for free-field intensity, frequency, permissible duration, and a tissue absorption coefficient.

Workplace monitoring and control requires careful attention to these parameters. For example, at the same intensity, noise at frequencies between 20 and 40 Hz is better tolerated by human ears than is noise between 2 and 4 kHz. Likewise, vertically polarized electromagnetic radiation at frequencies between 100 and 300 MHz delivers more energy to tissue of a standing adult human than either the same intensity electromagnetic (EM) radiation with horizontal polarization at the same frequency or any polarization at frequencies between 30 and 100 kHz.

Carrying this EM insight further, X-rays at a frequency higher than 30 PHz (30×10^{15} Hz) ionize molecules in tissue and body fluids, producing free radicals and peroxides that disrupt RNA and DNA molecules.

Hazard, Risk, Causation, and Threshold

Diseases associated with physical agents are also associated with other factors. It is important that the safety professional understand core concepts when discussing physical agent exposures. The first is the concept of dose-response, introduced by Paracelsus in 1567 (Ottoboni 1991):[2] "What is it that is not a poison? All things are poison and nothing is without poison. It is the dose only that makes a thing not a poison."

At doses below a sufficient dose, hazardous forms of energy are beneficial.[3] Hazard is a property of a stressor that causes harm at high doses. It is distinct from risk, which means that (1) conditions of use produce damage (suprathreshhold dose); (2) there is probability of harm; or (3) the rate of injury increases, as in the number injured in a cohort of 100,000 exposed workers.

Some argue that carcinogens, including ionizing radiation, have no threshold. Alice Ottoboni points out that there are practical threshold doses, even for carcinogens (Ottoboni 1991). As a population dose increases, members of the population show increasing cancer incidence rates and decreasing induction periods. A practical threshold exists when the exposure to a carcinogen is sufficiently small to reduce its cancer incidence rate to less than one case in the entire population, or to increase its induction period to more than the population life expectancy.

Cause is demonstrated when an exposure produces the same pathological symptoms in all exposed persons. For example, because an IR LASER beam burns a hole in the skin of every person who is exposed, the LASER is said to cause the burn. Likewise, when every hot dog in a microwave oven is heated, the oven is said to cause the heating. In contrast, 10+ years of cellphone use has not been shown to produce observable pathological effects in humans (Schüz 2006).

High ionizing radiation doses are associated with calculable risk of radiation sickness (acute effect) and of some cancers (chronic effect). Low doses are not. Even in the high-dose cohorts, not everyone develops cancer. Herman Cember discusses this situation quite cogently (Cember 1996, 233–237):

> Deterministic effects are characterized by three qualities:
>
> 1. A certain minimum dose must be exceeded before the effect is observed.
> 2. The magnitude of the effect increases with the size of the dose.
> 3. There is a clear, unambiguous causal relationship between exposure to the noxious agent and the observed effect.
>
> The stochastic [random] effects are those that occur by chance, and they occur in exposed as well as in unexposed individuals. Stochastic effects are therefore not unequivocally related to exposure to a specific noxious agent. . . . No pathologist can say with certainty that the cancer would not have occurred if the person had not been exposed to the carcinogen.

Review of Scientific Principles for Physical Agents

Energy is the ability to do work, measured in Joules (J). Power is energy per unit of time, or the rate at which work is done, in watts (W). Intensity is power per unit area and has dimensions of W/m^2 or J/m^2 s. Frequency is measured in cycles per second, called hertz (Hz) in the SI system of units. In an interaction between an electromagnetic field or an acoustic field and tissue, a portion of the intensity is absorbed by the tissue. The absorption efficiency is a function of the frequency (wavelength in tissue) and tends to peak when the tissue has a long dimension that is about 40% of the incident wavelength.

Primer on Physical and Physiological Systems of Units

The exposure to physical agents is controlled by the intensity of exposure. Intensity here is used as a precisely defined concept in physics that indicates the power transmitted by an electromagnetic wave or an elastic wave (acoustic wave) across a unit area perpendicular to the direction of propagation. To calculate intensity, it is sometimes convenient to multiply the energy density (J/m^3) of a traveling wave by its propagation velocity (m/s) to obtain intensity ($J/m^2s = W/m^2$).

Although all physical agent standards could, in principle, be expressed simply in units of J, W, and W/m^2, without reference to the time history or waveform of the exposure, the resulting standards would be overly restrictive. When a physical agent interacts with tissue, only that portion of the energy having appropriate frequency characteristics is absorbed. Thus, exposure standards are frequency dependent and based on the proportion of incident energy absorbed by critical organs.

Vibration standards are set with specific purposes. Along the spinal axis, the goal is to avoid destructive resonance that causes severe bending of the spine. Transverse acceleration, across the spinal axis, is set to avoid resonance in internal organs that might be bruised while bouncing off vertebral bodies or the rib cage. The hand–arm vibration endpoint is soft tissue damage in the forearm–wrist area and has different values in different directions relative to the bones.

Noise standards use units of power (W) to represent the radiated power from noise sources and units of intensity (W/m^2) to represent the rate at which acoustic power is transmitted, and they quantify intensity at a given point by using measurements taken with microphones that report root-mean-squared (*rms*) sound pressure (Pa). Exposure guidelines limit intensity and duration of exposure in order to limit absorbed energy, in J. In hearing conservation practice, standard frequency-weighting curves are applied to the pressure signal before these acoustic quantities are measured. The A-weighting approximates transmission of the acoustic power from the air to the inner ear at normal listening levels of 40 to 70 dBA. The C-weighting approximates the auditory system's transmission of acoustic power at higher occupational exposure levels of 90 to 115 dBC. The outer ear canal acts as an organ-pipe resonator to emphasize frequencies in the 1 to 4 kHz range. The middle-ear bones interact with the elasticity of the ear canal and oval window with more resonant enhancement in the same region, which is detuned by the stapedial reflex in the presence of loud sound, leading to the flatter pass-band of the C-weighting filter. Other weightings, called B- and D-weighting, are used for environmental and community noise standards.

Hearing conservation program guidelines are typically given in terms of A-weighting. Protection factors of hearing defenders (earplugs and earmuffs) are given in terms of C-weighting.[4] Infrasound standards have a weighting based on emotional effects and on soft-tissue resonances in the abdomen. Ultrasonic standards are based on a combination of emotional and subharmonic effects occurring as a result of nonlinear transmission of high-intensity signals from the environment to the inner ear and other tissues.

Electromagnetic (EM) standards for extremely low frequencies from microwave frequencies to infrared frequencies are based on limiting the direct heating of tissue and avoiding both localized and total-body thermal effects. As frequencies increase above those of microwaves, the depth of heating in tissue decreases and then increases again.[5] Radiated power is measured in W, intensity of a propagating wave in W/m^2, and average doses in J deposited during specified averaging periods—typically 6 minutes to account for the protection afforded as circulating blood carries localized thermal energy safely away (ACGIH Worldwide 2003).

In the spectral region near and including the *visible light* frequencies, the primary organs of concern are the eye and skin. The photon energy at these frequencies is sufficient to cause chemical reactions in rods and cones. Two complementary models apply: one measures intensity of radiation (W/m^2) and the other measures intensity in terms of the photon flux in [photons/(s m^2)]. The photon flux, measured in narrow frequency bands, can be summed to estimate total photon energy in J or intensity in J/m^2.

In the visible light region of the EM spectrum, two sets of units are in general use.

Radiometry is the science of quantifying the phenomena of electromagnetic radiation. Radiometry criteria are expressed in thermodynamic quantities: W, W/m^2, and J.

Photometry is the science of quantifying electromagnetic radiation in the visible light region of the spectrum[6] in units weighted by frequency according to the response of the human eye. Photometry is used to design lighting and projection systems for all kinds of human activities: entertainment, living, learning, driving, working, and so on. The photometric units have special names, recognized in the SI system, used to differentiate them from the radiometric units. The following table (Ohno 1997, 4–6) summarizes these differences. The problem set for this chapter includes exercises to illustrate the details more clearly.

Under an international standard created by the International Commission on Illumination (CIE), the dark-adapted standard eye (scotopic eye) has its best sensitivity at 505 nm wavelength (green light) and the light-adapted eye (photopic eye) has its best sensitivity at 555 nm (yellow light).[7] Light meters used for photometry may have both scotopic and photopic filters used to verify scene-lighting levels for both dark-adapted and light-adapted eyes, respectively.

Note that high intensity infrared ($\lambda > 780$ nm) or ultraviolet light ($\lambda < 380$ nm) registers no intensity on the photometric scale. The retina in a normal human eye does not respond to these frequencies because they are absorbed in the cornea, lens, and fluids of the eye. The radiometric standards for these frequencies exist because they heat skin and eye tissue (infrared) and high doses of UV energy are associated with sunburn, corneal burn, cataracts, and various cancers.

Table 1 summarizes the units of radiometry and photometry used by safety professionals and industrial hygienists.

The TLV uses spectral radiance of a light source (in Watts per steradian per square meter per nanometer of wavelength, W sr^{-1} m^{-2} nm^{-1}) or spectral irradiance incident to the eye (in Watts per square meter per nanometer of wavelength, W m^{-2} nm^{-1}). The coefficients describing this are called *spectral weighting coefficients* by ACGIH.

Although English units are discouraged in the United States, they continue to exist in safety and hygiene literature and in exposure limits promulgated by regulatory agencies. Illuminance in footcandles (fc) is defined as a lumen per square foot. Luminance in footlamberts (fL) is defined as (candela/π) per

TABLE 1

Quantities and Units for Photometry and Radiometry

Photometric Quantity	Unit	Radiometric Quantity	Unit
Luminous flux	lm (lumen)	Radiant flux	W (watt)
Luminous intensity	lm sr^{-1} = cd (candela)	Radiant intensity	W sr^{-1}
Illuminance	lm m^{-2} = lx (lux)	Irradiance	W m^{-2}
		Spectral irradiance factor	W m^{-2} nm^{-1}
Luminance	lm sr^{-1} m^{-2} = cd m^{-2}	Radiance	W sr^{-1} m^{-2}
	(per sr per m^2 of source)	Spectral radiance factor	W sr^{-1} m^{-2} nm^{-1}
Luminous exitance	lm m^{-2}	Radiant exitance	W m^{-2}
Luminous exposure	lm m^{-2} s = lx s	Radiant exposure	W m^{-2} s = J m^{-2}
Luminous energy	lm s	Radiant energy	W s = J (joule)
Color temperature	K (kelvin)	Radiant temperature	K

(*Source:* Ohno 1997, Ryer 2011)

TABLE 2

Ionizing Radiation Measurement Units

Units	Radioactivity	Absorbed Dose	Dose Equivalent	Exposure
Common	curie (Ci)	rad	rem	roentgen (R)
	3.7×10^{10} per s	10 mJ/kg	QF x AbsDos	
SI	becquerel (Bq)	gray (Gy)	sievert (Sv)	
	1/s	1 J/kg	QF x AbsDos	C/kg
Conversion	1 mCi = 37 MBq	1 rad = 0.01 Gy	1 rem = 0.01 Sv	1 R = 258 μC/kg
Conversion	1 MBq = 0.027 mCi	1 Gy = 100 rad	1 Sv = 100 rem	1 C/kg = 3880 R

(*Source:* Cember 1996)

square foot, the reflected luminance that results when a perfect diffuser is illuminated with 1 fc.[8] The luminance of a scene depends on its illumination, the orientation of its surfaces, and the proportion of incident light that is reflected specularly or diffusely, refracted, absorbed, or transmitted at each wavelength.

Ultraviolet frequencies increase from UV-A through UV-B to UV-C. There is a progressive increase in photon energy and in the proportion of molecules that can be ionized by such photons. The UV-C band ends at a wavelength of 0.1 nm, and all higher frequencies (shorter wavelengths) are considered strongly ionizing.

X-rays and *gamma rays* are photons with energies higher than those of UV light. By convention, an X-ray is emitted when an orbital electron jumps to a lower energy state, and a gamma ray is emitted when a nucleus relaxes to a lower energy level. These two types of photons are indistinguishable when they pass through tissue. The X-ray, γ-ray, and high-energy particle radiations are collectively known as *ionizing radiation*. Health hazards associated with ionizing radiation are the domain of the health physics profession and are expressed in specialized units, summarized in Table 2. In the case of light, one set of SI units expresses transport of energy, and a parallel set expresses the biological effectiveness in depositing energy in susceptible tissues.

The term *radioactivity* denotes the number of disintegrations per unit time. An atom may be unstable (*radioactive*) because its nucleus has too much mass, charge, or energy. To become stable, it emits mass, charge, and/or energy in a disintegration event. The rate at which this occurs in a given quantity of atoms is measured per second by the SI unit becquerel (Bq = 1/s) or in the older unit, curie (Ci = 3.7×10^{10}/s). The intensity of the resulting radiation field depends on the energy per emitted particle, whether alpha, beta, gamma, neutron, or other subatomic particle.

The SI unit of *absorbed dose* is the gray, the name for a quantity of absorbed energy totaling 1 J per kg of material. The older unit rad represents 0.01 J per kg of material. This is a physical unit and is not a good measure of the risk of adverse biological effect. For example, 1 Gy of internal alpha radiation poses far more risk than 1 Gy of external beta radiation. Rapidly dividing cell types are more susceptible than slowly dividing cell lines.

The *dose equivalent* is the product of absorbed dose in tissue multiplied by a quality factor—and then sometimes multiplied by other necessary modifying factors at the location of interest. It is expressed numerically in SI units called sieverts, or the older unit rem.

In the context of health physics, the term *exposure* represents the level of ionization realized in exposed material. Ionization is one means by which energy is deposited in tissue. It produces large quantities of peroxides and free radicals as well as a small amount of direct damage to life-critical molecules. Much, if not most, radiation damage is caused by secondary chemical reactions with peroxides and free radicals created in body fluids by ionization (Cember 1996).

Primer on Conservation Laws

Four quantities associated with physical agents are conserved in isolated systems: energy, linear momentum, angular momentum, and electric charge.[9] *Linear momentum* is a vector quantity formed by the product of particle mass and the velocity vector, with relativistic

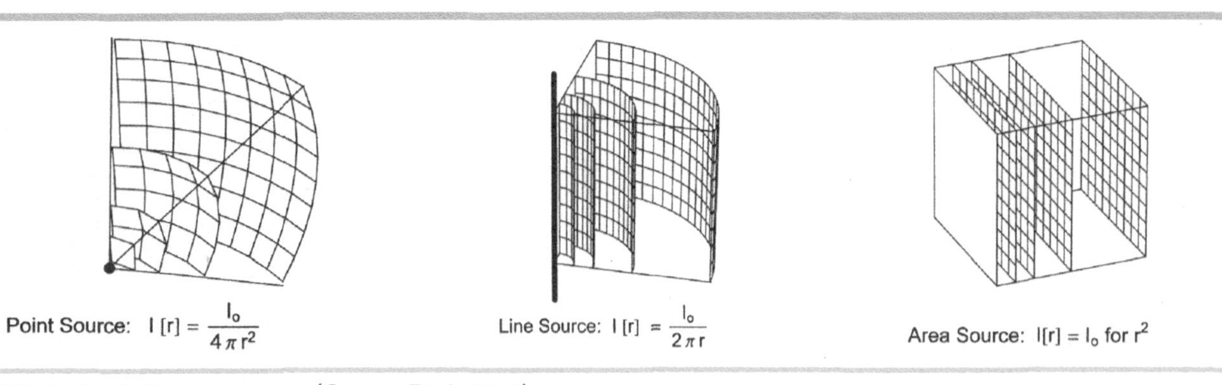

FIGURE 1. Radiation geometry (*Source:* Rock 2011)

corrections for sufficiently high velocities. *Angular momentum* is a vector quantity formed by the product of the moment of inertia and the angular velocity vector, or, equivalently, by the cross-product of linear velocity and radius to the reference point times the mass. *Electric charge* is a property of subatomic particles that is positive, negative, or zero and exists only in multiples of the proton charge.

Shielding for physical agents abides by these conservation principles, and its efficacy can often be checked by verifying conservation laws. Consider an incident wave with an intensity of 100 W/m^2. Measurements show that after it passes through the body of a worker, its intensity falls to 95 W/m^2. The principle of conservation of energy says that energy is neither created nor destroyed but may be changed in form; thus it is seen that 5 W/m^2 was either deposited in the tissue by the passing wave or reflected in another direction. If deposited, it may have caused physical motion, molecular ionization, molecular excitation, or simply thermal heating. If a portion is reflected, bystander exposures are possible.

Now consider the interaction of a photon with orbital electrons of a molecule, using the hydrogen atom to illustrate the principles involved. In this collision, charge, energy, linear momentum, and angular momentum are all conserved. Three events are possible during a collision between a photon and orbital electron: absorption, scattering, and ionization. A photon with energy equal to the transition energy between electron orbits[10] is absorbed, adding kinetic energy to the electron, and the atom is said to be in an excited state. Later, when the excited electron relaxes to a lower energy orbit, it emits a photon of the same or lower frequency (energy). If an excited state is metastable, as is the case of a carbon dioxide molecule, many electrons can be pumped to the excited state and then triggered to emit their radiation simultaneously in phase, a process called light amplification by simulated emission of radiation (LASER). A photon with energy between absorption bands may be scattered or partially absorbed and its excess energy scattered as lower-energy photons. A photon with sufficient energy (> 13.6 eV for hydrogen) ejects an electron from the atom, leaving behind a charged ion. The energy of the ejected electron is the difference between the energy of the incident photon and the ionization energy of the atom.

Primer on Radiation Geometry

Consider four radiation source geometries: point source, line source, surface source, and dipole source.[11] Understanding these allows intuitive professional judgment about numerous additional geometries that can be sketched as a mixture of these and analyzed by linear superposition (see Figure 1).

A point source radiates its power, P_{ps}, uniformly in all directions through a 4π steradian solid angle. At a radius, r_{ps}, the surface area is the product of the solid angle of a wave front and the square of its distance from the source: $4\pi r_{ps}^2$. The intensity of a spherical wave front is the ratio of power to its surface area, because energy is conserved. This is the inverse square law. I_{pso}

is defined as the intensity measured at $r_{ps} = 1$ m from the point source. Sources having a maximum dimension smaller than 0.1 wavelength can be approximated by a point source.

Equation: Point source intensity versus distance

$$I_{ps}(r_{ps}) = \frac{P_{ps}}{4\pi r_{ps}^2} \approx \frac{I_{pso}}{r_{ps}^2} \quad (1)$$

A line source radiates its power, P_{ls}, uniformly in all directions through a coaxial cylindrical surface. At a radius, r_{ls}, and length, L_{ls}, the surface area of a wave front is $2\pi r_{ls}L_{ls}$. The intensity is the ratio of power to surface area and is inversely proportional to r_{ls}.

Equation: Line source intensity versus distance

$$I_{ls}(r_{ls}) = \frac{P_{ls}}{2\pi r_{ls}L_{ls}} \approx \frac{I_{lso}}{r_{ls}} \quad (2)$$

A plane surface, or area source, radiates its power, P_{as}, uniformly in all directions away from a plane. At a distance, r_{as}, from a plane with dimensions length and width, the surface area of a wave front remains the product of its length and width, $A_{as} = L_{as}W_{as}$. In the near field, its intensity is the ratio of power to surface area, a constant independent of r_{as}.

Equation: Area source intensity versus distance

$$I_{as}(r_{as}) = \frac{P_{as}}{A_{as}} \approx I_{aso} \quad (3)$$

In the extreme near field, called the *reactive near field*, nonradiating energy is stored in both potential and kinetic modes. The intensity of the field includes all such energy, whether stored or radiating. For example, dipole sources follow an inverse cube law in the reactive near field, and exposures close to the source are much stronger than those associated with the radiating fields.[12]

Equation: Dipole source intensity versus distance in reactive near field

$$I_{dps}(r_{dps}) = \frac{I_{dps}}{r_{dps}^3} \quad (4)$$

A dipole source is two point sources close to one another. In this geometry, both constructive and destructive interference occur, and the two sources tend to fully or partially cancel one another in some directions while reinforcing in others. In the far field, intensity from a dipole source falls off as the inverse square of distance, just like a point source.

Primer on Waves: Elastic and Electromagnetic

A wave is a disturbance or variation that transfers energy progressively from point to point in a medium. It may take the form of elastic deformation, variation of pressure, magnetic intensity, electric or gravitational potential, or temperature (*Merriam-Webster's Online Dictionary* 2006). A traveling wave is described by its parameters: speed, wavelength, frequency, period, amplitude, impedance, and intensity (as illustrated in Figure 2).

Wavelength, λ, is the ratio of wave speed, c, to its frequency, f. The speed of a traveling wave depends on the properties of the media through which it propagates; its intensity is proportional to its frequency.

Equation: Speed, wavelength, period, and frequency

$$c = \lambda f = \frac{\lambda}{T} = \frac{\lambda\omega}{2\pi} \quad (5)$$

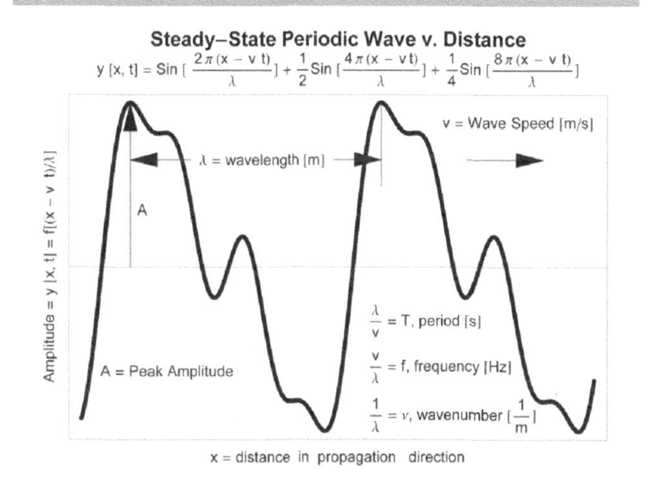

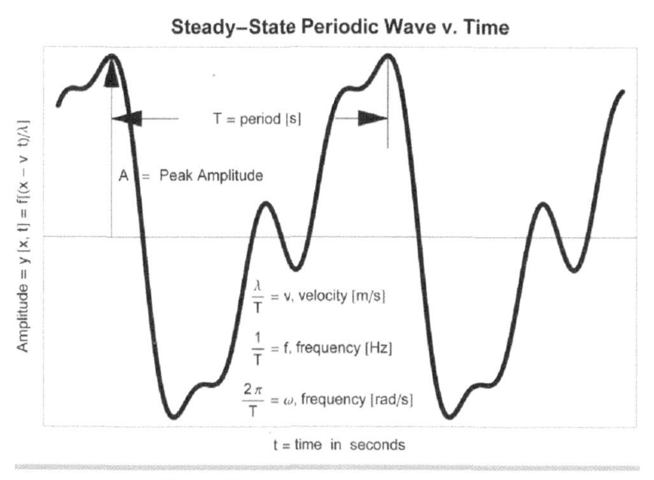

FIGURE 2. **Traveling wave parameters**
(*Source:* Rock 2011)

TABLE 3

Speed, Impedance, and Intensity of Traveling Waves

Wave Type	Wave Speed	Impedance	Intensity
(Eq. 6) Compression wave in ideal gas	$c_{gas} = \sqrt{\frac{\gamma_{gas} T}{M_{gas}}} \sqrt{T}$ [m/s]	$Z_{gas} = \rho_{gas} c_{gas}$ [rayl]	$\frac{P^2_{rms}}{Z_{gas}}$ [W/m^2]
	M in g/mol, T in K	ρ in kg/m^3, c in m/s	P in Pa, Z in rayl
(Eq. 7a) Sound in air	$c_{air} = \sqrt{\frac{\gamma_{air} RT}{M_{air}}} = 20.05\sqrt{T}$ [m/s]	$Z_{air} = \rho_{air} c_{air} = \frac{69.83\, P_{air}}{\sqrt{T_{air}}}$ [rayl]	$\frac{P^2_{rms}}{Z_{air}}$ [W/m^2]
	M in g/mol, T in K	ρ in kPa, T in K	P_{rms} in Pa, Z in rayl
(Eq. 7b) Ref values at 293 K = 20°C	$c_{0\,air} = 343$ [m/s]	$Z_{0\,air} = 400$ [rayl]	$\rho_{0\,air} = 1.2$ [kg/m^3]
(Eq. 8) Compression wave in liquid	$c_{liq} = \sqrt{\frac{\gamma_{liq} B_{liq}}{\rho_{liq}}}$ [m/s]	$Z_{liq} = \rho_{liq} c_{liq}$ [rayl]	$\frac{P^2_{rms}}{Z_{liq}}$ [W/m^2]
(Eq. 9a) Acoustic wave in pure water at P = 1 atm	$c_{water} \approx 1483 + 2(T - 293.15)$ [m/s]		For T = 293.15 K c_0 = 1481.4 m/s Z_0 = 1,480,000 rayl ρ_0 = 998.2 kg/m^3
(Eq. 9b) Acoustic wave in sea water	$c_{sea\ water} \approx 1449 + 4.6T_c - 0.055T_c^2 + 0.0003T_c^3 + (1.39 - 0.012T_c)(S - 35) + (0.017d)$ [m/s] $T_c = (T - 273.15)$, with T in K; S = salinity in ppt_{wt}; d = depth in m		c_0 = 1500 m/s Z_0 = 1.54 10^6 rayl S_0 = 35 parts/1000 d_0 = 1 m T_0 = 286.15 K = 13°C ρ_0 = 1026.4 kg/m^3
(Eq. 10) EM in homogeneous isotropic material	$c_m = \frac{1}{\sqrt{\mu_m \varepsilon_m}}$	$Z_m = \mu_m c_m = \sqrt{\frac{\mu_m}{\varepsilon_m}}$ in [Ω = V/A]	$\lvert\vec{S}\rvert = \frac{\lvert(\vec{E} \times \vec{B})\rvert}{\mu_m} \approx$ $\frac{\vec{E} \cdot \vec{E}}{Z_m} \approx$ $\left(\frac{\vec{B}}{\mu_m} \cdot \frac{\vec{B}}{\mu_m}\right) Z_m$ [W/m^2]
(Eq. 11) EM in vacuum	$c_0 = \frac{1}{\sqrt{\mu_0 \varepsilon_0}}$ [m/s] = 299,792,458 [m/s]	$Z_0 = \sqrt{\frac{\mu_0}{\varepsilon_0}} = 376.73\ \Omega$	$\lvert\vec{I}_{EM}\rvert = \left\lvert\vec{E} \times \frac{\vec{B}}{\mu_0}\right\rvert$ [W/m^2] $\lvert\vec{I}_{EM free field}\rvert \approx Z_0\left(\frac{B_{rms}}{\mu_0}\right)^2$ $\approx \frac{(E_{rms})^2}{Z_0}$ [W/m^2]

(*Source:* Rock 2011, using Wolfram Alpha, NIST, and various textbooks and Web sites)

The speed of an elastic compression or transverse wave equals the square root of the ratio of the bulk modulus (Pa = N/m^2) or string tension (in N) to its mass density (in kg/m^3 or kg/m). Similar concepts apply to electromagnetic waves. Permeability and permittivity of materials are analogous to elasticity and mass density. EM speed equals one over the square root of the product of permeability and permittivity. EM impedance is the square root of the ratio of permeability to permittivity.

As shown in Table 3, wave propagation speed is determined by the ratio of force to inertia. Impedance is the ratio of force to velocity. Intensity is the ratio of force squared to impedance, or, equivalently, the product of force and velocity. At a boundary between two materials (say air and human tissue), the ratio of wave impedances determines the proportions of energy reflected from, and penetrating, the boundary.

The speed of light in a vacuum, c_0, is a constant of nature found in Maxwell's equations that are identified in Einstein's theory of general relativity as the speed limit for all radiation, mass, and energy. When an electromagnetic wave passes through substances, it travels more slowly than c_0, because permittivity and permeability in materials are no less than those in a vacuum.

The impedance reveals important insights about behavior of a propagating wave. In real media $c_m < c_0$, and Z_m may differ from Z_I. When an electromagnetic wave enters or leaves such media, its frequency remains constant (conservation of energy) while its wavelength and its speed change in proportion (see Equation 5).[13]

The impedance of a traveling wave (the ratio of its potential to kinetic parameter) is approximately constant in the far field. There, average intensity is proportional to one of the *rms* quantities squared: P^2_{rms}, V^2_{rms}, F^2_{rms}, E^2_{rms}, B^2_{rms}, $dvol^2_{rms}$, I^2_{rms}, or Vel^2_{rms} and the constant of proportionality is the impedance or its reciprocal, the conductance. Most EM survey instruments measure E or H and calculate intensity as $E^2_{rms}/377$ or $H^2_{rms} \times 377$, and most noise survey instruments measure P_{rms}, calculating intensity as $P^2_{rms}/400$. These instruments are designed to measure the far-field intensity of propagating waves and may underestimate intensity in the near and transition fields, where the intensity of nonpropagating induction fields may exceed the intensity of the propagating fields by a large factor and the ratio of potential to kinetic quantities is neither constant nor equal to the impedance of the free field. Table 3 summarizes key features of acoustic and electromagnetic traveling waves that must be addressed when designing engineering controls to limit emission and absorbent and reflecting shielding to limit propagation of these occupational stressors.

Primer on Near and Far Fields

In general, the spatial distribution of intensity in the near field of an extended source is difficult or impossible to measure with common survey instruments. It is in the far field that the radiation field is well approximated by impedance between the potential and kinetic quantities. Further out, the intensity follows the simple inverse square law.

There is no single distance from a source beyond which near-field behavior suddenly becomes far-field behavior. OSHA has adequately summarized the situation for its field compliance officers (OSHA). Table 4 summarizes key points that apply equally to acoustic and EM radiation as a function of its wavelength, lambda (λ), originating from a source whose maximum transverse dimension is D, located a distance r away from the measurement point.

In the reactive near field, much more stored energy exists than does radiating energy. This energy can damage the tissue of any worker present in the field, even though it does not travel from its source. In the near and transition fields, the impedance is an adequate model neither for the ratio of the electric field to the magnetic field nor for the ratio of acoustic pressure to acoustic velocity. A satisfactory survey at distances closer than the far-field boundary requires direct measurement of all three vector quantities of interest for safety purposes: electric field strength, magnetic field strength and EM intensity for electromagnetic fields; or acoustic pressure, acoustic velocity, and acoustic intensity for airborne or waterborne sound fields. In the far field, intensity measurement is straightforward. The impedance at the point of measurement allows for the measurement of either the potential field (E_{rms} for EM, or P_{rms} for acoustic) or the kinetic field (H_{rms} for EM or Vel_{rms} for acoustic) and allows for the calculation of the intensity from the measured *rms* values.

TABLE 4

Near-Transition Far-Field Regions as a Function of $\lambda = c/f$

Region	Computatiion
Reactive near field: very high proportion of stored energy	(Eq. 12a) $r_{reactive\ near\ field} < \lambda/2\pi < 0.16\lambda$
Near field: more stored than propagating energy	(Eq. 12b) $r_{reactive\ near\ field} < r_{near} < \text{Max}\ [\lambda, D^2/\lambda]$
Transition region: more propagating than stored energy	(Eq. 12c) $r_{near} < r_{transition} < r_{far}$
Far field: for free-field impedance	(Eq. 12d) $r_{far} \leq \text{Max}\ [2\lambda, 2D^2/\lambda]$
Far field: for inverse square law behavior	(Eq. 12e) $r_{far} > \text{Max}\ [5\lambda, 2D^2/\lambda]$

(*Source:* OSHA 1990)

Primer on Parameter Dynamic Range

Many physical agents interact with human organs over wide dynamic ranges. It is common practice to describe their risk criteria, their perception, and the protection factors of personal protective equipment on a logarithmic scale. The two most important types of logarithmic scales for industrial hygiene and safety are the optical density and intensity of acoustic and EM fields.

Optical density is defined as the base 10 logarithm of the reciprocal of the transmittance, T_r. For a protective lens it is expressed as a dimensionless fraction.[14] The transmission loss is the optical density expressed in dB.

Equation: Optical density (OD), transmittance (T_r), and transmission loss (TL)

$$OD = \log_{10}(1/T_r);\ \text{and}\ TL = 10\ OD\ \text{in dB} \quad (13)$$

Level, used in acoustics and in EM surveys, is the base 10 logarithm of the dimensionless ratio of two intensities, powers, or energies. A *level* in decibels (dB) is 10 times the base 10 logarithm of the ratio between the two quantities. The dB can express a ratio or be written as "dB re Q_{ref}" where Q_{ref} identifies the size and units of the reference quantity. Reference quantities commonly encountered in safety guidelines include: 1 pW, 1 mW, 1 mV, 1 μPa, 20 μPa, 1 pW/m^2, and 1 mW/cm^2. The equation pair below converts between physical units and dB.

Equation: Level in decibel versus Q_{ref}

$$L_Q = 10 \log_{10}(Q/Q_{ref})\ [\text{dB re}\ Q_{ref}]$$
$$Q = Q_{ref}\ 10^{L_Q/10} \quad (14)$$

Because power is energy per unit time, a level in decibels may be used to describe the ratio between two power quantities when the length of observation for both is identical, as well as to describe the ratio between two intensities when the illuminated area and length of observation are the same. Average power is the product of an *rms* potential quantity (pressure, voltage, force, electric field, and so on) and a companion *rms* kinetic quantity (volume change, electrical current, velocity, magnetic field, and so on). It is important to know the inner workings of every survey instrument. Some measure intensity directly, but most measure either a potential or kinetic quantity, square it, average it, and multiply or divide by an assumed impedance[15] to report power levels. These common types may misrepresent risk in near and transition fields.

Primer on Thermal Effects

Small changes in tissue temperatures lead to dramatic changes in metabolic rates. Thermal energy is conveniently understood as independent, incoherent vibrations of molecules in material substances. In humans, a useful rule of thumb is that metabolic rates double with a temperature rise of 3 K (5°F) and are halved with a temperature fall of –3 K. To prevent acute physiological damage, including inability to complete complex mental tasks, like self-rescue, thermal stress standards are set to avoid more than ±1 K (2°F) changes in human body core temperature caused by occupational exposure factors. EM guidelines for specific organs are designed to prevent unacceptable temperature rises in those organs, considering blood as a coolant, and so typically have averaging times measured in minutes and seconds.

To prevent skin burns, limit the infrared intensity for radiated thermal energy, and limit the temperature for contact with gases, liquids, and solids having temperatures above 44°C (111°F). To prevent numbness, pain, and frostbite, limit the duration of contact with gases, liquids, and solids having temperatures below 16°C (60°F) (Ungar and Stroud 2007).

Primer on Physical Acoustics

In physical acoustics, sound pressure (P_{rms}) is a potential quantity easily measured by a microphone. Acoustic intensity is calculated from P_{rms} with acoustic impedance, which can be estimated by use of the ideal gas law:

Equation: Sound intensity in air

$$\vec{I}_{air} = \text{Mean}\ [P_{air}\overrightarrow{Vel}_{air}]$$

so that

$$\left|I_{air}\right| = \frac{P_{rms}^2}{Z_{air}} = \frac{P_{rms}^2}{Z_0} \cdot \frac{Z_0}{Z_{air}} \quad (15)$$

with P in kPa and Z in rayl.

Equation: Acoustical impedance of air

$$Z_{air} = \rho_{air} c_{air} = \frac{M_{air} P_{air} c_{air}}{R T_{air}} = \frac{69.846\, P_{air}}{\sqrt{T_{air}}} \qquad (16)$$

Hearing-damage risk is proportional to average intensity. Sound-level meters are designed to average P^2, take its square root and reporting

$$P_{rms} = \sqrt{\text{Mean}[P^2(t)]}$$

in terms of L_P in dB re 20 μPa. This makes L_P numerically equal to L_I when $Z_{air} \sim 400$. It is a happenstance of history that hearing conservation standards are presented in terms of sound pressure levels.[16] It is better practice to use sound intensity levels for comparison with hearing damage risk criteria. In any occupational setting involving wide departures from barometric pressure near 100 kPa or temperatures near 293 K (20°C), it is good practice to estimate the acoustic impedance and calculate the sound intensity level associated with the measured sound pressure level. First, look at the definitions of sound pressure level and of sound intensity:

Equation: Sound pressure level versus *rms* sound pressure

$$L_P = 10 \log_{10}\left(\frac{P^2_{rms}}{P^2_0}\right) = 20 \log_{10}\left(\frac{P^2_{rms}}{P_0}\right) \qquad (17)$$

in [dB re 20 μPa]

$$P_{rms} = P_0\, 10^{L_P/20}\ [\mu\text{Pa}]$$

Equation: Sound intensity level versus *rms* sound intensity

$$L_I = 10 \log_{10} \frac{I}{I_0}\ [\text{dB re } I_0 = 1\ \text{pW/m}^2] \qquad (18)$$

$$I = I_0\, 10^{L_I/10}\ [\text{pW/m}^2]$$

The corrected sound intensity level, L_I in [dB re 1 pW/m²] is a function of L_P measured with a microphone in [dB re 20 μPa], the air temperature during measurement [T_{air} in K] and the absolute atmospheric pressure at the location of the measurement [P_{air} in kPa].[17]

Equation: Sound intensity level pressure and temperature correction

$$L_I = L_P + 10 \log_{10}\left(\frac{400}{\rho_{air} c_{air}}\right) \qquad (19)$$

$$L_I(L_P, T_{air}, P_{air}) =$$

$$L_P + 10 \log_{10}\left(\frac{5.72693\sqrt{T_{air}}}{P_{air}}\right) [\text{dB re 1 pW/m}^2]$$

The correction factor to convert L_P to L_I, evident above, should be applied whenever the temperature is outside the range 200 K to 500 K (–100 to 440°F) or the atmospheric pressure is outside the range 80 kPa to 125 kPa (0.8 to 1.25 atm). People at work are seldom exposed to such temperatures, so the correction factor is needed primarily in workplaces at altitudes greater than ~5000 ft and in pressurized workplaces such as those connected with tunneling, commercial diving, and hyperbaric medicine.[18]

Primer on Photons

Electromagnetic phenomena exhibit two properties: waves and particles. During scattering events with molecules, the conservation of energy and momentum are explained by behavior of a particle called a photon. During propagation of energy through empty space, through materials, and in electromechanical equipment, the collective behavior of photons is well explained by Maxwell's wave equations with the Lorentz force equations.

A photon is a massless particle that travels at the speed of light, has a finite extent, behaves as a wave, and carries linear momentum, angular momentum (spin), and energy between molecules. It is the quantum of the electromagnetic field and, according to quantum electrodynamic theory, mediates the forces between electromagnetic fields and molecules. Photon energy and momentum can be transferred to a molecule or carried away by other subatomic particles during a collision. The principles of conservation of energy and conservation of momentum apply. The photon collision either raises the internal energy of the molecule or knocks an electron from the molecule in an ionizing event. When an ionized molecule captures an electron or an excited molecule relaxes from an excited state back into its state of equilibrium, photons may be emitted to carry away the excess energy and momentum. Both the energy and the momentum of a photon are proportional to its frequency, f, and the constant of proportionality is Plank's Constant, h. The speed of light equals the ratio of photon energy to photon momentum.[19]

Equation: Photon energy, photon momentum, and speed of light

$$U_{photon} = \frac{hc}{\lambda} = hf = hbar\ \nu\ [\mathrm{J}] \quad (20)$$

$$P_{photon} = \frac{h}{\lambda} = \frac{hf}{c} = \frac{hbar\ \nu}{c}\ [\mathrm{kg\ m/s}]$$

$$c = \frac{E_{photon}}{P_{photon}}\ [\mathrm{m/s}]$$

Primer on the Electromagnetic Spectrum

The EM spectrum displays the energy density of radiation as a function of frequency or vacuum wavelength.[20] Portions of the spectrum are assigned specific uses by national laws and international treaties. The dose of electromagnetic energy in tissue depends on tissue properties and radiation frequency. This primer lays the foundation for understanding the basis for regulations and guidelines discussed later in the chapter.

For nonionizing electromagnetic radiation (lower frequencies), models of collective effects are sufficient to specify health-related guidelines. Forces are proportional to an electric field, E in volts/meter, and a magnetic field, B in tesla or $H = B/\mu$ in amperes/m. The force on a stationary charged particle with net charge q in coulombs is a vector having the same sense as the electric field vector when q is positive and the opposite sense when q is negative. A magnetic field applies forces to moving charged particles that are at right angles to the magnetic field and to the velocity of the particle. The total Lorentz forces are the sum of the electric forces on all charged particles and the magnetic forces on moving charged particles.

Equation: EM forces experienced by a charged particle

$$\vec{F}_{elec} = q\vec{E}\ [\mathrm{N}] \quad (21)$$

$$\vec{F}_{mag} = q\overrightarrow{Vel} \times \vec{B}\ [\mathrm{N}]$$

$$\vec{F}_{Lorentz} = \vec{F}_{elec} + \vec{F}_{mag} = q\vec{E} + q\overrightarrow{Vel} \times \vec{B}\ [\mathrm{N}]$$

The (relativistic) relationships between electrical charge and electrical current distribution and their associated electric and magnetic fields are nearly[21] completely described by four equations known as Maxwell's equations. These equations predicted the speed of light as a constant of nature and form the basis for modern telecommunications, as well as the basis for safety guidelines for the use of electromagnetic devices in occupational settings. The differential form of these important equations (22a–22d) is offered in Table 5, along with an intuitive description.[22]

In the far field, or free field, there are no sources of electric or magnetic fields, neither charges nor currents. Here, the symmetry between Faraday's Law and Ampere's Law predicts that an EM wave will propagate long distances from its source through free space (charge-free, current-free space). Under these conditions, a simple relation exists between the radiating time-varying electric and magnetic field vectors. In space, they are orthogonal to each other and to the direction of energy propagation. In time, they are in a fixed phase with each other. Further, their amplitudes are in proportion to the speed of light. With E in V/m, H in A/m (so that $B = \mu_0 H$ is in T), and c in m/s,

Equation: Free-field ratio E to B (no charge or current sources)

$$\frac{E_{rms}}{B_{rms}} = c_0 \text{ with } c_0 = \frac{1}{\sqrt{\mu_0 \varepsilon_0}} \text{ in vacuum} \quad (23)$$

$$\frac{E_{rms}}{B_{rms}} = c_m \text{ with } c_m = \frac{1}{\sqrt{\mu_m \varepsilon_m}} \text{ in isotropic material}$$

The Poynting Vector, S, provides the intensity and direction of power flow in free space for a traveling EM wave. The Poynting vector allows the expression of the power density of a traveling EM wave in its far field in terms of the magnetic permeability of the medium and its time varying electric and magnetic fields. In the equation below, E is in V/m, H in A/m, B in T, and power density is in W/m².

Equation: Free-field Poynting Vector

$$\vec{S}_{EM} = \vec{E} \times \vec{H} = \vec{E} \times \frac{\vec{B}}{\mu_m}\ [\mathrm{W/m^2}] \quad (24)$$

The intensity at any point is defined as the time average of the Poynting vector at that point. This definition allows use of simple survey instruments measuring the *rms* values of E or B to measure the intensity. In the equation that follows, note that $Z_{EM} = Z_{tissue} \approx Z_0 \approx 377$ ohms.

TABLE 5

Maxwell's EM Equations in Free Space

Differential Form (Nave, 2011)	Sketch (Rock, 2007)	Comment (Rock, 2007)
(Eq 22 a) $Div(\bar{E}) = \frac{\rho}{\varepsilon_0}$ and $\int_{All A} \bar{E} \times d\bar{A} = \frac{\rho}{\varepsilon_0}$ A is a surface around charge ρ. For a sphere of radius r, with a point charge ρ at its center, $A = 4\pi r^2$.; $\lvert\bar{E}\rvert = \frac{\rho}{4\pi r^2 \varepsilon_o}$	+ −	(Eq 22a) Gauss' Law$_E$: Electric field strength through a closed surface is proportional to quantity of net charge enclosed by that surface. The Electric field lines diverge from the positive point charge (on left) and converge to negative charge (on right). Solid lines are lines of constant potential in volts. Arrows show direction and intensity of the E field. To imagine this image in its proper 3-D form, visualize two dandelion pods: field lines converge or diverge uniformly from each core.
(Eq 22 b) $Div(\bar{B}) = 0$ and $\int_{All A} \bar{B} \times d\bar{A} = 0$. A is any closed surface.	S N	(Eq 22b) Gauss' Law$_B$: Magnetic field lines do not diverge; they are closed on themselves (think rubber bands). There is no magnetic monopole.
(Eq 22 c) $Curl(\bar{E}) = -\frac{\partial \bar{B}}{\partial t}$ and $\int_{All S} \bar{E} \times d\bar{S} = -\frac{\partial \Phi_B}{\partial t}$ with $\Phi_B = \int_{All A} \bar{B} \times d\bar{A}$; S is the boundary of an open surface named A.	$\vec{E}$ $\frac{d\vec{B}}{dt}$	(Eq 22c) Faraday's Law: A time-varying magnetic field passing through an open surface creates an encircling electric field that curls around that surface. The minus sign agrees with Lenz' Law: E is directed to induce current flow in conductors that resist the change in the magnetic field. When dB/dt is negligible, the electric field resulting from a long charged wire is dominated by Eq 22 a.
(Eq 22 d) $Curl(\bar{B}) = \frac{1}{c^2}\left(\frac{\bar{J}}{\varepsilon_o} + \frac{\partial \bar{E}}{\partial t}\right)$ and $\int_{All S} \bar{B} \times d\bar{S} = \mu_0 i + \frac{1}{c_o^2}\frac{\partial \Phi_E}{\partial t}$ with $\Phi_E = \int_{All A} \bar{E} \times d\bar{A}$ and $i = \int_{All A} \bar{J} \times d\bar{A}$ S is the boundary of an open surface named A.	$\vec{B}$ $\vec{J}$ $\frac{d\vec{E}}{dt}$	(Eq 22d) Maxwell-Ampere Law: The net current through an open surface creates an encircling magnetic field that curls around that surface. Net current, in amperes, is the sum of ionic current and displacement current: $(\mu_o \bar{J})$ and $\frac{1}{c^2}\frac{\partial \bar{E}}{\partial t}$. When dE/dt is negligible, B at a distance r from a long wire carrying current I, is $\frac{\mu_o I}{2\pi r}$

Equation: Free-field EM intensity from measured E_{rms} and B_{rms} (valid in far field)

$$I_{EM} = E_{rms}H_{rms} = \frac{E_{rms}^2}{Z_{EM}} = Z_{EM}H_{rms}^2 = \frac{c_m B_{rms}^2}{\mu_m} \text{ [W/m}^2\text{]} \tag{25}$$

with $Z_{tissue} \approx Z_0 \approx 377$ [ohms]

Radiating EM waves exert pressure on the surfaces they illuminate that arises from the momentum of photons. According to Newton's third law, an object that reflects radiation must recoil with enough momentum to stop the incoming wave and send it out again—twice the momentum of the wave. If the energy is absorbed, however, the object must only stop it, recoiling with the momentum of the wave. When a photon is absorbed, its energy and momentum are transferred to the molecule that absorbs it. When a photon is totally reflected, its momentum change is twice its own momentum and the molecule that reflects it recoils twice as much as it would have from an absorption event (this is the principle underlying solar sails for space craft).[23] Radiation pressure is quantified by the equations below. The intensity of EM radiation is the time average of the Poynting vector,

$$I = \langle \vec{S} \rangle \text{ W/m}^2$$

The radiation pressure, or P_{EM} (force per unit area), exerted by electromagnetic radiation is proportional to its intensity.

Equation: EM radiation pressure from intensity I

$$P_{\mathrm{EM}_{absorption}} = \frac{I}{c_0}\ [\mathrm{Pa}] \tag{26a}$$

$$P_{\mathrm{EM}_{reflection}} = \frac{2I}{c_0}\ [\mathrm{Pa}] \tag{26b}$$

Intense LASER pulses deliver sufficient energy that retinal damage (and repair) can occur from both localized heating and mechanical impulses caused by momentum change.[24] Photon and radiation momentum are easily estimated from the ratio between energy and the speed of light.

Equation: Momentum change from a photon with energy, U_{photon} [J]

$$\Delta p_{photon\,aabsorbed} = \frac{U_{photon}}{c_0}\ [\mathrm{kg\ m/s}] \tag{27a}$$

$$\Delta p_{photon\,reflected} = \frac{2U_{photon}}{c_0}\ [\mathrm{kg\ m/s}] \tag{27b}$$

$$F_{photon} = \frac{\Delta p_{photon}}{\Delta t}\ [\mathrm{N}] \tag{27c}$$

A wide range of EM frequencies (and therefore of photon energies) may be encountered in occupational settings. A table or graph showing properties of electromagnetic waves across the full spectrum of interest is too large to publish in this text,[25] but an abridged illustration is offered in Figure 3 to illustrate some of the regions of interest for industrial hygiene and health physics.

According to classical electromagnetic theory, maximum energy transfer between radiated EM waves and an electrically conducting target occurs when the target size is about 0.4 wavelengths (if electrically isolated) or 0.2 wavelengths (if electrically bonded to a ground plane). That means for humans, energy from

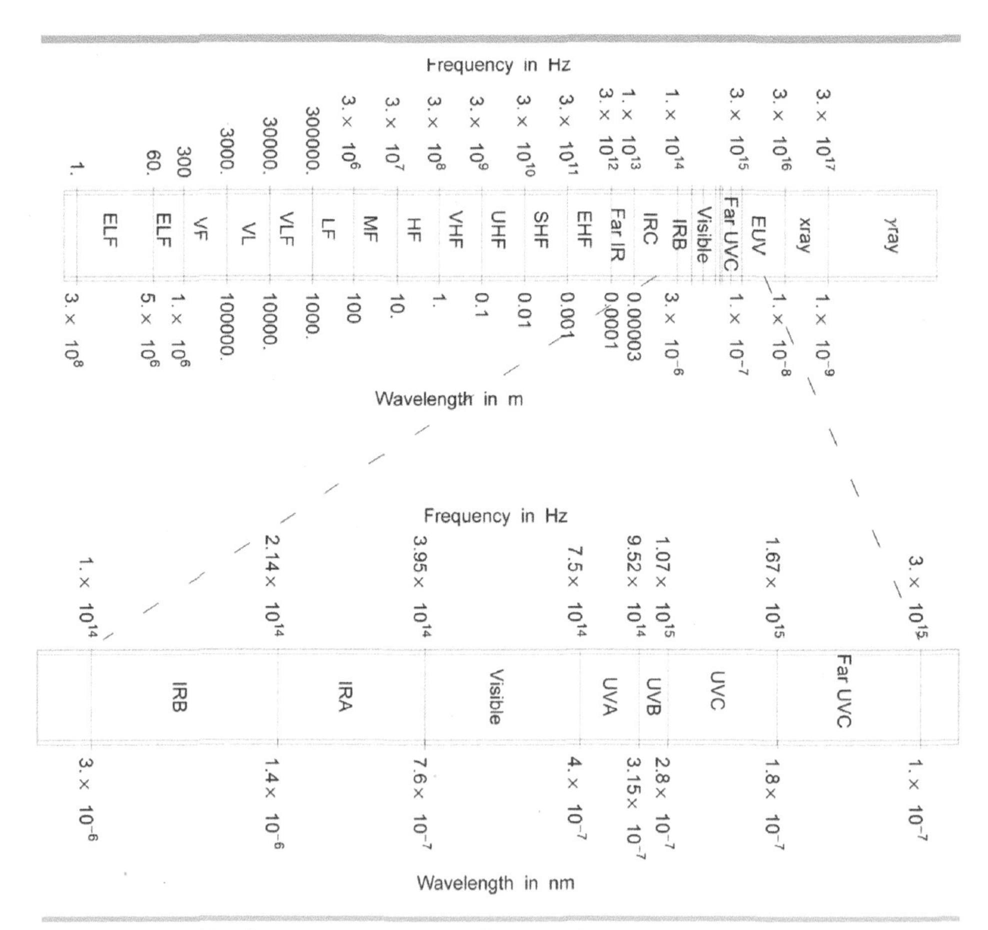

FIGURE 3. EM: Spectrum allocation (*Source:* Rock 2011, adapted from www.unihedron.com, Ryer 2011, NIST.gov, and other sources)

radio waves with frequencies between 30 and 300 MHz (wavelengths between 10 and 1 meter) are most strongly absorbed. Wavelengths shorter or longer than these tend to pass through the body while depositing only a small fraction of their propagating energy.[26] See Tables 6, 7, and 8 for wavelength and frequency summaries.

At low frequencies (wavelengths that are long in comparison to molecule and organ dimensions), exposure is controlled by controlling the electric field's strength in tissue. At low frequencies, high electric field strength can induce AC currents, but it is primarily contact with voltage sources that causes damaging current flow. Ohmic heating is the primary stressor for frequencies between DC and VLF. However, caution must be exercised; neuromuscular disturbance—such as cardiac fibrillation by contacting current with a frequency near 50 to 60 Hz—can be fatal.

Electronic and communications engineers describe various regions of the spectrum with names that may be unfamiliar to safety professionals. Common names for specific regions of the radio-frequency spectrum are summarized in Tables 6–9.

Radio-frequency bands pose primarily an ohmic heating risk. Microwave frequencies pose skin-effect risks where induced currents are concentrated near the surface and of microwave resonance absorption by some molecules common in tissues.

In far infrared frequencies, the penetration depth is small, causing primarily surface heating. Symptoms include welder's flash and skin erythema that looks like sunburn. At frequencies of visible light, very little penetration occurs except in specialized tissues of the cornea, lens, and aqueous humor of the eye. At ultraviolet frequencies, ionization occurs as photons interact with molecules and are almost completely absorbed near the surface of the human body (see Table 9).

At frequencies above extreme UV, a high proportion of X-rays and gamma rays penetrate the body completely, allowing medical imaging of the skeleton and of some organ systems. A small proportion of X-ray and γ-ray photons collide with tissue molecules and produce copious quantities of ionization.

TABLE 6

DC to Very Low Frequency EM Spectral Bands

Name	Symbol	Frequency	Wavelength/km
Approximate direct current	~DC	0 Hz to1 Hz	> 300,106
Extremely low frequencies	ELF	1 Hz to 300 Hz	300,000 to 1000
Voice frequencies	VF	300 Hz to 3 kHz	1000 to 100
Very low frequencies	VLF	3 kHz to 30 kHz	100 to 10

(*Source:* www.unihedron.com)

TABLE 7

Radio-Frequency Spectral Bands

RF Band Name	Symbol	Frequency/MHZ	Wavelength
Low frequency	LF	0.03 to 0.3	10 km to 1 km
Medium frequency	MF	0.3 to 3	1 km to 100 m
High frequency	HF	3 to 30	100 m to 10 m
Very high frequency	VHF	30 to 300	10 m to 1 m

(*Source:* www.unihedron.com)

TABLE 8

Microwave Spectral Bands

Band Name	Symbol	Frequency/GHZ	Wavelength
Ultra high frequency	UHF	0.3 to 3	1 m to 10 cm
Super high frequency	SHF	3 to 30	10 cm to 1 cm
Extremely high frequency or millimeter band	EHF or mm band	30 to 300	10 mm to 1 mm
Micrometer band	μm band	300 to 3 000	1 mm to 100 μm

(*Source:* www.unihedron.com)

Ionization events are widely associated with alterations in RNA and DNA. If these are not repaired in a timely fashion, they are associated with increased risk of cancer in some tissue types. Fortunately, humans are equipped with robust repair mechanisms; peer-reviewed epidemiological studies have shown that low levels of radiation exposure actually reduce the risk of cancers. An undated critical report available on the Internet that criticizes these studies is referenced here for the convenience of readers who wish to evaluate minority arguments (Nussbaum, et al. u.d.). However, subthreshold levels seem to represent exposures low enough that the rate of damage remains below the rate of repair, keeping damage from

TABLE 9

Summary Effects of IR, Vis, and UV Photons

Band	Name	Photon Energy/eV	λ/nm	Eye	Skin
Far IR	IR-C	0.00124–0.0413	1×10^6–30×10^3	Corneal burn	Skin burn
Thermal IR	IR-C	0.0413–0.413	30×10^3–3×10^3	Corneal burn Aqueous flare IR cataract	Skin burn
Near IR	IR-B	0.413–0.886	3000–1400	Corneal burn Aqueous flare IR cataract	Skin burn
Near IR	IR-A	0.866–1.63	14000–760	IR cataract Retinal burns	Skin burn
Visible	Vis	1.63–3.1	760–400	Photochemical Retinal burns	Skin burn Photosensitive reactions
Near UV	UV-A	3.1–3.94	400–315	Photochemical UV cataract	Pigmentation Skin burn DNA changes
Medium UV	UV-B	3.94–4.43	315–280	Photokeratitis	Sun tan Pigmentation Skin aging
Far UV	UV-C	4.43–6.89	280–180	Photokeratitis Germicidal	Skin cancer Skin burn Germicidal
Far UV	FUV	6.89–12.4	180–100	Photokeratitis Germicidal	Skin cancer Skin burn Germicidal
Extreme UV	EUV	12.4–124	100–10	Photokeratitis Germicidal	Skin cancer Skin burn Germicidal

Photobiological system: UV-A1 (400–340 nm) tans skin, a protective mechanism; UV-A2 (340–315) changes DNA; UV-B provides energy for producing Vitamin D.[1] UV-C, FUV, and EUV are germicidal and carcinogenic.

Physics system: far UV (FUV) is 280–100 nm, and extreme UV (EUV) is 100–10 nm. Vacuum UV extends from 200–10 nm, is absorbed in the atmosphere and propagates only in a vacuum. Near IR is 0.76–3 μm, thermal IR is 3–30 μm, and far IR is 30–100 μm.

[1] The ozone layer partially filters UV-B and nearly completely filters UV-C, FUV, and EUV from the sun. Arguably, the ozone layer makes life on earth possible.

(*Source:* Rock 2011, Ryer 2011, OSHA 2003)

accumulating. (See Figure 4 on the biological effects of EM radiation.)

Primer on Ionization

Ionizing radiation interacts with tissue (or any material) when high-speed subatomic particles (including photons) collide with electrons or nucleons of atoms in molecules. These collisions conserve mass, charge, and momentum. An ionizing event occurs when an electron or other charged particle is added to, or removed from, a molecule. Particle energy for ionizing weakly bound orbital electrons is as low as ~7 eV for amines; most molecules are ionized by energies above 12.4 eV.[27] Ionization in modern occupational settings is typically caused by common high-energy subatomic particles, including helium nuclei (alpha particles), electrons (beta$^-$ particles), positrons (beta$^+$ particles), photons (UV, X-, and γ rays), protons, neutrons, and cosmic rays (subatomic and subnucleonic particles).

Ionization in material, including in human tissue, produces ion pairs, conserving charge in the universe. The first ionization occurs when an ionizing particle knocks one or more electrons out of their orbital position, giving the parent molecule a net positive charge. A second ionizing event occurs quickly when the freed electrons are captured by another molecule, which becomes a negatively charged ion. When a particle has sufficiently high energy, an ion track may be created as the particle bounces between molecules, successively ionizing a series of molecules along its path. Very high-energy charged particles and uncharged particles can disrupt

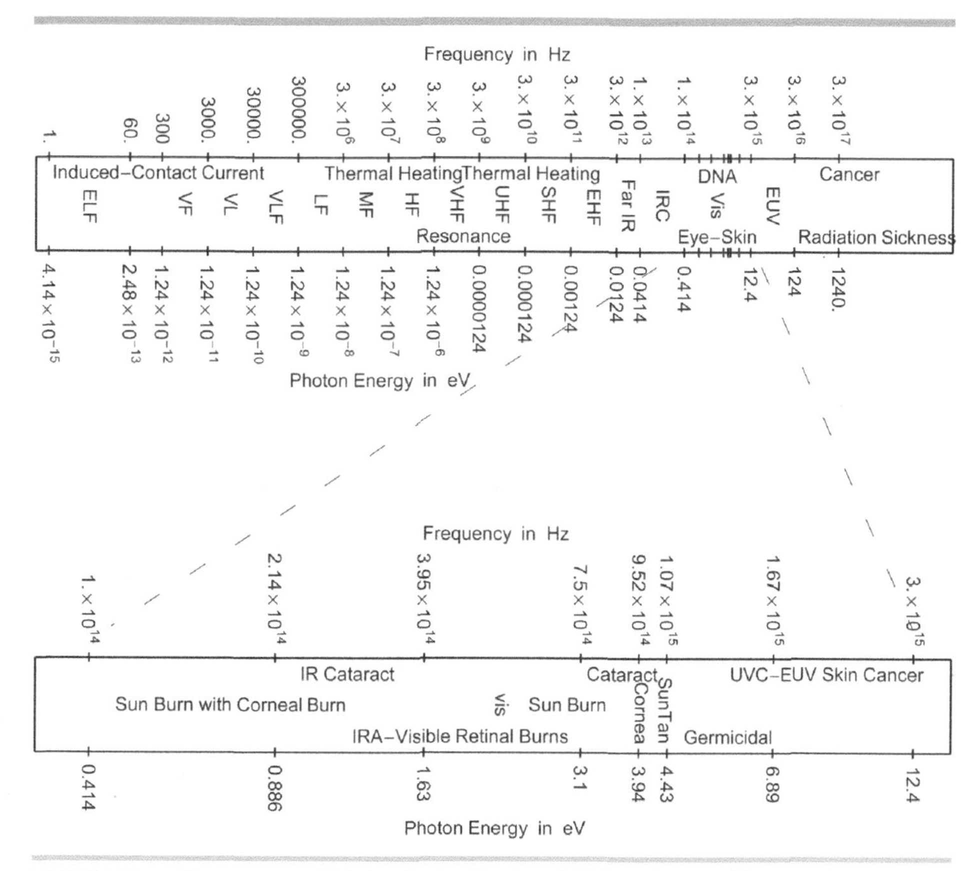

FIGURE 4. Summary of biological effects of EM radiation (*Source:* Rock 2011, adapting material from OSHA, NRC, and EPA)

the nucleus of an atom by emitting secondary ionizing radiation in the form of gamma rays, neutrons, protons, beta particles, neutrinos, muons, and so on. This principle is used in neutron activation analysis, in which neutrons excite nuclei so that characteristic gamma rays are emitted, allowing a gamma spectrometer to identify the elements in the unknown substance.

Primer on Ionizing Radiation

It will be helpful to understand the nature of several of the various forms of energy, which range from the mildly ionizing ultraviolet light to the highly ionizing X-, alpha, beta, and γ rays and high-energy neutrons.

The dominant tissue-damage mechanism of ionizing radiation is the oxidation of life-critical molecules by free radicals and peroxides created along the aqueous ion track left in tissue by a passing ray of highly ionizing radiation. Excess consumption of oxidant-rich foods produces the same kinds of damage as low-level exposure to ionizing radiation. No matter the source of damage, the same repair mechanisms work to repair damaged tissue. If the damage rate is lower than the repair rate, neither acute nor chronic injuries are observed clinically. We live in a radiation-filled environment that includes cosmic background radiation and radiation from naturally occurring environmental radio nuclides, and our bodies experience internal radiation from radio nuclides in tissue that enter in chemicals from air, water, and food. This has been the case throughout human history.

Environmental Background Radiation Levels

At sea level, the average radiation level is approximately 0.03 microsieverts per hour. As altitude increases, radiation exposure increases exponentially. Mexico City, which is 2240 m above sea level, is exposed to about 0.09 microsieverts per hour; La Paz, Bolivia, at ~3640 m the highest city in the world, endures cosmic

TABLE 10

Common Sources of Everyday Radiation

Source	Amount
1 kg of coffee	1000 Bq
1 kg super-phosphate fertilizer	5000 Bq
The air in a 100 m^2 Australian home (radon)	3000 Bq
1 adult human weighing 70 kg (100 Bq/kg)	7000 Bq
The air in many 100 m^2 European homes (radon)	30,000 Bq
1 household smoke detector (with americium)	30,000 Bq
Radioisotope for medical diagnosis	70,000,000 Bq
Radioisotope source for medical therapy	100,000,000,000,000 Bq

(*Source:* Adapted from the American Nuclear Society (AMS) n.d. and Health Physics Society (HPS) n.d.)

and solar radiation of about 0.23 microsieverts hourly, more than seven times the tropical sea-level value.

Naturally occurring background radiation is the main source of exposure for most people. Levels typically range from about 1.5 to 3.5 millisieverts per year. In Brazil and Sudan many people have average exposures up to 40 mSv yearly. Several places are known in Iran, India, and Europe where natural background radiation, including radon gas, gives an annual dose exceeding 50 mSv and even up to 260 mSv (at Ramsar in Iran). Lifetime doses from natural radiation range from 120 to 20,000 mSv and there is no evidence of increased cancers or other health problems arising from these high natural levels.[28] Clearly, the 50 mSv/yr (5 rem/yr) PEL for annual occupational exposure is well below the threshold for identifiable disease in humans.

There are many common sources of radiation in our lives. Table 10 summarizes some of these, and an EPA Web site (EPA 2007) allows users to estimate their own annual radiation dose by answering some simple multiple-choice questions.

Ultraviolet Radiation (UV Rays)

UV radiation is divided into three bands, called UV-A (400–315 nm, or 3.1–3.94 eV/photon), UV-B (315–280 nm, or 3.94–4.43 eV/photon) and UV-C (280–100 nm, or 4.43–12.4 eV/photon). Some UV-B and most UV-C photons are able to ionize some biochemical molecules. In most occupational settings vacuum UV wavelengths (180–100 nm, or 6.89–12.4 eV/photon) are of no consequence, because these photons are so completely absorbed that they travel no further than 4 cm (1.5 inch) in air at sea level. Commercial IH survey instruments, called photo ionization detectors, measure the airborne concentration of some vapors and gases based on UV ionization. Typically, photo ionization detectors have interchangeable UV sources that produce 8.4 eV, 9.5 eV, 10.0 eV, 10.6 eV, or 11.7 eV photons (International Sensor Technology n.d.).

Alpha Particles or Alpha Rays

Alpha radiation is the name for fast-moving, positively charged helium nuclei emitted from a nucleus during a disintegration event. Alpha particles have a mass number $A = 4$ and atomic number $Z = 2$, indicating a double positive charge. They have high energy—typically in the MeV range—but because of their large size are stopped by just a few inches of air, the human epidermis (the outer layer of skin, made up of dead cells), or a piece of paper. Alpha particles are emitted having discrete energies, and alpha spectra are used to identify the parent radio nuclide. Because alpha radiation does not penetrate the skin, external exposure poses little hazard. When alpha-emitting radio nuclides are inhaled or ingested, their radiation causes extensive localized internal damage.

Beta Particles or Beta Rays

Beta particles are fast-moving, charged particles emitted from a nucleus during a disintegration event that changes its net charge, and thereby its position in the periodic table. They carry either a single negative charge (electron) or single positive charge (positron) and typically have energies in the range of a few hundred keV to several MeV. Radio nuclides responsible for spontaneous beta emissions exhibit continuous energy distributions. The maximum energy of beta emission is characteristic of the nuclide present. Beta rays are more penetrative than alpha particles but less so than gamma rays. Beta particles penetrate several feet of air, several millimeters of plastic, and lesser amounts of very light metals.

Gamma-Ray and X-Ray Photons

X-rays and gamma rays are photons having higher energy (higher frequency and shorter wavelengths) than UV-C. Industrial hygienists consider energies greater than 12.4 eV to be ionizing soft X-rays. Health physicists note that those of significant health concern typically range from several keV to several MeV in occupational settings. X-rays and gamma rays differ only in their sources; X-rays originate from the sudden acceleration of a charged particle (bremsstrahlung radiation) outside the nucleus of an atom, and gamma rays originate within the nucleus of the atom when nucleons relax to lower energy states from an excited state. Gamma rays are emitted at characteristic frequencies and gamma spectroscopy is useful for identifying the elemental content of unknown substances. Like all photons, X-rays and gamma rays carry no charge, have zero rest mass, and deliver energy and momentum to an atom during a collision. X- and gamma-ray photons damage living cells by energy transfer when they scatter from molecules in living tissue. A collision of this sort most frequently leaves a free radical or ion that can produce a cascade of damaging chemical reactions. High-Z materials are the most effective shield for high-energy photons, which interact primarily with their numerous orbital electrons. To a first approximation, more electrons per atom mean better shielding from a solid made up from that atom. Soft X-rays can be stopped by a thin piece of aluminum foil, but hard X-rays can penetrate several inches of lead.

Transitions that result in gamma emission leave A (the mass number) and Z (the atomic number) of the element unchanged and are called *isomeric transitions*. Gamma emissions carry energy and momentum away from an unstable nucleus as it adjusts to a lower energy state and are emitted as photons whose frequencies are characteristic for each atom. Because gamma photons are usually emitted following radioactive decay that also includes alpha, beta, or neutron emissions, a full health physics assessment is required to discover the limits on time, shielding, and distance that will protect workers.

Neutrons

A neutron is uncharged and has slightly more mass than a proton. Free neutrons are unstable and decay into protons by beta emission, having a half life of about 11 minutes (Christenson, et al. 1972, 1628–1640). Neutrons are stable only when in a nucleus and bound to protons (Williams 2010). Neutrons are emitted as a by-product of fission or by nuclear reactions involving other particles. Neutrons can cause much damage in tissue and cells by creating ions, peroxides, and free radicals in all tissue types. Secondary reactions by the free radicals and ions created by neutrons are the primary cause of biochemical damage—especially that occurring to life-critical RNA and DNA molecules.

Primer on Human Vision

The human eye is a remarkable organ that has automatic control of focal length, of the retinal illumination level, and of retinal photochemical gain. The cornea and lens are made of specialized cells organized as highly parallel bundles of proteins wrapped in bilipid layers. These are transparent to photons in the visible spectrum, between infrared and ultraviolet light (700–400 nm). The retina is a complex, multilayered structure having photosensitive elements (called *rods* and *cones*) at the back; initial image processing occurs in layers of neurons toward the front of the eye. The neural network acts like a screen door, casting shadows on the image plane containing the rods and cones. However, the short distances between neurons in the front layers allow real-time image preprocessing with minimal time delay. The processed image is collected and sent to the visual cortex through the fovea, a hole in the retina through which the optic nerve passes. It forms a blind spot in the visual field of each eye. The overlapping images received in the visual cortex have nonoverlapping blind spots, completing the perceived image with binocular vision.

Occupational injuries to the eyes include physical trauma, corneal burns, lens burns, and retinal burns. Figures 5a–c show injury to the eye caused by high-intensity radiation of various wavelengths.

As shown in Figure 6, the idealized human eye responds to light intensity over nearly nine orders of magnitude, the brightest (6) by the response of the cones and the dimmest (3) by the rods (Graham 1965). Visual acuity is monotonic with intensity and is best near about 10 millilamberts for the cones and about 100 microlamberts for the rods. The best visual acuity of rods is much poorer than the best of cones. To max-

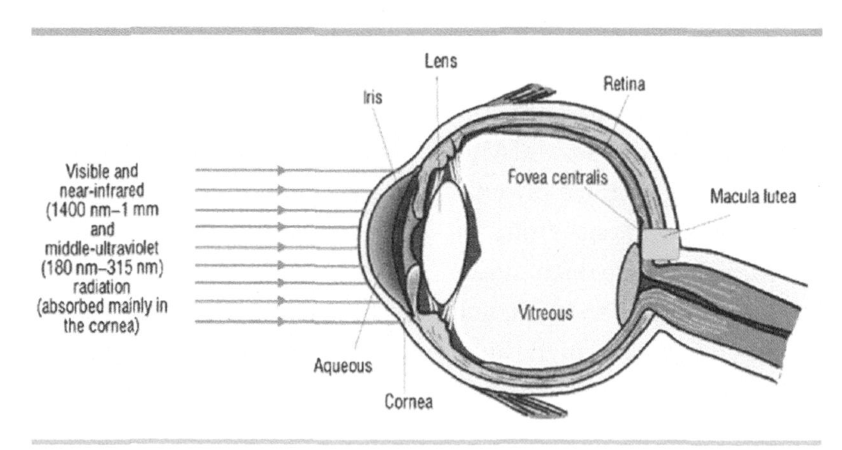

FIGURE 5a. Example of wavelength sensitivity of the human eye (*Source:* www.agamemnon.cord/stip_online/st1-2/st/2ei/1.htm)

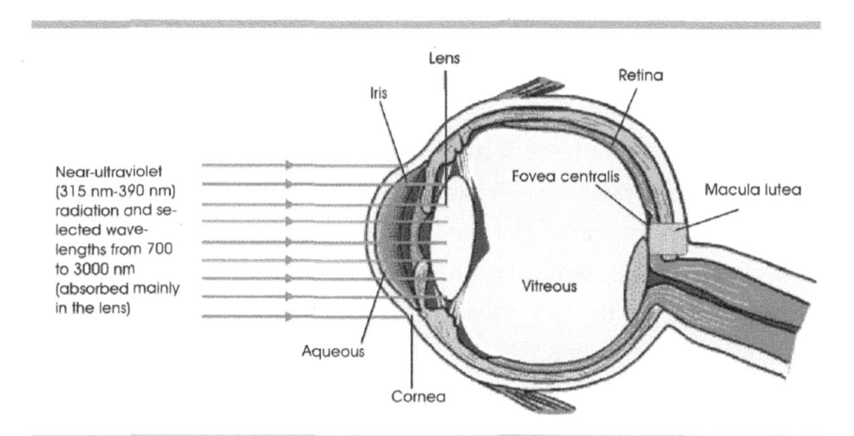

FIGURE 5b. Example of wavelength sensitivity of the human eye (*Source:* www.agamemnon.cord/stip_online/st1-2/st/2ei/1.htm)

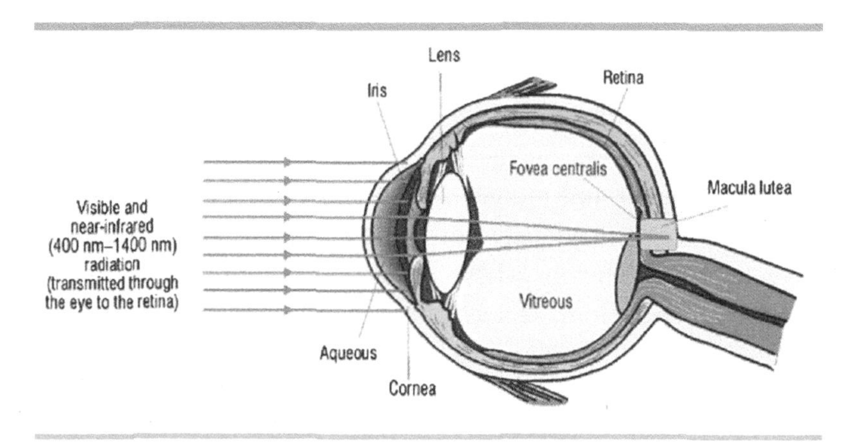

FIGURE 5c. Example of wavelength sensitivity of the human eye (*Source:* www.agamemnon.cord/stip_online/st1-2/st/2ei/1.htm)

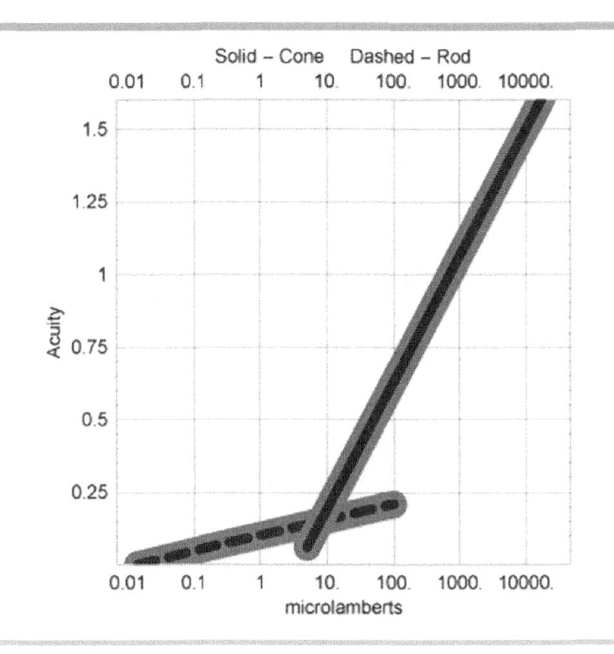

FIGURE 6. Human visual acuity (*Source:* Graham 1965)

imize visual performance in critical work areas, control the level of illumination and the quality of contrast and limit reflections.

Recent evidence supports tetrachromic response of light-sensitive molecules in rods and cones, as illustrated in Figure 7 (Fulton 2006–2011, MacEvoy 2009). The human retina responds well to ultraviolet photons. In a normal eye, this does not happen, because UV photons are absorbed in the cornea and lens. In an aphakic eye, the lens has been removed and the UV sensitivity allows color perception that is more varied than that normally experienced. Additionally, normally tolerated UV photon flux can cause retinal damage in an aphakic eye. Therefore, separate exposure limits apply to individuals who have no lens (aphakic individuals).

In terms of eye damage, one must consider both the frequency (a measure of energy per photon) and intensity (number of photons per unit area). Damage occurs when too much energy is absorbed (primarily by the cornea, the lens, and the retina, or when an intense LASER pulse is reflected). The wavelengths responsible for such damage are detailed in the exposure guidelines sections that follow.

Primer on Human Hearing

Noise is a wave that propagates through material.[29] It is convenient to think of noise as collective coherent vibrations moving as elastic waves through a gas, liquid, or solid. The elastic waves have alternating compression and rarefaction peaks along their direction of travel. Occupational noise usually originates from vibrating solids or turbulent fluid flow. When the noisy medium (air, liquid, or solid) is in contact with some portion of the body, it can transfer mechanical energy from its alternating pressurized and rarified peaks. This energy creates vibrating waves in that portion of the body. The induced motion, if it exceeds the elastic limit of the moving parts, may cause direct mechanical damage. If it merely moves some parts—including molecules—relative to one another, frictional heating increases temperature and the resulting increased molecular motion increases reaction rates. At ultrasonic frequencies there may be a direct effect on the rate of chemical reactions in tissue as individual molecules are rapidly rotated, flexed, and bounced into each other, producing reaction rates similar to those expected at higher temperature. Focusing of acoustic energy in fluids is known to cause cavitation bubbles that experience transient pressures sufficient to melt most metals by adiabatic heating when they collapse.

Noise is here defined as small pressure oscillations of less than a few Pa around an average ambient air pressure of ~50,000–200,000 Pa. These alternating pressurization and rarefaction peaks induce vibrations in the tympanic membrane (eardrum). In turn, the eardrum vibrates the middle-ear bones (hammer, anvil, and stirrup). The footplate of the stapes transfers the

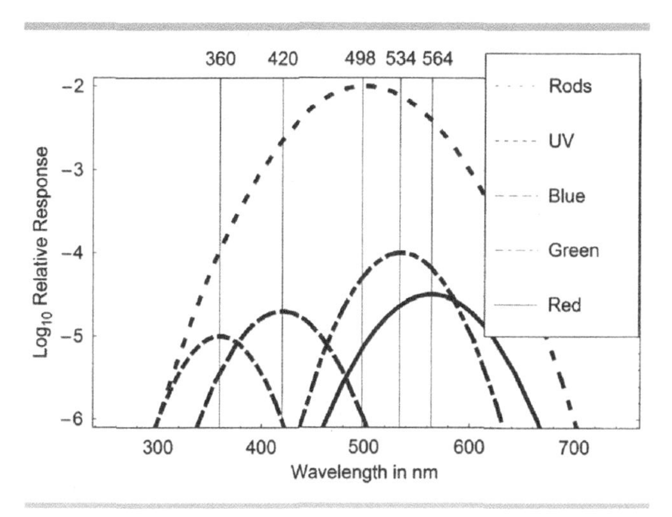

FIGURE 7. Tetrachromic vision (*Source:* Adapted by Rock, based on Fulton 2006)

vibrations through the oval window into the fluid in the inner ear. The fluid motion bends the inner and outer hair cells of the cochlea. The cochlea acts as a harmonic analyzer and directs different frequencies to different neurons in the auditory nerve. Signals from the left and right auditory nerves combine and spread out over the surface of the auditory cortex. The complex features appear spatially separated so that humans are able to identify speakers, identify threats, localize the source of sound in their 3-D world, and communicate by means of spoken language.

Remarkably, because noise and speakers' phonemes tend to be localized in differing regions of the auditory cortex, verbal communication remains possible in the presence of interfering noise.

Sound that vibrates the eardrum and stimulates the cochlea lies in the frequency range of 20 Hz to 20 kHz. The outer ear canal acts as a tuned organ pipe with one end open and the other closed by the eardrum. Its resonant behavior emphasizes sound with frequencies from 1–4 kHz while attenuating sound at much higher or much lower frequencies. The middle-ear bones also emphasize sound in this preferred speech range. When sound intensity is dangerously high, small muscles contract to pull the middle-ear bones into a protective geometry that reduces signal strength delivered to the cochlea, a protective mechanism called the *stapedial reflex*.[30]

In the cochlea, the organ of Corti is a nonlinear frequency-tuned transmission line that moves with high-frequency sound near its base and with low-frequency sound around the 2.75 turns of its helix all the way to its distal end. As it bends, those of its hair cells located near the base of the cochlea respond to all frequencies, and those near the apex respond preferentially to low frequencies. The hair cells stimulate neurons in the auditory nerve; these signals are sent to the auditory cortex for processing. The net result is that the human sensitivity to hearing behaves with maximum sensitivity in or near the range 2 to 4 kHz for most adults and at higher frequencies for young children, who have shorter external ear canals.

The ear adjusts to intensities over 12 orders of magnitude, from 10^{-12} to 1 W/m^2. The root-mean-square sound pressures associated with these intensities range from 20 μPa (197×10^{-12} atm) to 20 Pa (197×10^{-6} atm) in normal occupational settings.

Damage to the ear is mediated by sound power and total energy received. Incident sound power is a quantity that equals the product of sound intensity and the area of the tympanic membrane (eardrum). Under normal occupational conditions of sea-level barometric pressure (P_{air} ~100 kPa) and comfortable temperatures (T_{air} ~293 K), the reference quantities for sound pressure level and sound intensity level are such that the two are approximately numerically equal. It is best practice to compare the sound intensity level in dB re 1 pW/m^2 with the appropriate hearing-damage risk criteria expressed in dB.

Exposure Guidelines for Physical Agents

Thermal Stress

Thermal stress occurs when the tissue temperature rises (heat stress) or falls (cold stress) too far from its normal temperature. Occupational thermal stress standards are designed to keep the core temperature within ±1.0°C (2°F) of the normal human body temperature of 37°C (98.6°F) and to keep the surface temperature of skin within the approximate range of 16–35°C (60–95°F). Hand and finger temperatures need to be kept warmer than 16°C (60°F) to preserve manual dexterity. There are ear-canal thermal monitors that can be used for real-time monitoring of a core-temperature surrogate—and surface-temperature monitors can be used as well.

Heat Stress

Heat stress[31] depends upon environmental conditions (temperature, humidity, air velocity, radiant-heat load) and on the worker (metabolic rate, type of clothing worn, acclimatization, sweat rate, evaporation rate, cardiovascular health). When in doubt of stress levels, or when conditions are extreme, encourage use of continuous ear-canal temperature monitoring. When conditions are within a normal range, a description of the work environment using the wet-bulb globe temperature (WBGT) is sufficient to establish the baseline work schedule.

The WBGT is calculated by one of two formulas: the first is used in cases not involving a solar load and the second is used when outdoors working with a solar load.

Equation: Wet-bulb globe temperature (WBGT)

$$WBGT_{no\ sun} = 0.7\ T_{NWB} + 0.3\ T_{GT} \qquad (28a)$$

where

T_{NWB} = natural wet bulb; T_{GT} = globe temperature.

$$WBGT_{in\ sun} = 0.7\ T_{NWB} + 0.2\ T_{GT} + 0.1\ T_{DB} \qquad (28b)$$

where T_{DB} = dry bulb.

The work–rest schedule outlined by OSHA has been modernized by the TLV committee since OSHA adopted its older version into law. The revised version, reproduced as Table 11, will provide reasonable assurance that assigned tasks will not result in heat exhaustion, heat stroke, or worse.

These TLVs are based on the assumption that nearly all acclimatized, fully clothed[32] workers with adequate water and salt intake should be able to function effectively under the given working conditions without exceeding a deep body temperature of 38°C (100.4°F).[33] They are also based on the assumption that the WBGT of the resting place is identical or near to that of the workplace. When the WBGT of the work area is different from that of the rest area, a time-weighted average may be used to estimate the effective WBGT each hour.

TABLE 11

Work–Rest TLV for Controlling Heat Stress

	Workload			
Work-Rest Regimen	**Light**	**Moderate**	**Heavy**	**Very Heavy**
Continuous work	29.5°C	27.5°C	26.0°C	
75% work–25% rest each hour	30.5°C	28.5°C	27.5°C	
50% work–50% rest each hour	31.5°C	29.5°C	28.5°C	27.5°C
25% work–75% rest each hour	32.5°C	31.0°C	30.0°C	29.5°C

Light: Sit with moderate hand–arm motion; use table saw; some walking.
Moderate: Walk at 6 km/hr carrying 3-kg load on level terrain; scrubbing while standing.
Heavy: Carpenter sawing by hand; intermittent shoveling dry sand; pick and shovel use.
Very heavy: Continuously shoveling wet sand; emergency rescue wearing SCBA.

(*Source:* Assembled from ACGIH 2010a, and OSHA)

In addition to the work–rest schedule, other control measures for heat stress include access to cool nonalcoholic drinks (10–16°C, or 50–60°F), wearing cooling vests (or vortex coolers with air-supplied hoods when mobility is not required), air-conditioned rest areas, and scheduling hot work during cool parts of the day. Although fans can help, their use must be judicious. In any environment where the WBGT of the air streaming from the fan is higher than 35°C (95°F), the convective heat transfer from the air will cause a temperature increase in the exposed worker. Fans are primarily useful when the WBGT of the air currents directed on workers is less than the tabulated value for 100% work under the appropriate metabolic rate. This means fans are truly useful when they produce drafts with measured WBGT below 26–29.5°C (79–85°F).

All workers should be trained to recognize the symptoms of heat stress in themselves and others so heat exhaustion and heat stroke can be prevented. The OSHA technical manual points out that the signs and symptoms of *heat exhaustion* are headache, nausea, vertigo, weakness, thirst, and giddiness. Fortunately, this condition responds readily to prompt treatment. *Heat cramps* are usually caused by performing hard physical labor in a hot environment and have been attributed to an electrolyte imbalance caused by sweating. Cramps can be caused by either too much or too little salt. Because sweat is a hypotonic solution (±0.3% NaCl), excess salt can build up in the body if the water lost through sweating is not replaced. Thirst cannot be relied on as a guide to the need for water; instead, water must be taken every 15 to 20 minutes when in hot environments. In *heat collapse*, the brain does not receive enough oxygen because blood pools in the extremities. An exposed individual may lose consciousness suddenly and with little warning. To prevent heat collapse, the worker should gradually become acclimatized to the hot environment. *Heat rashes*, however, are the most common problem in hot work environments. *Prickly heat* manifests as red papules and usually appears in areas covered by restrictive clothing. As sweating increases, these papules give rise to a prickling sensation in that skin which is persistently wetted by unevaporated sweat. Heat-rash papules may become infected if they are not treated. In most cases, heat rashes will disappear when the affected individual returns to a cool environment.

Cold Stress

On cold, windy days, the rate of cooling is a function of both windspeed and air temperature. NOAA published the modern windchill formula, intended for worldwide use (National Weather Service 1991). When windspeed is less than 3 mph, the windchill formula is unnecessary; use the dry-bulb temperature instead. For higher windspeeds, the windchill temperature is computed from the dry-bulb temperature (T) and windspeed (V):

$$T_{\text{windchill}\,°F} = 35.74 + 0.6215\,T_{°F} - (35.75 - 0.4275\,T_{°F})\,Vel_{mph}^{0.16};\ \text{for } V_{mph} > 3 \quad (29a)$$

$$T_{\text{windchill}\,°C} = 13.13 + 0.6215\,T_{°C} - (13.95 - 0.4863\,T_{°C})\,Vel_{mps}^{0.16};\ \text{for } V_{mps} > 1 \quad (29b)$$

Exposed skin will suffer frostbite in a few minutes at low temperatures. Table 12 summarizes the approximate effect of windchill temperature on exposed skin and also contains recommendations for work–rest schedules for use by properly clothed personnel. Together, these two aspects of the human response to cold can be used to conservatively manage occupational cold exposure in a program that includes specific worker training about symptoms requiring self-rescue and use of a buddy system—allowing every worker to observe and be observed by another.

TABLE 12

Guidelines for Cold Stress

$T_{windchill}$ (°F)	Time for Frostbite of Exposed Skin[1]	Maximum Continuous Work	Number of 10-min Warm-Up Breaks in 4-hr Shift
Warmer than −18	> 30 minutes	115 minutes	1
−20 to −24	~30 minutes	115 minutes	1
−25 to −29	~30 minutes	75 minutes	2
−30 to −34	10 to 30 minutes	50 minutes	3
−35 to −39	< 10 minutes	40 minutes	4
−40 to −44	5 to 10 minutes	30 minutes	5
Colder than −45	< 5 minutes	Emergency work only	

Notes:

Be more cautious and shorten these times in the cases of young children and senior citizens.

Do not administer hot liquids to hypothermia victims; tepid liquids are better.

Do not heat the extremities of a hypothermia victim, which drives cold blood to the heart.

Seek immediate medical attention for any hypothermia victim.

[1]The complete NOAA windchill chart indicates slightly longer times to frostbite at lower temperatures than these at some wind speeds. Full details are on the Internet (www.nws.noaa.gov/om/windchill/).

(*Source:* National Weather Service (NWS) 1991)

Contact Thermal Stress

Rat skin suffers superficial, deep, and full-thickness skin burns from extended contact with solids at surprisingly low temperatures: 37.8°C (100°F), 41.9°C (108°F), and 47°C (119°F) (Suzuki, et al. 1991). Human studies of cold-surface contact support a recommended standard (Marklund 2003).

To prevent numbness that interferes with manual dexterity, keep skin temperatures above 15°C (Marklund 2003, Fig. 34). The tolerable contact duration for various cold surfaces depends on the material properties of thermal capacity and thermal conductivity and on contact pressure. For example, for surfaces at 0°C, the tolerable touching times to prevent numbness are measured in seconds: 3 seconds for aluminum, 13 seconds for steel, and progressively longer than 100 seconds for stone, nylon, and wood, respectively. If pain is the end point rather than numbness and if gripping is required rather than touching, another set of guidelines were proposed (Marklund 2003, Fig. 36). For gripping these materials at 0°C and releasing before the pain threshold is reached, the tolerable duration of grip is: 400 seconds for aluminum, 470 seconds for steel, 630 seconds for stone, 790 seconds for nylon, and 880 seconds for wood. These studies show the wisdom of long-standing engineering rules of thumb that well-engineered equipment with exposed surfaces, situated such that personnel contact is likely or required, should be insulated to operate with surface temperatures between 5°C (41°F) and 51°C (125°F). Durations for other surface temperatures are plotted in Marklund (2003, Figs. 34 and 36).

Noise and Vibration

Noise and vibration standards are designed to prevent direct tissue damage and to limit discomfort from non-damaging sound pressure levels. Because damage and control mechanisms differ, separate noise exposure guidelines exist for infrasonic sound (< 20 Hz), acoustic sound (20 Hz to 20 kHz), and ultrasonic sound (> 20 kHz). Similarly, vibration damage mechanisms differ depending on the included angle between the vibration vector and key body axes. The vibration standards are separately specified for vibration directed along or transverse to the spine for standing, sitting, and prone positions, and along or transverse to the forearm.

The tissues most sensitive to acoustic energy are those found in the outer, middle, and inner ears. Control measures have been well summarized by OSHA and are available via the Internet.

Noise

All noise control, whether using the PEL[34] (legally required) or more protective TLV[35] (ISO standard), involves only three equations: $D(C,T)$, $T(L)$, and $L(C,D)$. D is the noise dose with an acceptable daily value between 0 and 1. Daily doses > 1 and weekly doses > 5 should be avoided by appropriate use of personal protective equipment (insert earplugs and circum-aural earmuffs). L is the sound pressure level and is numerically equal to the sound intensity level in most workplaces having ambient pressures near 100 kPa (1 atm). Good hearing conservation programs reduce L by (1) substituting quieter machinery for older, noisy machinery to the maximum extent practical; (2) adding engineering controls such as sound barriers, which contain noise and reduce transmitted waves; and (3) installing sound-absorbing materials to minimize noise reflection.

Infra sound at frequencies between 1 and 80 Hz is to be kept below 145 dB. Compliance may be inferred when an unweighted sound-level meter reads less than 150 dB re 1 pW/m^2. Lower levels may be required if workers complain of resonance in their lungs (50–60 Hz).

The OSHA hearing-damage risk criteria, expressed as T_I, is the maximum allowed duration of exposure at sound intensity level L_I. The TLV criteria, expressed as T_{TLVi}, is the recommended maximum duration of exposure at sound intensity level L_I. (See Tables 13a and b.) Noise dose in either system is based on measured sound intensity levels, L_I, each lasting for a period C_I hours. Note the difference between these two criteria in Table 13a. In other words, the OSHA PEL uses a 5-dB doubling rate, and the TLV uses a 3-dB doubling rate. OSHA allows 8 hours/day at 90 [dBA re 1 pW/m^2],[36] while the TLV allows 85 [dBA re 1 pW/m^2]. Protect hearing by keeping nonoccupational exposures below 80 dBA and sleeping areas below 70 dBA to allow the ears to rest between work cycles.

TABLE 13a

PEL and TLV Hearing-Damage Risk Criteria

OSHA PEL		ACGIH TLV	
L_i	T_i	L_{TLVi}	T_{TLVi}
85	16	82	16
90	8	85	8
95	4	88	4
100	2	91	2
105	1	94	1
110	0.5	97	0.5
115	0.25	100	0.25
		103	0.125
		106	0.0625

Graphical Comparison

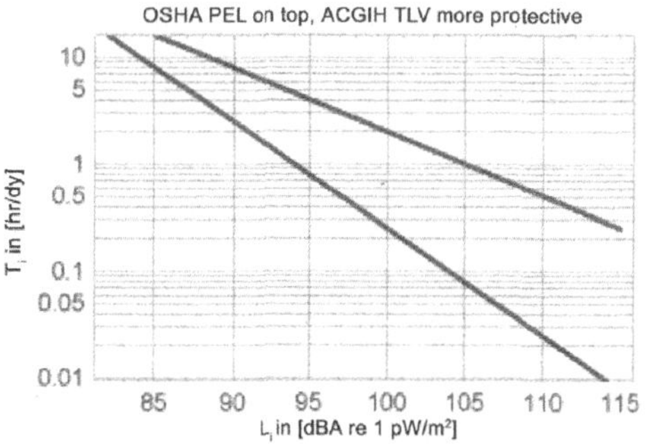

OSHA PEL on top, ACGIH TLV more protective

T, in [hr/dy]
10
5
1
0.5
0.1
0.05
0.01
85 90 95 100 105 110 115
L, in [dBA re 1 pW/m^2]

(*Sources:* OSHA 2008 and ACGIH 2010a)

TABLE 13b

Equations for PEL and TLV Hearing-Damage Risk Criteria	
(Eq. 30) OSHA Noise Dose (29CFR1910.95)	**(Eq. 31) ACGIH Noise Dose (ACGIH TLV Booklet 2010a)**
$T_{PEL_i} = 2^{\frac{105 - L_i}{5}}$ [hr]	$T_{TLV_i} = 2^{\frac{94 - L_i}{3}}$ [hr]
$D_{OSHA} = \sum_{i=1}^{N} \frac{C_i}{T_{PEL_i}}$ [unitless]	$D_{TLV} = \sum_{i=1}^{N} \frac{C_i}{T_{TLV_i}}$ [unitless]
$C_{total} = \sum_{i=1}^{N} C_i$ [hr]	$C_{total} = \sum_{i=1}^{N} C_i$ [hr]
$L_{OSHA} = 105 - 5\log_2\left(\frac{C_{total}}{D_{OSHA}}\right) = 105 - 7.2135\log_{10}\left(\frac{C_{total}}{D_{OSHA}}\right)$ in dB re 1 pW/m^2	$L_{TLV} = 94 - 3\log_2\left(\frac{C_{task}}{D_{TLV}}\right) = 94 - 4.3281\log_{10}\left(\frac{C_{total}}{D_{TLV}}\right)$ in dB re 1 pW/m^2

(*Sources:* OSHA 2008 and ACGIH 2010a)

When noise emissions have not been controlled at sources, hearing protection must be used for exposed workers. In the United States, earplugs and earmuffs are labeled with a noise reduction ratio (NRR) that averages 22 dB. Extensive field testing has demonstrated remarkably lower performance in practice (Berger 2000). It is recommended that the effective NRR be computed as half the labeled NRR. When C-weighted sound intensity levels are available, the A-weighted ear-canal level is estimated to be NRR/2 smaller than the free-field C-weighted level. When only A-weighted sound intensity levels are available, the estimated ear-canal level is reduced by about (NRR – 7)/2. For example, when NRR = 22 dB, the practical A-weighted ear-canal level is approximately 11 dB smaller than the free-field C-weighted level and approximately 7.5 dB smaller than the free-field A-weighted level. With proper training and care, an individual can achieve the advertised NRR = 22 dB. With sloppy use, however, hearing loss is likely.

$$L_{A,\,Ear\ Canal} = (L_C - \text{NRR}/2) \quad [\text{dBA re } 1\ \text{pW/m}^2] \tag{32a}$$

$$L_{A,\,Ear\ Canal} = (L_A - (\text{NRR} - 7)/2) \quad [\text{dBA re } 1\ \text{pW/m}^2] \tag{32b}$$

The analysis above makes it clear that earplugs alone are insufficient in workplaces with OSHA equivalent levels above 95 dBA. Elliott Berger has confirmed this by measuring threshold shifts in workplaces. When the noise is more intense, use both earplugs and earmuffs. NRR values are not additive; when used together there is an additional 5-dBA augmentation of the NRR of the better-performing of the two devices. Earplugs with an NRR of 22 dB and circumaural muffs with an NRR of 28 dB have a combined NRR of 33 dB.

The TLV for ultrasound at 1/3 octave center frequencies between 10 kHz and 100 kHz is separately specified depending upon whether the worker's head is underwater or not. In water, the ceiling values are 167 dB between 10 kHz and 20 kHz and 177 dB between 20 kHz and 100 kHz. In air, the ceiling values are 105 dB from 10 to 20 kHz, 110 dB at 25 kHz and 115 dB from 31.5 to 100 kHz. Furthermore, the 8-hour-TWA TLV is 88 dB at 10 kHz, 92 dB at 16 kHz, and 94 dB at 20 kHz, although subjective annoyance and discomfort may occur in some individuals when exposed to tonal sound above 75 dB in this frequency range.

Occupational hearing protection with the TLV considers those chemicals and drugs that increase susceptibility to noise-induced hearing loss. Chemicals already of concern include toluene, lead, manganese, and n-butyl alcohol, and chemicals proposed for addition to this list include arsenic, carbon disulfide, carbon monoxide, mercury, styrene, toluene, trichloroethylene, and xylene. When these are present, periodic audiograms should be administered and carefully reviewed.

Vibration

Vibration damage mechanisms depend upon whether the vibrating object is in direct contact with a small spot on the body, with the whole body, or with only the hand or arm. Within the variety of possible whole-body vibration exposures, the potency of the vibration depends on the included angle between the vibration vector and critical body axes, as well as on the frequency and the amplitude of vibration. Vibrations or motion at frequencies below 1 Hz cause motion sickness in some individuals and are not part of the vibration TLV. Vibrations above 4 kHz are unimportant from a whole-body or hand–arm standpoint, but localized injury can occur when ultrasonic transducers in the range of 4 kHz to 100 kHz or more are applied directly to the skin.[37]

Vibration survey meters have one or more internal frequency-weighting networks.[38] For hand–arm vibrations, the frequencies between 4 and 8 Hz are measured without attenuation and higher frequencies are attenuated progressively at –20 dB per decade so that the weighting at 160 Hz is –20 dB (a factor of 1/10) and at 1600 Hz is –40 dB (a factor of 1/100). The weighting network for longitudinal acceleration (in the direction of the spine) is flat between 4 and 8 Hz, rolls off at –20 db per decade between 8 and 80 Hz, and rolls off at –3 dB per octave between 4 Hz and 1 Hz. The weighting network for transverse whole-body acceleration is flat between 1 and 2 Hz with a gain of 1.414 to represent an observed resonance of the human body in these vibration directions. The response rolls off at –20 dB per decade between 1 and 80 Hz; these features are illustrated in Figure 8.

Vibration is properly measured with 3-axis accelerometers. Along each axis, either adjust the raw data to reflect body-frequency sensitivity with weighting from Figure 8, or make the measurements with an instrument equipped with equivalent internal filter networks.[39] Each measurement period is characterized by three numbers, the *rms* value of acceleration along each axis in m/s^2.

Equation: Frequency-weighted acceleration for x-axis

$$A_{wxn} = \sqrt{\sum_{f_{min}}^{f_{max}}[W(f_i) \cdot A_{xn}(f_i)]^2} \ [m/s^2] \qquad (33)$$

Vibration intensity may vary during a work shift. If so, a time-weighted average (TWA) acceleration is computed from the frequency-weighted acceleration for each axis for each period. Use *rms* addition for the time-weighted average calculation, as shown in Equation 34.

Equation: TWA acceleration along one axis, illustrated by x-axis

$$A_{wx} = \sqrt{\frac{\sum_{n=1}^{N}(C_n \cdot A_{wxn}^2)}{\sum_{n=1}^{N} C_n}} \ [m/s^2] \qquad (34)$$

The *rms* resultant vibration is computed from the TWA values for individual axes.

Equation: Resultant TWA frequency-weighted acceleration

$$A_{wt} = \sqrt{A_{wx}^2 + A_{wy}^2 + A_{wz}^2} \ [m/s^2] \qquad (35)$$

The TLV committee and the European Commission both use an action level of 0.5 m/s^2 for 8 hours of exposure to the resultant whole-body acceleration, as computed above. The implied OEL is 1 m/s^2. The TLV committee recommends 4 m/s^2 as the TLV for 4- to 8-hour periods of hand–arm vibration exposure. Periods other than 8 hours have a nonlinear relationship between acceleration level and allowed duration of exposure. The data are tabulated in summary in the TLV booklet (ACGIH 2010a) and in their entirety in the ANSI standards. However, there is a shortcut for those who have computed the resultant acceleration from Equation 35. The allowed duration of exposure depends on whether the area of concern is hand–arm or whole-body vibration.[40] For hand–arm vibration, the allowed duration in hours is calculated from the

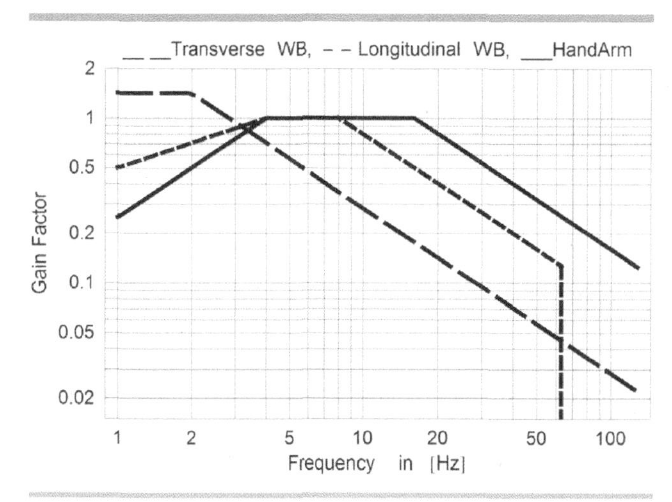

FIGURE 8. TLV vibration guidelines, frequency weighting, *W(f)* (*Source:* ACGIH 2010a, 2010b, 2011)

resultant *rms* hand–arm acceleration vector in m/s² with a valid range of 10 minutes to 16 hours.

Equation: Hand–arm vibration criteria

$$T_{HA} = \frac{98}{A_{wt}^2} \text{ [hr]} \quad (36)$$

For whole-body vibration, the allowed duration in hours is calculated from the resultant *rms* whole-body acceleration vector in m/s² with a valid range of 1 minute to 24 hours.

Equation: Whole-body vibration criteria

$$T_{WB} = \frac{0.7994}{A_{wt}^2} - \frac{0.006532}{A_{wt}^4} \text{ [hr]} \quad (37)$$

Let C_i be the observed duration of resultant *rms* acceleration A_{wt} that has an allowed daily duration of T_{TLV} hours. The daily dose is C_i/T_i and should be maintained less than 1 daily and less than 5 weekly.

A summary of steps for vibration analysis during a workday includes:

- Measuring the vibration frequency spectrum along three orthogonal axes. (Units for *rms* acceleration are [m/s²] along each of three orthogonal axes.)
- Applying frequency weighting reflecting human sensitivity.
- Recording the duration for each period of this vibration in hours, called C_i.
- Estimating TWA *rms* acceleration along each axis.
- Calculating the resultant vibration in *rms* acceleration units of m/s².
- Calculating allowable daily exposure duration.
- Calculating the daily exposure dose.
- Verifying that vibration dose is < 1 daily and < 5 weekly.

Electromagnetic Radiation

Electromagnetic radiation is energy propagating in the form of oscillating electric and magnetic fields that spans an infinite range of frequencies. One of the most complete graphical summaries of the electromagnetic spectrum is that copyrighted by Unihedron in 2006.[41]

This section is organized and moves progressively through the electromagnetic spectrum from the lowest frequencies to the highest frequencies. At the low frequencies, up to radio frequencies and microwaves, the standards limit electrical current flow in tissue to minimize tissue heating rates below normal homeostatic thermal regulatory-system capabilities. As frequencies increase from infrared up through extreme ultraviolet, photon energies increase from a fraction of an electron volt (eV) to more than 100 eV. The genetic damage threshold due to ionization starts near 3.7 eV and continues beyond 100 eV, sufficient for ionization damage to all tissues.

Photons with vacuum wavelengths shorter than 100 nm have photon energies greater than 12.4 eV and frequencies greater than 3 PHz and are considered to be ionizing. When these are scattered by a molecule, free electrons (ionization event) and lower-energy photons typically result.

Nonionizing Radiation

Nonionizing radiation is freely propagating electromagnetic radiation. Orthogonal electric and magnetic fields propagate at the local speed of light in all media. The photons are nonionizing for frequencies ranging from very low frequency of seconds per cycle through radio frequencies, microwave frequencies, infrared frequencies, and visible light frequencies. The EM waves discussed in this section do not have enough energy to knock electrons free from the parent atoms or molecules; these low-energy photons do not cause ionization.

The primary mechanisms of action for nonionizing EM radiation are the vibration, flexing, and twisting of polyatomic molecules. Such vibrations may directly increase reaction rates by bending reactant molecules enough that they fit one another, or indirectly—by causing a chemical chain reaction resulting in increased temperature. People have experience with nonionizing radiation when they use microwave or stone ovens to heat food or when they warm themselves by a campfire on a cool evening or bask in the warm sun on a beach.

Microwaves and infrared light are used in industry for accelerating two-part glues, drying coatings, curing some polymeric materials, and heat-sealing some thermal plastics. Control of exposures to nonionizing radiation is based on the twin concepts of limiting local temperature rise in susceptible tissue and limiting induced electrical current flows to levels that do not interfere with normal neuromuscular events such as fine motor control, heart rate, blood pressure, and respiratory rate.

Engineering control recommendations have evolved separately and are discussed separately for quasistatic electric and magnetic fields, extremely low-frequency (ELF) electromagnetic fields, radio-frequency (RF) electromagnetic fields, infrared (IR) radiation, visible light, ultraviolet (UV) light, and the coherent monoenergetic light from a LASER (primarily in the infrared to ultraviolet frequencies). Work is underway to extend the frequency range of LASERs, and exposure guidelines are under consideration.

Static Electric and Magnetic Fields

Between 0 and 100 Hz, the electric field strength should be kept smaller than 25 kV/m.

Between 0 Hz and 1 Hz, the magnetic flux density should not exceed a ceiling of 2 T, with an 8-hour TWA of 60 mT for whole-body exposures or 600 mT for extremity exposures.[42]

Sub-Radio-Frequency Electric and Magnetic Fields

The ACGIH TLV book is a convenient source of guidance for these frequencies. Table 14 has been constructed by estimating values for *H* and *D*, which are equivalent to the *B* and *E* criteria given in the TLV guidelines. Measure the free field without the worker.

Figure 9 shows sub-radio frequency for *E* and *H* fields (ACGIH 2010a).

TABLE 14

TLV Guidelines for Electric and Magnetic Fields

Frequency/Hz	*B* = Magnetic Flux Density/(mT) 8-hr TWA	*H* = Magnetic Field Strength/(A/m) 8-hr TWA	*D* = Electric Field Displacement/(nC/m^2) Ceiling	*E* = Electric Field Strength/(V/m) Ceiling
< 1	60*	47,700	221	25,000
$1 < f < 100$	$60/f$	$47{,}700/f$	221	25,000
$100 < f < 300$	$60/f$	$47{,}700/f$	$221/f$	$2{,}500{,}000/f$
$300 < f < 4{,}000$	0.2	15.9	$221/f$	$2{,}500{,}000/f$
$4000 < f < 30{,}000$	0.2	15.9	5.53	625
	$B = \mu_0 H$		$D = \varepsilon_0 E$	

*60 mT 8-hr TWA is for whole body with 2 T ceiling and 600 mT 8-hr TWA is for extremities.
Keep ceiling exposures below 0.1 mT for pacemaker and medical device patients.
In this table, f is in hertz (Hz). $\mu_0 = 4\pi\ 10^{-7}$ [V s/(A m)], $\varepsilon_0 = 1/(\mu_0 c_0^2) \approx 10^{-9}/(36\pi)$ [A s/(V m) = C/(V m)].

(*Source:* ACGIH 2010a)

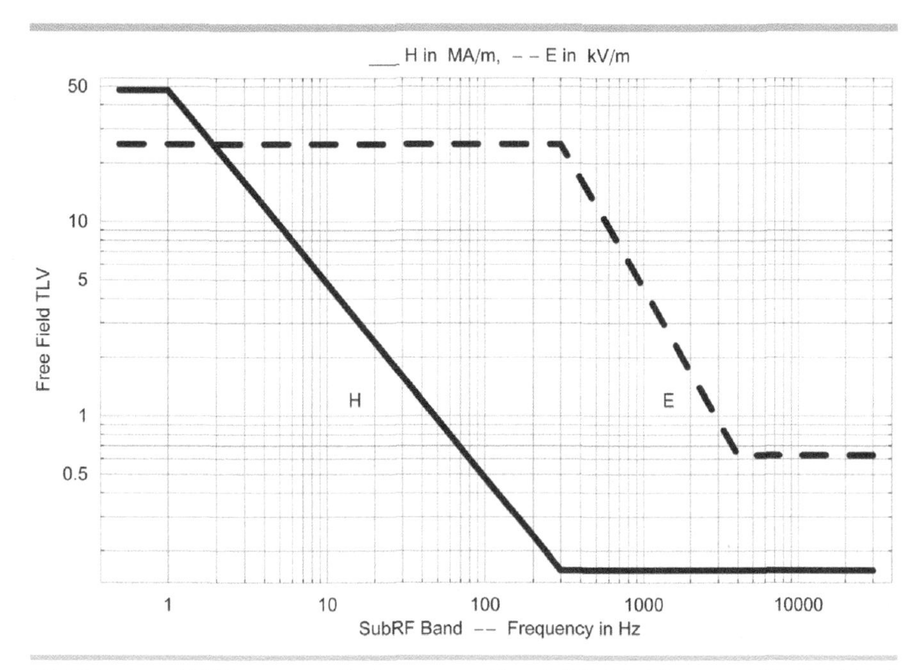

FIGURE 9. TLV for sub-radio-frequency *E* and *H* fields (*Source:* ACGIH 2010a)

TABLE 15

EM Guidelines for RF Through Far-IR

Frequency*	Wavelength	$S = E \times H$** *rms*/(mW/cm²)	E = Electric Field *rms*/(V/m)	H = Magnetic Field *rms*/(A/m)	Averaging Time† for E^2, H^2, or S
30–100 kHz	10–3 km	10^5–10^5	614	163	360 s
0.1–3 MHz	3000–100 m	10^5–3333	614	16.3/f	360 s
3–30 MHz	100–10 m	3333–3.33	1842/f	16.3/f	360 s
30–100 MHz	10–3 m	3.33–1	61.4	16.3/f	360 s
10–300 MHz	3–1 m	1	61.4	0.163	360 s
0.3–3 GHz	100–10 cm	f/300			360 s
3–15 GHz	100–20 mm	10			360 s
15–300 GHz	20–0.1 mm	10			$(36.95 \times 10^6)/(f^{1.2})$
300 GHz	0.1 mm	10			10 s

*In this table, when the frequency appears in a formula, its units are in MHz.

**The Poynting Vector, S, is the cross-product of E and $H = B/\mu$. S gives the *rms* power density and propagation direction of a radiating electromagnetic field. $S/(W/m^2) = E/(V/m) \times H(A/m)$. There is additional energy in the nonpropagating reactive near field, close to a source of radiation.

†The impedance of free space is $z = (\mu_0/\varepsilon_0)^{1/2} = 376.7$ ohms. Because $z = E/H$, it follows that the Poynting Vector amplitude can be estimated by $S = E^2/z = zH^2$. In units listed in this table, $S = EH/10$, $S = E^2/3767$, and $S = 37.76\ H^2$. These are plotted in Figure 10.

(*Source:* ACGIH TLV 2010a)

Radio Frequency and Microwave Electromagnetic Radiation

Radio frequency and microwave radiation limits are set to limit the *rms* body currents induced by the electromagnetic field over the frequencies ranging from 30 kHz to 300 GHz. The TLV guidelines limit the potential for electrostimulation, *shock* (for frequencies < 0.1 MHz) or perceptible heating (for frequencies > 0.1 MHz).

In all cases, the whole-body specific absorption rate (SAR) should be kept below 0.4 W/kg. The exposure limits listed assume the worker has no physical contact with electrically conductive devices (including metallic jewelry) and is insulated from earth ground. When these conditions are not met, consult more detailed references.[43]

TLV guidelines are conservatively tabulated in Table 15. These values are deemed tolerable. Under special conditions identified in the documentation for TLVs, some of these values can be relaxed.

Table 15 and Figure 10 summarize TLV guidelines for the radio-frequency and microwave portions of the electromagnetic spectra. Note that for frequencies above 100 MHz it is often easier to measure power density than to measure either the magnetic or electric field strength. Additionally, the averaging time is 6 minutes for frequencies between 30 KHz and 15 GHz.[44] The TLVs apply to a spatial average of the electromagnetic field strength over the cross-sectional area of the worker. When surveying, measure the field intensity at the worker's location without the presence of the worker.

Ultra Wideband Radiation (UWB)

This is radiation that typically takes the form of short pulses, $T_{pw} << 1\ \mu s$ with rise times < 1 ns. UWB pulses have bandwidth greater than their center frequency and may have measurable energy in frequencies between DC and 30 GHz. UWB signals may interfere with safety-related electronic equipment, including fire alarms, automatic process controls, avionics, and communications and computing equipment. Emerging evidence shows that UWB signals can be used to preferentially destroy cancerous tissue while producing minimal damage in nearby healthy tissue with pulse durations shorter than 1 μs and rise times of a few ns (Schoenbach 2006, 20–26).

The TLV (ACGIH 2010a) for this exposure category is designed to keep specific absorption below W_{al} = 0.4 (W/kg) for periods longer than 6 minutes and below a specific energy absorption limit of, E_{al} = 144 (J/kg), in any 6-minute period. With incident radiation power density, S (mW/cm²), conservative SAR coefficient, S_c = 0.25 (W/kg)/(mW/cm²), and pulse duration (including ring-down time), T_{pw} (s), the specific absorption per pulse is SA_{pp} (J/kg). The specific absorption rate is the product of the specific absorption per pulse and the pulse repetition rate in pulses/s.

Equation: Specific absorption per UWB pulse and specific absorption rate

$$SA_{pp} = S \cdot T_{pw} \cdot S_c \text{ [J/kg]} \tag{38}$$

The permitted pulse repetition rate is a function of the *SA* per pulse, the 6-minute energy absorption limit (E_{al} = 144 J/kg), and the 6-minute thermal averaging time (T_{at} = 360 s).

Equation: Allowed *PRF* for UWB radiation

$$PRF = \frac{E_{\text{al}}}{T_{at} \cdot SA_{pp}} \text{ [pulses/s]} \tag{39}$$

If the actual average pulse repetition rate, *prf*, is higher than the allowed *PRF* estimated above, then exposure duration must be shortened to less than 6 minutes. The permissible exposure duration, $T_{\max} <$ 360 s, is inversely proportional to the square of the specific absorption rate. The numerator is the product of tissue energy and tissue power absorption limits: ($E_{al} \times W_{al}$).

Equation: Allowed duration of UWB radiation exposure at *PRF* [pulse/s]

$$T_{\text{max}_{\text{UWB}}} = \frac{E_{al} W_{al}}{SA_{pp}\, prf} \text{ [s]} \tag{40}$$

Infrared (IR) and Visible Radiation

These frequencies form a continuum near the portion of the spectrum called the visible light. Infrared light is of lower frequency and longer wavelengths than the red end of the visible light spectrum. Visible light (760–400 nm) passes through the cornea, the lens, and the aqueous humor before it excites rods and cones in the retina through photosensitive chemical reactions that make vision possible. Infrared radiation primarily serves to warm the skin, even while air temperature is cool.[45] Photochemical damage is possible if the intensity of short-wavelength visible (blue to violet) light is not controlled. Such damage is called the blue light hazard.

To avoid retina thermal injury, use the retinal weighting function, $R\lambda$, to adjust measured spectral radiance according to its thermal damage potential. Keep the total effective radiance within the limits in the following equation, where t is in s, and α is the mean angle[46] (radian) subtended by the lamp.

Equation: Retina thermal TLV; for $T_{\max} \leq 10$ [s]

$$L_{retina} = \sum_{\lambda=380}^{1400} (L\lambda R\lambda \Delta\lambda) \leq \frac{5}{\alpha (T_{\max})^{0.25}} \text{ [W/cm}^2\text{ sr]} \tag{41a}$$

$$T_{\max} \leq \left(\frac{5}{\alpha L_{retina}}\right)^4 \text{ [s]}$$

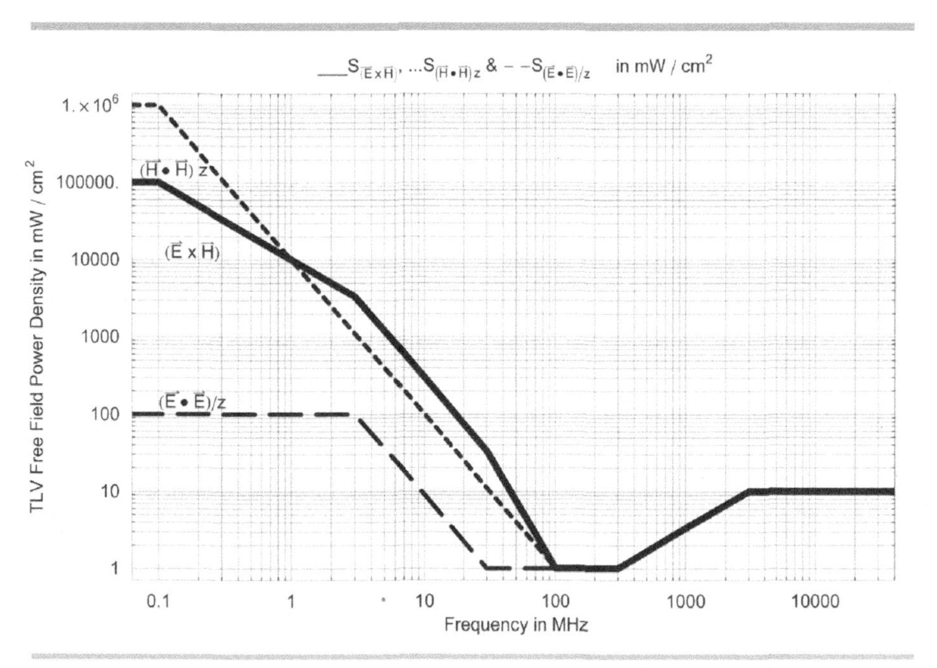

FIGURE 10. TLV for RF and microwave exposures (*Source:* ACGIH 2010–2011)

Equation: Retina thermal TLV; for $T_{max} > 10$ [s]

$$L_{retina No Vis} = \sum_{\lambda=380}^{1400} (L\lambda R\lambda \Delta\lambda) \leq \frac{0.6}{\alpha} \text{ [W/cm}^2\text{ sr]} \quad (41b)$$

$$T_{max} \leq \left(\frac{5}{\alpha L_{retina No Vis}}\right)^4 \text{ [s]}$$

To avoid photochemical injury to rods and cones in the retina, limit *blue* light exposure. Use the blue weighting function, $B\lambda$, to adjust measured blue spectral radiance according to its photochemical damage potential. This TLV is not protective for LASER light at these frequencies because of the especially potent effects of monochromatic and coherent light. The TLV in the following equation can be relaxed for very small light sources, using procedures in the TLV booklet (ACGIH 2010a, 139).

Equation: Blue light TLV (photochemical retina damage), for $T_{max} \leq 10^4$ [s]

$$L_{blue} = \sum_{\lambda=305}^{700} (L\lambda B\lambda \Delta\lambda) \leq \frac{100}{T_{max}} \text{ [W/cm}^2\text{ sr]} \quad (42a)$$

$$T_{max} \leq \frac{100}{L_{blue}} \text{ [s]}$$

Equation: Blue light TLV (photochemical retina damage), for $T_{max} > 10^4$ [s]

$$L_{blue} = \sum_{\lambda=305}^{700} (L\lambda B\lambda \Delta\lambda) \leq 0.01 \text{ [W/cm}^2\text{ sr]} \quad (42b)$$

To protect from photochemical damage in an aphakic eye (no lens and no blue light filter), use the aphakic weighting function, $A\lambda$.

Equation: Aphakic TLV (photochemical damage, no lens), for $T_{max} \leq 10^4$ [s]

$$L_{aphakic} = \sum_{\lambda=305}^{700} (L_\lambda A\lambda \Delta\lambda) \leq \frac{100}{T_{max}} \text{ [W/cm}^2\text{ sr]} \quad (43a)$$

$$T_{max} \leq \frac{100}{L_{aphakic}} \text{ [s]}$$

Equation: Aphakic TLV (photochemical damage, no lens), for $T_{max} > 10^4$ [s]

$$L_{aphakic} = \sum_{\lambda=305}^{700} (L_\lambda A\lambda \Delta\lambda) \leq 0.01 \text{ [W/cm}^2\text{ sr]} \quad (43b)$$

To protect from thermal heating damage to the lens and cornea, it is sufficient to use the weighting function called $IR\lambda$ in the following equation. $IR\lambda$ is a function that equals unity between 770 and 3000 nm. The TLV booklet distinguishes between IR sources that include visible light and those that are invisible to the human eye. The following equations are at least as protective as those in the TLV booklet under these circumstances (ACGIH 2010a).

Equation: Cornea and lens TLV (thermal heating); for $T_{max} \leq 10^3$ [s]

$$E_{IR} = \sum_{\lambda=770}^{3000} (E_\lambda T_\lambda \Delta\lambda) \leq \frac{1.8}{(T_{max})^{0.75}} \text{ [W/cm}^2\text{]} \quad (44a)$$

$$T_{max} \leq \left(\frac{1.8}{E_{IR}}\right)^{4/3} \text{ [s]}$$

Equation: Cornea and lens TLV (thermal heating); for $T_{max} > 10^3$ [s]

$$E_{IR} = \sum_{\lambda=770}^{3000} (E_\lambda T_\lambda \Delta\lambda) \leq 0.01 \text{ [W/cm}^2\text{]} \quad (44b)$$

Figure 11 shows five defined spectral weighting functions: $A\lambda$, $B\lambda$, $R\lambda$, $IR\lambda$, and $S\lambda$. The aphakic weighting (absent a lens to absorb UV and blue light), $A\lambda$, is defined over the wavelength range of 305 nm to 700 nm and shows relative potencies of photon energies for photochemical damage in the retina. The blue weighting function, $B\lambda$, is defined over the same range and shows the photochemical potency of photon energies to damage the retina, taking into account the filtration of the lens. The retinal weighting function, $R\lambda$, defined over the wavelengths between 380 nm and 1400 nm, shows relative potency of these wavelengths for overheating the retina, also accounting for cornea, lens, and optic media filtration. The actinic UV weighting function, $S\lambda$, defined over the wavelengths between 180 nm and 400 nm, shows relative potency of these wavelengths for skin and cornea damage.

Ultraviolet Radiation

OSHA does not have a PEL for UV radiation, instead referring employers to the ACGIH TLV (OSHA, 2003). The UV TLV represents conditions to which it is believed nearly all healthy workers may be repeatedly exposed without acute adverse health effects, such as erythema of the skin and photokeratitis of the cornea and conjunctiva. The TLVs apply to UV radiation from arcs, gas and vapor discharges, fluorescent sources, in-

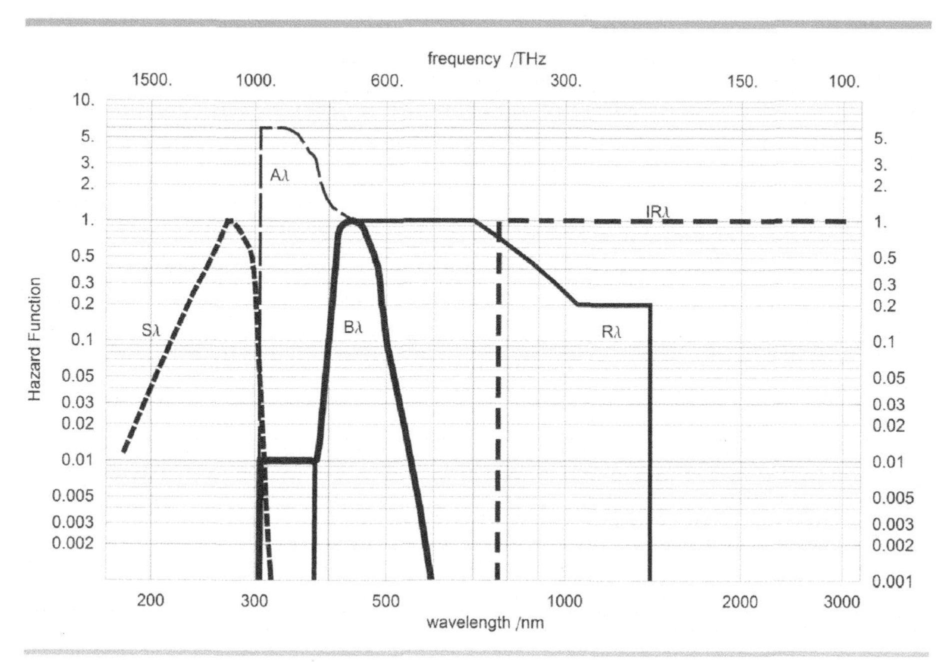

FIGURE 11. Spectral weighting for IR, visible, and UV TLV guidelines
(*Source:* Graphic by Rock 2011 from data from ACGIH 2010–2011)

candescent sources, and solar radiation, but not from UV lasers. The UV spectrum lies above the high-frequency (violet) end of the visible spectrum and has photon energies sufficient to ionize electrons held in relatively weak chemical bonds.

The TLVs may not be protective for aphakes (missing lens) or for individuals who are photosensitized by chemicals, drugs, genetic makeup, or diseases. Many chemicals and some liver diseases cause skin or corneal photosensitization reactions. Examples include some antibiotics (such as tetracycline and suphathiazole), some antidepressants (such as imipramine and sinequan), extracts from some agricultural plants (such as celery, lime oil, and blue-green algae) and many other chemicals used in cosmetics, dyes, and antipsychotic drugs.

The TLV for radiant exposure to UV-A is limited to energy of 1 J/cm^2 for periods < 1000 s, and the irradiance is limited to 1 mW/cm^2 for periods longer than 1000 s. Because the lens absorbs UV radiation, aphakes (no lens) are at risk of UV-induced retinal injury at lower levels than these.

Because ozone is produced in air by photons with $\lambda < 250$ nm (extreme UV-B plus UV-C), good hygiene practice requires that the ozone level be controlled below its TLV, which ranges from 0.05 ppm for heavy work to 0.1 ppm for light work.

The UV-weighting function shows that humans are most susceptible at wavelengths of 270 nm and have better tolerance for longer or shorter wavelengths. Because sodium vapor lamps have strong emission lines near 270 nm, they are normally encased in a UV filtering envelope. When that envelope is broken, exposed workers are at risk.

A UV survey is easy with a UV radiometer having a spectral response that implements the relative spectral effectiveness values provided in the TLV book and reports effective irradiance, E_{UV} in mW/cm^2. To protect eyes and skin from adverse consequences of UV light, use the actinic spectral effectiveness function, $S(\lambda)$, to adjust measured UV spectral irradiance according to its skin- and eye-damage potential.

Equation: UV TLV (skin and eyes genetic damage)

$$E_{UV} = \sum_{\lambda=180}^{400} (E_\lambda S_\lambda \Delta\lambda) \leq \frac{0.003\ [\text{J/cm}^2]}{T_{max}}\ [\text{W/cm}^2] \quad (45)$$

$$T_{max} < \left(\frac{0.003\ [\text{J/cm}^2]}{E_{UV}\ [\text{W/cm}^2]}\right) [\text{s}]$$

Note that the TLV for UV radiation can be exceeded by a few minutes in the noonday sun in the

TABLE 16

Hazards by LASER Classification

Class	UV	Vis	NIR	IR	Hazards: Direct Ocular	Hazards: Diffuse Ocular	Hazards: Fire
I	x	x	x	x	No	No	No
IA		x			Yes, < 1000 s	No	No
II		x			Yes, < 0.25 s	No	No
IIIA	x	x	x	x	Yes	No	No
IIIB	x	x	x	x	Yes	Yes, near 500 mW	No
IV	x	x	x	x	Yes	Yes	Yes

x indicates that a LASER in this wavelength range can be classified in this class by ANSI guidelines:

I: No emissions at known hazard levels (~0.4 μW continuous wave visible). Can mean enclosed LASER of higher power if enclosure is interlocked to prevent operation while open.

IA: LASERs "not intended for viewing" that are safe for direct exposures up to 1000 s. Power limit is 4 mW. Supermarket scanners are an example.

II: Low-power visible LASER < 1 mW. Human aversion to bright light will limit exposure duration. Minimal controls. Use ANSI "Caution Label."

IIIA: Intermediate power LASER (1–5 mW). Only hazardous for direct intrabeam viewing. Use "Caution Label" if < 2.5 mW, "Danger Label" if 2.5–5 mW.

IIIB: Moderate power lasers (5–500 mW continuous or the lesser of 10 J/cm^2 pulsed or the diffuse reflection limit). Not expected to ignite ordinary flammable substances. Controls are strongly recommended. Use ANSI "Danger Label."

IV: High-power LASER > 500 mW continuous or >10 J/cm^2 per pulse. Viewing can be hazardous in direct beam, or by specular or diffuse reflection/scattering. Type IV LASERs generally pose both eye and skin hazards. Controls and ANSI "Danger Labels" are required.

(*Source:* ACGIH TLV 2010a)

tropics or near the time of the summer solstice in the mountains of subtropical and temperate zones. For example, in a location where the effective irradiance is $E_{eff} = 0.001$ W/cm^2, the allowable duration is $T_{max} =$ 3 s. Note also that unfiltered ophthalmologic slit lamps and some microscope illumination can exceed both the blue light and the UV TLV in a few minutes (Sliney 1997, 981–996).

LASER Radiation

OSHA notes the distinguishing features of LASER light sources:

1. a nearly single-frequency output (i.e., an almost pure monochromatic light beam)
2. a beam with a Gaussian intensity profile
3. a beam of small divergence
4. a beam of enormous intensity
5. a beam which maintains a high degree of temporal and spatial coherence
6. a beam that is, in many devices, highly plane polarized[47]
7. a beam with enormous electromagnetic field strengths (Liu 2001)[48]

It takes an entire book to properly describe all LASER safety considerations (ACGIH, 1990).[49] In the interest of space, the principles are described here and the reader is encouraged to use more extensive references as needed (see Table 16). OSHA citations for LASER violations are issued by invoking the general duty clause or, in some cases, Subpart I. In such cases, the employers are required to revise their reportedly unsafe workplace using the recommendations and requirements of such industry consensus standards as the ANSI Z136.1 standard and the ACGIH TLV and LASER monograph.

To implement a LASER safety program, a qualified LASER safety officer (LSO) will be appointed. The LSO will implement appropriate controls, not less than those required by ANSI, ACGIH, and the OSHA construction standard. In addition to labels, Class IIIB and Class IV lasers may require other precautions. A LASER-controlled area is required during periods of operation of any LASER installation that inadequately encloses the beam. The controlled area will encompass the entire no-hazard zone (NHZ) determined by the LSO using guidance from the OSHA technical manual and ANSI standards. Personnel inside the NHZ will wear LASER safety goggles with optical density OD = $\log_{10}(H_0/\text{MPE})$, where H_0 is the anticipated worst-case exposure in J/cm^2 for a pulsed LASER or W/cm^2 for a continuous LASER, as appropriate. MPE is the maximum level of laser radiation to which a person may be exposed without hazardous effects or biological changes in the eye or skin. The MPE is determined by the wavelength of the laser, the energy involved, and the duration of the exposure. The ANSI 136.1 standard tables 5, 6, and 7 summarize the MPE for particular wavelengths and exposure durations (Princeton 2007).

The following facts are useful for training laser personnel about symptoms of possible overexposure (Bader 2006):

- Exposure to the invisible carbon dioxide laser beam (10,600 nm) can be detected by a burning pain at the site of exposure on the cornea or sclera.
- Exposure to a visible laser beam can be detected by a bright color flash of the emitted wavelength and an after-image of its complementary color (e.g., a green 532-nm laser light would produce a green flash followed by a red after-image).
- When the retina is affected, there may be difficulty in detecting blue or green colors secondary to cone damage, and pigmentation of the retina may be detected.
- Exposure to the Q-switched Nd:YAG laser beam (1064 nm) is especially hazardous and may initially go undetected because the beam is invisible, and because the retina lacks pain sensory nerves. Photoacoustic retinal damage may be associated with an audible *pop* at the time of exposure. Visual disorientation caused by retinal damage may not be apparent to the operator until considerable thermal damage has occurred.

Ionizing Radiation

Many recommend that ionizing radiation exposures be kept as low as reasonably achievable (ALARA). This cannot mean zero exposure; practically speaking, humans are continuously exposed to ionizing radiation that includes solar radiation, cosmic radiation, external radiation from environmental radio nuclides, and internal radiation from radio nuclides in the air, water, and food that are incorporated into body tissues.

Most radiation sources in the United States are regulated by the Department of Energy and the Nuclear Regulatory Commission; OSHA and the EPA play only a minor role.[50] Key regulatory limits are summarized in Table 17.

To determine acceptable health protection, use radiation-weighted measures of dose—the sievert and

TABLE 17

Regulatory Limits for Ionizing Radiation

	NRC		OSHA	
Whole body	50 mSv/yr	5 rem/yr	12.5 mSv/qtr	1.25 rem/qtr
Lens of eye	150 mSv/yr	15 rem/yr	12.5 mSv/qtr	1.25 rem/qtr r
Skin	500 mSv/yr	50 rem/yr	75 mSv/qtr	7.5 rem/qtr
Extremities	500 mSv/yr	50 rem/yr	187 mSv/qtr	18.75 rem/qtr
Embryo/fetus	5 mSv/yr	0.5 rem/ gestation	--	--
Minor	10% of adult		10% of adult	
Cumulative occupational from birth to age *n* yrs			< 50 (*n*−18) mSv	< 5(*n*−18) rem[1]
General public	1 mSv/yr	0.1 rem/yr	--	--
General public	0.01 mSv/hr	0.002 rem/hr	--	--

[1]Found in 29 CFR 1910.1096(b)(2)(ii)

TABLE 18

Quality Factors for Ionizing Radiation

Energy	Quality Factor	Neutron Fluence per Sievert	Neutron Fluence per Rem
Unknown γ	1	--	--
Unknown β	1	--	--
< 0.01 MeV *n*	2	(81–98) × 10^9/cm^2/s	810–980 million/cm^2/s
0.01 MeV *n*	2.5	101 × 10^9/cm^2/s	1010 million/cm^2/s
0.1 MeV *n*	7.5	17 × 10^9/cm^2/s	170 million/cm^2/s
0.5–1 MeV *n*	11	(3.9–2.7) × 10^9/cm^2/s	39–27 million/cm^2/s
Unknown *n*	10	(1.4–2.7) × 10^9/cm^2/s	14–27 million/cm^2/s
Unknown *p*	10	--	--
Unknown α	20	--	--

(*Sources:* Cember 1996, OSHA 2011, NRC 2011)

the rem. These equivalent doses are derived from physical dose measurements, reported in grays and rads, made by using a quality factor specified by the Nuclear Regulatory Commission. The quality factors in Table 18 depend both on the type of radiation and on its energy.

X-Ray and Gamma Radiation

X-rays and gamma rays are best shielded with electron-rich materials such as the high-Z elements. Lead is commonly used. Because this type of radiation does not activate any elements, people exposed do not become radioactive. The quality factor is unity, so the effective exposure in sieverts is numerically equal to the measured dose in grays.

Alpha Particulate Radiation

Alpha radiation, which does not penetrate the outer layers of dead skin or even a thick sheet of fine paper, poses no external radiation hazard. If ingested and metabolized, however, alpha-emitting radio nuclides do pose a health threat. The best protection is to prevent inhalation and ingestion by engineering design. The quality factor for alpha particles emitted inside the body is 20. The effective dose in sieverts, to be compared with exposure guidelines, is 20 times the measured dose in grays.

Beta Radiation

Electrons and positrons penetrate several millimeters of tissue and deposit their energy in potentially damaging ways. Low-energy beta radiation is adequately shielded by electrical conductors—such as a few millimeters of aluminum—but higher-energy particles need more complete design, often employing a low-Z substance thick enough to stop all beta rays followed by a high-Z substance thick enough to absorb all bremsstrahlung photons generated in the first layer (Cember 1996). Beta particles have a quality factor of unity, so the effective exposure in sieverts is numerically equal to the measured dose in grays.

Neutron and Proton Radiation

Neutrons readily penetrate long distances in most materials and are best shielded by thick barriers of hydrogen-rich materials. Neutron shields are commonly made from pools of water, polyethylene, and concrete. The quality factor for neutrons depends on their energy, but a default value of 10 is authorized by the NRC when the energy is unknown.[51] Design of shielding systems for protons is a task proper to a fully qualified health physicist who specializes in such designs.

ENDNOTES

[1]Modern physics textbooks and a useful Web site summarize concepts central to this chapter: www.hyperphysics.phy-astr.gsu.edu/hbase/hph.html.

[2]Paracelsus' 1567 book was published in Switzerland 27 years after his death.

[3]Henry F. Smyth, Jr. introduced sufficient dose to toxicology in *Food and Cosmetics Toxicology* 5:51 (1967). It applied dose-response and is consistent with hormesis, the beneficial effects of low doses of hazardous stressors. The modern basis for radiation hormesis is found in a pivotal paper by T. D. Luckey, "Physiological benefits from low levels of ionizing radiation," *Health Physics* 43:771–789 (1982). For further details, see www.angelfire.com/mo/radioadaptive/inthorm.html and www.belleonline.com.

[4]See Review Questions 4–6 for a NIOSH summary of attenuation factors for A- and C-weighting filters.

[5]At specialized microwave frequencies, energy is deposited in the skin at the depth of pain endings of neurons and equipment exists for crowd control using this principle. At the higher frequencies of IR B and IR C some of the incident intensity passes completely through the human body—medical imaging devices are being produced that take advantage of this.

[6]As discussed in NIST SP 250-37 (July 1997), the sensitivity curve for human vision is given by proportional response coefficients called V_λ. The CIE visual response curve shows that $0.0001 < V_\lambda < 0.0001$ for wavelengths between 380 to 780 nm and essentially zero for all wavelengths outside this range.

[7]This easily demonstrated shift in wavelength of best sensitivity is called the Purkinje shift. Consider a yellow sunflower in a field of green grass. At high noon, light-adjusted eyes see the yellow appear brighter. As the sun sets, the eye's sensitivity to yellow falls and its sensitivity to green rises. At dusk, green appears brighter than the yellow to dark-adapted eyes. When color perception is important to safety, it is important to control illumination.

[8]In SI units, the luminance of a perfect diffuser is $(1/\pi)$ (cd/m^2) when it is illuminated with 1 lx = 1 lm/m^2.

[9]The equations for these terms are found in the glossary.

[10]For the hydrogen atom, these energies are characterized by the visible light Balmer Series, the Lyman Series in UV, the Paschen Series in near-IR, and the Brackett, Pfund, and Humphreys Series at longer wavelengths. Every atom and molecule has characteristic energy gaps that are revealed by characteristic spectra.

[11]Dr. Dan Russell, Kettering University, Applied Physics Department, has a very nice animation of monopole, dipole, and quadruple geometries (accessed April 11, 2011). www.kettering.edu/~drussell/Demos/rad2/mdq.html.

[12]Well described in textbooks describing the physics of acoustics and of electromagnetic radiation. See also Straus, I. "Near and Far Fields—From Statics to Radiation." *Conformity* 2001 (accessed April 11, 2011). www.conformity.com/past/0102 reflections.html.

[13]The energy of a photon is proportional to its frequency. Conservation of energy means constant frequency when a photon moves between materials. The wavelength and speed of propagation change as photon radiation passes from one material to another.

[14]For example, a welder's lens that transmits 0.0001 of the incident intensity has an optical density of 4. A welder's lens with an optical density of 7 transmits 1.0×10^{-7} of the incident intensity.

[15]Impedance is usually taken to be 377 ohms for EM measurements and 400 rayls for acoustic measurements.

[16]From the 1940s through the 1960s, many thought that hearing damage was proportional to sound pressure with its 6-dB doubling rate (force per unit area). Physicists thought it was proportional to sound intensity (work per unit area) with its 3-dB doubling rate. In the early 1970s OSHA chose a 5-dB doubling rate as a conservative compromise between these two camps. It is now generally agreed that sound intensity is the appropriate metric, and NIOSH, ACGIH, and ISO all recommend the 3-dB doubling rate with an 85 dBA 8-hour TWA goal.

[17]Pressure reported by NOAA and the U.S. Weather Bureau is published after being corrected to sea level and is not useful for calculations during a sound survey taken at altitudes not at sea level. Atmospheric pressure at other altitudes is estimated from the NOAA standard atmosphere tables published as *U.S. Standard Atmosphere*, 1976, U.S. Government Printing Office, Washington, D.C., 1976. These have been republished in the *CRC Handbook of Chemistry and Physics*, which may be more generally accessible. An FAA rule of thumb says that pressure decreases by ~1 inch Hg for each 1000 feet above mean sea level up to about 12,000 ft MSL. Digitaldutch offers a free online calculator for the U.S. Standard Atmosphere (accessed 11 Aug 2011). www.digitaldutch.com/atmoscalc/

[18]It is good practice to carefully study the manual for your sound-level meter to discover if it is internally corrected for nonstandard T and P.

[19]A photon has linear momentum because of its speed plus angular momentum, called spin by modern physics.

[20]When an EM wave propagates through material, its wavelength is generally shorter than in a vacuum, a phenomenon expressed by means of the refractive index of the material. See hyperphysics.phy-astr.gsu.edu/hbase/geoopt/refr.html (accessed Apr 2011).

[21]See www.distinti.com for evidence that an expanded set of equations more completely describes electromagnetic phenomena than Maxwell's Equations. For purposes of this chapter, however, the classical equations are sufficient. Also see www.physicsandbeyond.com/DymnamicTheory.html for evidence of a deeper connection between mass, gravitational forces, and electromagnetic forces than is yet incorporated into the standard model of physics. (Web sites verified April 2011.)

[22]Many textbooks discuss the use of these equations to solve practical problems. When charges are in the region of propagation, or if polarizable or magnetic materials are in region of propagation, a more complex set is required. For more detail, see, for example, www.hyperphysics.phy-astr-gsu.edu/hbase/emcon.html#emcon (accessed April 11, 2011).

[23]See www.en.wikipedia.org/wiki/Solar_sail (accessed April 11, 2011) for more discussion of this device.

[24]The impulse momentum theorem calculates force as the ratio of momentum change to the time needed for the change. In its simple form, $F = \Delta p/\Delta t$.

[25]See a remarkably detailed EM spectrum which shows use, wavelength, frequency, photon energy, and other useful characteristics of EM radiation at www.unihedron.com/projects/spectrum/index.php (accessed April 11, 2011).

[26]These guidelines are violated by resonant structures. The 9-cm ferrite antenna in an AM radio is too small to absorb meaningful energy from a 1 MHz AM radio wave with λ = 300 m unless it is tuned with a capacitor to resonate at 1 MHz. A hydrogen atom with a diameter of 0.5 nm absorbs and emits EM radiation at the H_{alpha}, a red line with wavelength = 656.3 nm. This transition is between quantum state $n = 2$ and $n = 3$ in the hydrogen atom. These states are reasonably viewed as resonant nonradiating states for the orbital electron.

[27]The ACGIH uses 12.4 eV as the boundary between ionizing and nonionizing radiation.

[28]See www.world-nuclear.org/education/ral.htm and www.nrc.gov for summaries of radiation effects and sources in everyday life (accessed April 15, 2011).

[29]See OSHA's online *Technical Manual*, Chapter 5, "Noise and Hearing Conservation." For additional information: www.osha.gov/dts/osta/otm/noise/index.html (accessed April 11, 2011).

[30]Impulse noise, like a hammer hitting an anvil, is so short that it has ended before these reflexes can protect the cochlea. This is why impulse noise is more hazardous than steady sound intensity levels between 85 to 115 dBA.

[31]OSHA's quick card for heat stress is available online at www.osha.gov/Publications/osha3154.pdf. Detailed discussions for safety professionals are in the OSHA *Technical Manual*, Section III, Chapter 4, available at: www.osha.gov/dts/osta/otm/otm_iii/otm_iii_4.html (both accessed April 11, 2011).

[32]Assumes a light, loose-woven cotton summer work uniform allowing free air circulation to evaporate perspiration and maintain the evaporative cooling needed by the human thermoregulatory system. Add 3.5°C (6.3°F) to measured WBGT if close-woven coveralls are worn, and add 5°C (9°F) if two layers of woven or knit coveralls are worn. Compare the corrected WBGT with the guidelines in the table.

[33]See the current version of the booklet *TLVs and BEIs* from ACGIH for guidance on unacclimatized workers. OSHA recommends that a new worker be given five days to reach acclimatization with 20% exposure on day 1, increasing by 20% each day to 100% of the work schedule on day 5.

[34]OSHA PEL for Noise & Vibration: 29 CFR 1910.95 and 1926.10.

[35]The ACGIH TLV is consistent with the ISO standard and most other national standards while being more protective than the OSHA standard. Recommend use of TLV.

[36]90 dBA for 8 hours is the maximum OSHA dose. However, an OSHA noise dose of 50%, representing an OSHA equivalent 85 dBA for 8 hours, is the dose above which OSHA requires a hearing conservation program.

[37]The TLV committee recommends avoiding direct contact with transducers producing intensities greater than 15 dB above 1 g rms. This means keep direct contact below 5.6 g (55 m/s^2).

[38]These attenuation plots are based on data in the *ACGIH TLV Booklet for 2010*, Physical Agent section, under Hand Arm Vibration and Whole Body Vibration (ACGIH 2010a).

[39]The next three equations are discussed in the ACGIH TLV booklet (ACGIH 2010a), some textbooks, and ANSI standards. Also see Wasserman 2006.

[40]These equations for allowed duration of vibration as a function of *rms* acceleration were fitted by linear regression to tabulated values in the 2010 TLV book (ACGIH 2010a). The correlation coefficient for the fit was $R^2 = 0.995$ with p-value < 0.000000005 for the whole-body fit and was $R^2 = 0.997$ with p-value < 0.00004 for the hand–arm fit.

[41]This remarkable summary of the electromagnetic radiation spectrum remained available as of April 11, 2011 at www.unihedron.com/projects/spectrum/downloads/spectrum_20100428.pdf.

[42]$B = (\mu_0 \times H)$, with B in T, H in (A/m) and $\mu_0 = 4\pi\ 10^{-8}$ (V s)/(A m)

[43]ACGIH Worldwide 2003 and IEEE Std C 95.1-1999 or newer.

[44]Localized heating is the problem of concern, and blood flow through body tissues can control localized heating in an averaging time of 6 minutes.

[45]This is the principle of radiant heating, by which wall, floor, and ceiling panels are kept at a higher temperature than the air, conserving energy by minimizing the air-temperature change required in the tempered spaces.

[46]The solid angle of a lamp with measurements $l = 1$ m, $w = 0.03$ m at a distance of 2 m is the ratio of its average transverse dimension, $(l + w)/2 = 0.515$ m, to its distance from the observer, $\alpha = 0.515/2 = 0.257$ radian.

[47]A perfectly polarized beam would have its electric field vector continuously oscillating in one direction. A nonpolarized beam has an E field oscillating in random directions or in multiple simultaneous directions.

[48]For example, beam power in a 300 Hz, 21 fs pulsed laser focused to a 1.6 μm spot is reported to exceed 4×10^{18} W/m^2, corresponding to an electric field strength of nearly 4×10^{10} V/m. This has produced 100 keV X-rays from a 7 μm spot in solid targets.

[49]ANSI has six monographs dealing with LASER safety, numbered Z136.1 through Z136.6. All ANSI LASER standards are available from www.ANSI.org. The overarching standard is: Z136.1-2007, "Safe Use of Lasers."

The OSHA *Technical Manual*, Chapter 6 is a very well-written summary of LASER safety considerations and is available at www.osha.gov/dts/osta/otm/otm_iii/otm_iii_6.html as of April 11, 2011.

[50]Department of Energy (DOE): 10 CFR 835, "Occupational Radiation Protection."

Nuclear Regulatory Commission (NRC): 10 CFR 20, "Standards for Protection Against Radiation."

OSHA: 1910.1096, "Ionizing radiation (general industry)"; 1926.53, "Ionizing radiation (construction)"; 1915.57, "Uses of fissionable material in ship repairing and shipbuilding and ionizing radiation requirements for ship repairing and shipbuilding activities"; 1910.120 and 1926.65, "Hazardous waste operations and emergency response."

The two HAZWOPER standards regulate ionizing radiation at hazardous waste sites.

[51]There is more detail provided in NRC Table 1004(b).2 from 10 CFR 20.1004 and OSHA Table G-17—Neutron Flux Dose Equivalents from 29 CFR 1910.1096(a)(7)(v). See also the National Institutes of Health radiation safety Web site at www.drs.org.ors.nih.gov/training/index.htm (accessed April 11. 2011).

References

American Conference of Governmental Industrial Hygienists (ACGIH) Worldwide. 1990. *A Guide for Control of Laser Hazards*. www.acgih.org

______. 2010a. *2010 TLVs and BEIs*. www.acgih.org

______. 2010b. *Documentation for the TLVs and BEIs*. www.acgih.org

______. 2011. *Physical Agent TLVs Under Study: Elecrtomagnetic Radiation and Fields* (accessed April 11, 2011). www.acgih.org/tlv/PATLVStdy.htm

American Nuclear Society (ANS). n.d. *Radiation Dose Chart* (accessed November 14, 2011). www.and.org/pi/resources/dosechart

Armstrong T. J., T. E. Bernard, and M. S. Lopez. 2007. "Hand–Arm Vibration Exposure Guidelines in the United States with Special Reference to the ACIGH TLV." Proceedings of the 11th International Conference on Hand Arm Vibration, Bologna, Italy, pp. 674–680.

Bader, O., and H. Lui. 2006. *Laser Safety and the Eye: Hidden Hazards and Practical Pearls*. www.derm.ubc.ca/laser/eyesafety.html#What

Berger E. 2000. *The Naked Truth about NRRs*. Earlog Technical Monograph 20. www.e-a-r.com/pdf/hearingcons/earlog20.pdf

Cember, H. 1996. *Introduction to Health Physics*. New York: McGraw-Hill.

Christensen, C. J., A. Nielsen, A. Bahnsen, W. K. Brown, and B. M. Rustad. 1972. "Free-Neutron Beta-Decay Half-Life." *Phys.* 7:1628–1640.

Environmental Protection Agency (EPA). 2007. *Calculate Your Radiation Dose*. www.epa.gov/radiation/students/calculate.html

Fulton, J. T. 2006. *Processes in Biological Vision Including Electrochemistry of the Neuron*. www.4colorvision.com/pdf/17Performance1a.pdf

Graham, C. H., ed. 1965. *L. A. Visual Acuity*. New York: John Wiley & Sons. www.webvision.med.utah.edu/imageswv/KallSpat18.jpg

Griffen, M. G. et al. 2006. "Guide to Good Practice on Hand–Arm Vibration (V7.7 English)—Implementation of EU Directive 2002/44/EC" (December 6) (retrieved November 18, 2007). www.humanvibration.com/EU/VIBGUIDE/HAV%20Good%20practice%20Guide%20V7.7%20English%20260506.pdf

Health Physics Society (HPS). n.d. *Radiation Basics* (accessed November 14, 2011). www.hps.org/public information/ate/facts/aqs/radiation.html

International Sensor Technology. *Photoionization Detectors*. u.d. (retrieved August 2006). www.intlsensor.com/pdf/photoionization.pdf

Liu, J., H. Wang et al. 2001. "An Ultra High Intensity Laser at High Repetition Rate." www.sunysb.edu/icfa2001/Papers/th2-2.pdf#search = 'laser%20beam%20intensity

MacEvoy, Bruce. 2009. *Light and the Eye* (accessed August 11, 2011), www.handprint.com/HP/WCL/color1.html#aberration

Marklund, S. ed. 2003. *Temperature Limit Values for Cold Touchable Surfaces*. Arbete halsa | vetenskaplig skriftserie (accessed April 11, 2011). http://gupea.ub.se.dspace/bitstream/2077/4303/1/ah2003_07.pdf

Merriam-Webster's Online Dictionary. www.m-w.com/cgi-bin/dictionary

National Institutes for Occupational Safety and Health (NIOSH). 1998. NIOSH Publication No. 98-126, *Criteria for a Recommended Standard: Occupational Noise Exposure*. www.cdc.gov/niosh/docs/98-126/chap4.html

National Weather Service (NWS). u.d. *NWS Windchill Chart* (retrieved July 6, 2005). www.nws.noaa.gov/om/windchill/

Nussbaum, R., and W. Kohnlein. u.d. *Radiation Hormesis & Zero-Risk Threshold Dose: Two Scientifically Refuted, but Stubborn Myths* (retrieved April 2007). www.gfstrahlenschutz.de/docs/hormeng2.pdf

Occupational Safety and Health Administration (OSHA). 1990. *OSHA RF Radiation Electromagnetic Field Memo*. www.osha.gov/SLTC/radiofrequencyradiation/electromagnetic_fieldmemo/electromagnetic.html

______. 1990. *Near and Far Field Guidance* (accessed August 11, 2011). www.osha.gov/SLTC/radio frequencyradiation/electromagnetic_fieldmemo/electromagnetic.html

______. 2001. *Energy Evaluation and Management for Antenna Sites* (accessed August 11, 2011). www.osha.gov/SLTC/radiofrequencyradiation/corley_motorola_eme_report.pdf

______. 2003. *OSHA Standard Interpretation: Workplace Exposure Limits for UV Radiation*. www.osha.gov/pls/oshaweb/owadisp.show_document?p_table = INTERPRETATIONS&p_id = 24755

______. 2008. *1910.95, Occupational Noise Exposure* (accessed November 15, 2011). www.osha.gov/pls/oshaweb/oeadisp.show_document?p_table=standards&p_id=9735

______. STD 01-05-001, PUB 8-1.7, *Guidelines for Laser Safety and Hazard Assessment*. www.osha.gov/pls/oshaweb/owadisp.show_document?p_table = DIRECTIVES&p_id = 1705

______. u.d. *Noise Control. A Guide for Workers and Employers*. www.nonoise.org/hearing/noisecon/noisecon.htm

Ohno, Y. 1997. "Photometric Calibrations." United States Department of Commerce, National Institute of Standards and Technology.

Ottoboni, M. A. 1991. *The Dose Makes the Poison*. New York: Van Nostrand Reinhold.

Princeton University. *2007 Laser Safety Guide*. Section 4: "Laser Control Measures" (modified 10/3/2007). www.princeton.edu/sites/ehs/laserguidesec4.htm

Ryer, A. 2011. *The Light Measurement Handbook* (accessed August 15, 2011). ilsales@intl-lighttech.com

Schoenbach, K. H., R. Nuccitelli, and S. J. Beebe. 2006. "Extreme Voltage Could Be a Surprisingly Delicate Tool in the Fight Against Cancer." *IEEE Spectrum*. www.spectrum.ieee.org/aug06/4257

Schüz, J., R. Jacobsen, J. H. Olsen, J. D. Boice, Jr., Joseph K. McLaughlin, and C. Johansen. 2006. "Cellular Telephone Use and Cancer Risk: Update of a Nationwide Danish Cohort." *Journal of the National Cancer Institute* (Dec.) 98(23):1707–1713.

Sliney, David H. 1997. "Optical Radiation Safety of Medical Light Sources." *Phys. Med. Biol.* 42:981–996.

Suzuki, T., T. Hirayama, K. Aihara, and Y. Hirohata. "Experimental Studies of Moderate Temperature Burns." *Burns* (Dec.) 17(6):443–451.

Taylor, Barry N. 1995. NIST Special Publication 811, *Guide for the Use of the International System of Units (SI)*. Washington, D.C.: Department of Commerce, National Institute of Standards and Technology. www.physics.nist.gov/cuu/Units/bibliography.html

Tominaga, Y. 2005. "New Frequency Weighting of Hand–Arm Vibration." *Industrial Health* 43:509–515.

Ungar, E., and K. Stroud. 2007. *A New Approach to Defining Human Touch Temperature Standards* (accessed August 12, 2011). http://ntrs.nasa.gov/archive/nasa/casi.ntrs.nasa.gov/20100020960_2010020520.pdf

Wasserman, D. E. 2006. *Hand-Arm Vibration Standards: The New ANSI S2.70 Standard* (accessed April 17, 2011). www.public.navy.mil/navsafecen/Documents/acquisition/wasserman_HAV_stds_06.pdf

Williams, P. E. 2010. *Physics: Against the Odds* (accessed September 6, 2011). www.createspace.com/3371910

Appendix: Glossary of Mathematical Symbols and Physical Constants

SI units are in square brackets [ ].

A Ampere, SI base unit of electric current

$\vec{A}$ Area element with direction orthogonal to surface area

A_{xxx} Acceleration [m/s^2]

wxn—weighted along *x*-axis during *n*th time interval

wx—time weighted average acceleration along *x*-axis

wt—total resultant TWA acceleration, a composite of three-axis measurement data

$A\lambda$ Wavelength weighting function to prevent photochemical retina damage in lensless eye

Amu Atomic mass unit = Dalton—1/12 mass of ^{12}C: 1 amu = $1.6605402 \times 10^{-27}$ kg

$\vec{B}$ Magnetic field = magnetic flux density = $\mu\vec{H}$ [Tesla, T = V s/m^2]

B_{med} Bulk modulus of a compressible medium [Pascal, Pa = N/m^2 = kg/ms^2]

$B\lambda$ Blue light wavelength weighting function to prevent photochemical retina damage in normal eye

C Symbol for capacitance, measured in Farads [F = C/V = A s/V]

C Coulomb, quantity of charge or quantity of electricity [C = A s]

cd Candela, base unit for luminous intensity [cd]

c_{med} Speed of a wave in a compressible medium [m/s]

c_{air} Speed of sound in air [m/s]

c_m Speed of light in medium *m*, $c_m = \dfrac{1}{\sqrt{\mu_m \varepsilon_m}}$ [m/s]

c_0 Vacuum speed of light or electromagnetic wave; $c_0 = 299792458 \approx 3 \times 10^8$ [m/s]

cm Centimeter [m/100]

dB Decibel, base 10 logarithm of a ratio of two energy quantities [dB], or a ratio of one energy, *Q*, to a reference energy, Q_0 [dB re Q_0].

dBA A-weighted sound intensity level, used for hearing conservation [dBA re 1 pW/m^2]

$\vec{D}$ Electric displacement field [A s/m^2 = C/m^2 = F V/m^2]

D_{xxx} Noise dose where *xxx* = PEL for OSHA and *xxx* = TLV for ACGIH [unitless]

$\vec{E}$ Electric flux density [J/m C] = electric field = [V/m]

e Unit charge on electron and proton, 1.60218×10^{-19} [C]

EM Abbreviation for electromagnetic

E_{al} Allowed limit of specific energy deposited in tissue in a specified time, E_{al} = 144 [J/kg]

E_{IR} Effective irradiance incident to skin or eye in 770 nm $< \lambda <$ 1400 nm, [W/cm^2]

E_{UV} Effective irradiance incident to skin or eye weighted by $S\lambda$, [W/cm^2]

$E\lambda$ (λ) Spectral irradiance at wavelength = λ, incident to skin or cornea, [W/cm^2 sr nm]

eV Electron volt, energy of an electron accelerated by 1 V (1.60218×10^{-19}) [J]

f Frequency in cycles per second [Hz]

F Farad, quantity of capacitance [F = C/V = A s/V]

F Force [N]

G Gauss, cgs measure of magnetic flux density [T = 10^4 G]

h Planck constant = 6.6207×10^{-34} [J s = kg m^2/s]

hbar Dirac constant = Planck constant/2π; $h/2\pi$ = 1.0547×10^{-34} [J s]

H Henry, measure of inductance [H = s V/A]

$\vec{H}$ Magnetic field strength, $\vec{H} = \beta/\mu_0$ [A/m]

I Electric current [A = W/V = C/s]

I_{xxx} Intensity for radiation source geometries defined by *xxx* [W/m^2]

xxx ps means point source

xxx ls means line source

xxx as means area source

xxx dps means dipole source

$\vec{I}_{air}$ Sound intensity [W/m^2]

$\vec{I}_{EM}$ Electromagnetic intensity [W/m^2]

$\vec{I}_{ff}$ Electromagnetic intensity in radiating far field = $|\vec{S}|$ [W/m^2]

I_0 1 pW/m^2, reference sound intensity

J Joule, unit of energy J = Nm = kg m^2/s^2

$\vec{J}$ Electric current density vector [A/m^2]

L Symbol for inductance, measured in Henrys, H = s V/A

L_I Sound intensity level, 10 $\log_{10}(I/I_0)$ [dB re I_0 = 1 pW/m^2]

$$L_I = L_P + 10 \log_{10}\left(\frac{400}{\rho_{air} c_{air}}\right)$$

L_P Sound pressure level, 20 $\log_{10}(P_{rms}/P_0)$ [dB re P_0 = 20 μPa *rms*]

$L_{aphakic}$ Effective radiance of light source weighted by $A\lambda$ for lenseless eye [W/cm^2 sr]

L_{blue} Effective radiance of light source weighted by $B\lambda$ [W/cm^2 sr]

L_{retina} Effective radiance of light source weighted by $R\lambda$ [W/cm^2 sr]

L_λ Spectral radiance of light source at λ [W/cm² sr nm]

lm Luminous flux, lumen [lm = cd sr]

lux Illuminance [lux = lm/m² = cd sr/m²]

M Molar mass [g/mol]

M_{air} Molar mass of NOAA standard air, 28.964 [g/mol]

m Meter, SI base unit of length

m_α the alpha particle mass = 6.644656×10^{-27} [kg]

m_d the deuteron mass = $3.34358309 \times 10^{-27}$ [kg]

m_e the electron mass = 9.109382×10^{-31} [kg]

m_n the neutron mass = $1.6749272 \times 10^{-27}$ [kg]

m_p the proton mass = $1.6726216 \times 10^{-27}$ [kg]

m_{length} mass per unit length of a string or rod [kg/m]

mW milliWatt [10^{-3} watt]

n A neutron, an uncharged nucleon with $m = m_p$ and $q = 0$

N Newton, unit of force to accelerate 1 kg at 1 [ms^{-2}]; N = kg m/s²

OD Optical density, $\log_{10}(1/T_r)$ [unitless]

p A proton, a positively charged nucleon with $m = m_p$ and $q = e$

$\vec{p}$ Momentum vector of a particle with mass.

Linear momentum vector = $\dfrac{m\vec{v}}{\sqrt{1-(v/c)^2}}$;

Angular momentum (AM) vector = **L**, of a particle of position vector (**r**) and linear momentum (**p**) is defined as **L** = **r** × **p**.

p_{photon} Momentum of a photon [J S/m = kg m/s]

P_{rms} Pressure or *rms* sound pressure [Pa]

P_{EM} Radiation pressure of EMS wave [Pa]

P_{air} Barometric pressure with standard atmosphere, reference value = 101.325 [kPa]

Pa Pascal, the SI pressure exerted by a force of 1 Newton over 1 square meter [N/m²]

P_0 20 μPa, reference *rms* sound pressure

prf Observed pulse repetition frequency [pulses/s]

PRF Allowed pulse repetition frequency [pulses/s]

pW picoWatt = [10^{-12} Watt]

q Charge [Coulomb = C]

Q An energy or power quantity used in converting to and from dB

R Molar gas constant, R = 8.31447 J/KMole

rms Root mean square = square root of the average value of the square of a time-varying signal over a defined interval or over one period of a periodic signal.

r_{xxx} Distance between observer and source, [m]. See I_{xxx} for meaning of *xxx*.

$R\lambda$ Wavelength weighting function to prevent IR thermal damage to retina

s Second, SI base unit of time

$\vec{s}$ A vector along a line or path to be integrated

$\vec{S}$ Poynting vector indicating power density and direction of traveling EM wave $\vec{S} = \vec{E} \times \vec{H}$ in [W/m²] $|\vec{S}|\ |\vec{E}| \times |\vec{H}|$ in a free-field plane wave [W/m² = A V/m²]

SA_{pp} Per pulse specific absorption of energy in tissue [J/kg]

$S_c(f)$ Specific absorption coefficient for tissue bathed by EM waves with frequency = f in Hz [$S_c(f)$ is unitless]

SI base units

meter: m
kilogram: kg
second: s
ampere: A
kelvin: K
mole: mol
candela: cd

Units used with SI system

minute (time)	min	1 min = 60 s
hour	h	1 h = 3600 s
day	d	1 d = 24 h = 86,400 s
degree (angle)	°	1° = (π/180) rad
minute (angle)	′	1′ = (1/60)° = (π/10,800) rad
second (angle)	″	1″ = (1/60)′ = (π/648,000) rad
liter	L	1L = 1 dm³ = 10^{-3} m³
metric ton (tonne)	t	1 t = 10^3 kg
neper (dimensionless)	Np	1 Np = 1; $\log_e$ [power ratio]
bel (dimensionless)	B	1B = 1; $\log_{10}$ [power ratio]
electronvolt	eV	1 eV ≈ 1.602 18 × 10^{-19} J
unified atomic mass unit	u	1 u ≈ 1.660 54 × 10^{-27} kg
astronomical unit	ua	1 ua ≈ 1.495 98 × 10^{11} m

Units still used in the USA

nautical mile	nm	1 nm = 1852 m
knot	kt	1 kt = 1 nm/h = (1852/3600) m/s
are	a	1 a = 100 m²
hectare	ha	1 ha = 1 hm² = 10,000 m²
bar	bar	1 bar = 0.1 MPa = 100 kPa = 10^5 Pa
ångström	Å	1 Å = 0.1 nm = 10^{-10} m
barn	b	1 b = 100 fm² = 10^{-28} m²
curie	Ci	1 Ci = 3.7 10^{10} Bq
roentgen	R	1 R = 2.58 10^{-4} C/kg
rad	rad	1 rad = 1cGy = 0.01 Gy
rem	rem	1 rem = 1 cSv = 0.01 Sv

Partial SI prefixes				
atto	$a = 10^{-18}$	Exa	$E = 10^{18}$
femto	$f = 10^{-15}$	Peta	$P = 10^{15}$
pico	$p = 10^{-12}$	Tera	$T = 10^{12}$
nano	$n = 10^{-9}$	Giga	$G = 10^{9}$
micro	$\mu = 10^{-6}$	Mega	$M = 10^{6}$
milli	$m = 10^{-3}$	Kilo	$k = 10^{3}$
centi	$c = 10^{-2}$	Hecto	$h = 10^{2}$
deci	$d = 10^{-1}$	Deka	$da = 10$

S_λ Wavelength weighting function to prevent UV damage to skin and cornea

T Tesla, magnetic flux density, $T = s\ V/m^2$

T Tension in a vibrating string [N]

T Period of a traveling wave, $T = 1/f = 2\pi/\omega$ [s]

T_{air} Absolute temperature of air in Kelvin [K]

T_{at} Averaging time for reversible tissue thermal effects, $T_{at} = 360$ [s]

$T_{°F}$ Temperature in degrees Fahrenheit or in degrees Celsius [°C] or Kelvin [K]

T_i OSHA allowed duration of exposure to sound intensity level, L_i [hr]

T_{pw} Pulse width including rise, fall, and ring-down time [s]

T_r Transmission through a medium, $0 \le T_r \le 1$

T_{max} Maximum duration of exposure to radiation [s]

T_λ Wavelength weighting function to prevent IR thermal damage to cornea and lens

U Energy [Joule = J]; $U_{photon} = hf$; hf is energy of a photon

V Volt, electrostatic potential difference, energy per unit charge, [V = W/A = J/C]

V_m Molar volume, ideal gas law estimate $= RT/P$ [V in L when T in K and P in kPa]

Vel Velocity [m/s] or Vel_{mph} in [mi/hr] when subscript is shown

$\vec{Vel}_{air}$ Vector acoustic (oscillating) velocity in air [m/s]

W Watt, unit of work at rate 1 Joule per second [W = J/s = V A]

W_{al} Allowed limit of specific power deposition in tissue [W/cm^2]

Z_{air} Acoustic impedance of air with P_{air} in [kPa] and T_{air} in [K]

$$Z_{air} = \rho_{air} c_{air} = \frac{M_{air} P_{air}}{RT_{air}} \left(20.05\sqrt{T_{air}}\right) = \frac{69.7758\ P_{air}}{\sqrt{T_{air}}}$$

in [Pa s/m]

Z_m EM impedance of medium m characterized by μ_m and ε_m: $Z_m = \sqrt{\frac{\mu_m}{\varepsilon_m}}$ [V/A = Ohm]

Z_0 EM impedance of a mass-free vacuum:

$$Z_0 = \sqrt{\frac{\mu_0}{\varepsilon_0}} \text{ [V/A = Ohm]}$$

Z_{0air} Reference acoustic impedance of air, $Z_{0air} \equiv 400$ Rayls = 400 [Pa s/m] = 400 [N s/m^3]

α Alpha particle, a fully ionized helium nucleus, He^{++} with $m \sim 4$ amu and $q = +2e$

β Beta particle, a free electron (β^-) or a free positron (β^+) with $m = m_e$ and $q = e$

γ Gamma particle, a photon with $m = 0$, $q = 0$, and finite momentum

γ_{air} Adiabatic constant for air and diatomic gases ~1.4

$\Delta\lambda$ A short wavelength interval on a spectrum [m or nm]

ε_m Permittivity in a material [A s/(V m) = F/m]

ε_r Relative permittivity, $\varepsilon_r = \frac{\varepsilon_m}{\varepsilon_0} \ge 1.0$ [unitless]

ε_0 Vacuum permittivity or dielectric constant, $\varepsilon_0 = 8.854187817 \ge 10^{-12} \approx 10^{-9}/36\pi$ [A s/V m = F/m]

μ_m Permeability in a material, $\mu_m \ge \mu_0$ [V s/A m = H/m]

ν (nu) $= 2\pi f$ [radians/s] with frequency, f, in Hz

μ_0 Vacuum permeability or magnetic constant, $\mu \equiv \pi/2{,}500{,}000$ [V s/A m = H/m]

μ_r Relative permeability, $\mu_r = \frac{\mu_m}{\mu_0} \ge 1.0$ [unitless]

Φ_E Electric flux $\int_A \vec{E} \cdot d\vec{A} \approx \vec{E} \cdot \vec{A}$ [N m^2/C] → [J m/C] → [W m/A] → [V m]

Φ_M Magnetic flux $\int_A \vec{B} \cdot d\vec{A} \approx \vec{B} \cdot \vec{A}$ [T m^2] →[N m/A] → [J/A] → [W s/A] → [V s]

λ Wavelength in [m], used herein for both elastic and electromagnetic waves

π (Circumference of circle)/diameter ≈ 3.14159, π radians = 180 degrees

ω Frequency in radians per second ($\omega = 2\pi f$) [rad/sec]

Ω Ohm $1\,|\Omega| = 1$[V/A]

ρ_{air} Density of air, $\frac{M_{air}}{V_{molar\,air}} \approx \frac{M_{air} P_{air}}{RT_{air}}$ [ρ in kg/m^3 when M in kg/kmol, P in kPa, T in K]

ρ Mass density [kg/m^3] or charge density [C/m^3]

$\nabla \cdot \vec{A}$ = Div ($\vec{A}$) = Divergence of a vector field, $\vec{A}$, quantifying the flux away from or toward the point of analysis

$\nabla \times \vec{A}$ = Curl ($\vec{A}$) = Curl of vector field $\vec{A}$ is a vector operator quantifying its vorticity at the point of analysis

5

Biological Hazards

Michael A. Charlton

LEARNING OBJECTIVES

- Become well-versed in the anticipation, recognition, evaluation, and control of biological hazards in an occupational setting.
- Learn where to find reference information on biological hazards in an occupational setting.
- Become familiar with the bloodborne pathogens and recombinant DNA regulatory and safety requirements.
- Outline the operation and uses of primary biological safety containment devices (e.g., biological safety cabinets).

A RELATIVELY NEW paradigm in the last 50 years is the anticipation, recognition, evaluation, and control of biological hazards in the workplace. Exponential growth in basic sciences, microbiology, and medicine has led to unparalleled advances in human morbidity and mortality. Improving human health pushes researchers to study the fundamentals of disease genesis and transfer in our population. This chapter studies biological safety aspects of anticipation, recognition, evaluation, and control, especially in the occupational environment.

Human medicine in developed countries has evolved greatly over the past 50 years. The ability to diagnose, treat, and ultimately cure infectious diseases has significantly increased the human life span over the past century. The prevalence of infectious disease cases in developed countries has given way to other chronic diseases, such as coronary heart disease and solid tumor cancers.

The practicing safety professional should be aware of the techniques for anticipating, recognizing, evaluating, and controlling biological hazards in the workplace. Naturally occurring biological hazards exist in almost any workplace that involves plant and animal contaminants, meat processing, farming, laboratories, or health care (Heubner 1947; Sulkin and Pike 1951; Oliphant et al. 1949). In particular, laboratory-acquired infections have become very significant safety concerns. More than 3500 laboratory infections and 160 deaths have been reported worldwide (Wedum 1997).

Biological safety programs must be founded on fundamental safety principles. Pike (1979) once concluded that "common sense, good work practices and using the appropriate equipment should protect workers from the risks related to the use of hazardous biological agents." These guiding principles should be emphasized throughout acceptable biological safety programs.

Anticipation and Recognition

The primary focus of biological safety in the United States today occurs in the highly specialized realm of clinical testing and microbiology laboratories. Through the years, numerous case-prevalence studies have reported biological hazards in these occupational settings. The most well known are a series of laboratory surveys published by Sulkin and Pike from 1949 to 1979. By 1976, Pike had reported a stunning 3921 cases of laboratory-acquired illness. The most common diseases reported were brucellosis, typhoid, tularemia, tuberculosis, and hepatitis. Most noteworthy, approximately 70 percent of Pike's reported cases were not associated with a known accident or incident (Pike 1976). Table 1 summarizes the reported causes of 3497 laboratory infections (Wedum 1997). It is presumed that these illnesses may have occurred via outdated laboratory techniques (e.g., mouth pipetting), a lack of engineering controls, or a loss of containment.

TABLE 1

Reported Cause of 3497 Laboratory-Acquired Illnesses

Reported Cause	Count	Percentage
Aerosol exposure	466	13.3
Accident (reported)	566	16.2
Unknown cause	2465	70.5
TOTAL	3497	100.0

(*Source:* Wedum 1997)

Routes of Transmission

These exposure data illustrate the most common exposure routes in an occupational setting. The National Research Council (NRC 1989) reported five primary routes of exposure in the biomedical research laboratory. The oral ingestion and respiratory routes are frequent safety risks for many hazardous materials. However, biological agents may also be transmitted through direct contact (e.g., droplets contacting unprotected skin), ocular contact, and self-inoculation (e.g., percutaneous or needlestick injury). These routes are especially important in industries that routinely utilize aerosol-generating equipment and sharp implements (e.g., syringes and scalpels).

Clinical testing laboratories were found to have biological safety hazards, particularly posed by bloodborne pathogens. Skinholj (1974) reported a retrospective case study in which Danish clinical testing laboratories reported an incidence of hepatitis that was seven times higher than the incidence in the general Danish population. Anticipation of biological safety hazards associated with bloodborne pathogens represents a critical program for safety professionals.

A clear record of occupational biological hazard is available in the literature. Table 2 shows an interesting distribution of infections as a function of self-reported occupation (Wedum 1997). These hazards are pronounced in the occupational setting but less established as a community health risk. Clearly, foodborne pathogens have resulted in community health risks, especially in sensitive populations, such as the elderly and transplant, oncology, and pediatric patients. The record of community health risk from occupations handling biological agents and human specimens is not well established. Richardson (1973) observed no secondary cases (to the community) from 109 laboratory infections reported to the Centers for Disease Control and Prevention (CDC) from 1947 to 1973. A limited number of secondary cases are available in the literature, ranging from sexual transmittal of Marburg disease (Martini and Schmidt 1968) to Q-fever among commercial laundry workers handling contaminated linens (Oliphant et al. 1949). Q-fever transmission from close household contact (presumably as a result of infectious aerosol generation) and percutaneous transmission from a B-virus spousal exposure were also reported by Holmes et al. (1990). The highly infectious nature of Q-fever supports the notion that enclosed and improperly ventilated operations have the potential for creating secondary community infections. The sporadic nature of these secondary community infections makes it difficult for the safety professional to anticipate biological hazards. However, plans for post-exposure decontamination, contaminated laundry procedures, and proper hand hygiene appear to be warranted.

The two most common early biological safety hazards include aerosol transmission via centrifuging

TABLE 2

Percent Occurrence of Laboratory-Acquired Infection as a Function of Self-Reported Occupation

Self-Reported Occupation	Ft. Detrick Data (%) ($n = 369$)	Pike and Sulkin Data (%) ($n = 1286$)
Trained scientific personnel	58.5	78.1
Laboratory technical assistants	21.7	
Animal attendants	2.1	10.3
Contaminated glassware washer	3.8	
Housekeeping	0	
Administrative and clerical	3.7	
Maintenance employees	7.8	6.7
Personal contacts	2.4	
Students not in research	0	4.9
TOTAL	100.0	100.0

(*Source:* Wedum 1997)

and ingestion transmission via oral pipetting of infectious materials. Oral pipetting was reported to account for 6 to 18 percent of known accidental inoculations from 1893 to 1968 (Wedum 1997). Wedum noted various causes, including a loose cotton plug, incorrect selection of the type of pipette, excessive suction, removal of the pipette from the liquid, and even presence of a nose cold in the laboratory technician. The onset of mechanical, calibrated pipettes has virtually eliminated the oral exposure pathway from most occupations in the past twenty years.

Due to the ability of the pathogens to rapidly entrain in air, microbial aerosols containing pathogens can be released during centrifugation. In particular, aerosols can be created by infectious fluid remaining on the lip of the tube, leakage of a tube when the fluid head angle is less than 45 degrees, distortion of a nonrigid tube by centrifugal forces, or even residual fluid in the cap screws (Wedum 1997). Anticipation of these biological safety hazards is critical because two of the reported cases resulted in fatalities. A risk-assessment procedure that incorporates sealed rotors, routine decontamination, tube inspection, vigorous training, and emergency spill procedures is warranted from these data.

The data from Table 2 indicate that approximately 10 percent of laboratory-associated illnesses occur via percutaneous injuries. Although these data may be dated, safety professionals should heed the general trend of occupational biological hazards.

Types of Biological Agents

It is critical for the safety professional to understand the subtle differences in biological agents. This knowledge should yield improved control measures and emergency response procedures in the occupational environment. However, knowledge of biological interactions and human disease onset is not fully defined and is rapidly developing. Visit the Centers for Disease Control (CDC) Web site for the current guidance on specific biological agents. Another excellent regulatory reference comes from the Public Health Agency of Canada (PHAC 2006). These pathogen safety data sheets (PSDS) are produced by Canadian health authorities with the stated purpose of providing guidance to employees and employers regarding biological agents in the workplace. They contain succinct hazard information organized in alphabetical order and include excellent safety information for rapid reference.

A common source of health information is the *Merck Manual of Diagnosis and Therapy* (Porter and Kaplan 2006), which conveys basic understanding of infectious diseases especially from the patient perspective. The following summary is drawn from the *Merck Manual*.

Bacteria

These common and familiar biological agents may be further subdivided into gram-positive cocci, gram-negative cocci, gram-positive bacilli, gram-negative bacilli, spirochetes, mycobacteria, and anaerobics. Each one has unique traits, especially in relation to the effect on humans and potential therapies.

Staphylococcal infections are extremely common in humans, especially in hospitals or related environments. These infections appear in circumstances involving newborns, postoperative surgeries, internal catheters, certain pulmonary disorders, and even some bone maladies.

Streptococcal infections are another group of common bacterial agents and are generally evaluated by growth on sheep-blood agar media. Another common way to classify streptococci is by the amount of carbohydrates in the cell wall. The most familiar of these gram-positive cocci infections are rheumatic fever, scarlet fever, and familiar tonsillitis/pharyngitis diseases. The most common disease among these agents is streptococcal pharyngitis characterized by sore throat, fever, and tonsillar exudate. Most streptococcal infections are generally considered virulent, and some subgroups have known resistance to drug therapies. However, many safety professionals will be familiar with the symptoms of these diseases because of their commonality. With proper diagnosis and pharmacological therapy, most healthy workers will have an excellent long-term prognosis from gram-positive cocci.

The general term *gram-positive bacteria* indicates a dark-colored reaction to a Gram-staining procedure. This purple-colored reaction is caused by incorporation of the Gram stain throughout the cell via the cell wall. This clinical laboratory procedure is extremely common in order to highlight bacterial cells against other cells. A counterstain involves the addition of safranin to the biological sample. This counterstain allows gram-negative bacteria to turn a light red or pink color to easily differentiate the dark purple gram-positive bacteria.

Pneumococcal infections are another type of gram-positive lancet-shaped encapsulated diplococcus, with more than 85 different types. These bacteria are readily spread person to person via aerosolized droplets (e.g., coughing or sneezing). These infections are so common that nearly half of a healthy workforce may harbor these pathogens during the winter months. Further, extreme care should be observed for special populations in the workplace (or patients) with immunological deficiencies, for oncology patients, and for those with sickle cell diseases.

Gram-negative cocci include the genus Neisseria. These bacteria differ from the gram-positive stain because their cell wall structure does not readily take up the primary Gram stain. Generally, gram-negative cells appear red or pink because of a secondary counterstain added during the staining procedure. The most familiar gram-negative cocci bacterial agent is *N. gonorrhoeae*, which is the causative agent for the sexually transmitted disease gonorrhea. Another significant human pathogen is *N. meningitides*, which causes a clinically significant bacterial meningitis. Normally, these gram-negative cocci are not strongly associated with occupational exposures. Gram-negative rod or bacilli include significantly more species than the cocci groups. Thousands of subspecies have been observed, including many clinically significant species. Of particular importance to a safety professional, in the gram-negative bacilli category, are the respiratory hazards caused by *Legionella pneumophila* and the ingestion/foodborne hazard posed by *Salmonella enteritidis* or *Salmonella typhi*.

GRAM-POSITIVE BACILLI

The most important occupational gram-positive bacilli is *Erysipelothrix rhusiopathiae*, which causes a common skin irritation. Bacterial infection with *E. rhusiopathiae* occurs via dermal abrasions and cuts resulting in local infection. The most commonly associated occupational-exposure settings include animal husbandry, handling animal carcasses or excreta, and extremity contact with animal derivatives.

GRAM-NEGATIVE BACILLI

This broad group of organisms is gram-negative, oxidase-positive, and readily cultured. These organisms also ferment glucose. One of the most common bacteria is *Escherichia coli*, which commonly inhabits the gastrointestinal tract of healthy humans. *E. coli* is extremely invasive and toxic when the host system is disrupted via trauma, disease, or pharmaceutical induction. External introduction of some strains into a human may occur through undercooked animal products, especially beef. *E. coli* is extremely common in research laboratories. Laboratory-acquired cases of *E. coli* enterohemorrhagic disease have been reported in the literature (Rao et al. 1996).

Many farm animals in the United States may host the toxic strains of *E. coli*. Occupational exposure to farm animal excreta, especially bovines, is generally considered to have a strong correlation with *E. coli*.

Gram-negative bacilli are extremely widespread and include common hospital-acquired infections (*Klebsiella*, *Enterobacter*, and *Serratia*), *Salmonella*, *Shigella*,

Haemophilus, *Brucella*, and *Cholera*. Of these, *Brucella* has been responsible for numerous occupational exposures. The infectious dose of *Brucella* spp is extremely low, and hence it was the first biological agent (*Brucella suis*) weaponized by the United States in 1954 (Gilligan and York 2004). Prohibitions on ingestion of unpasteurized milk (especially goat) have led to case-incidence reductions, and approximately 100 cases are reported in the United States each year (Gilligan and York 2004). Occupational exposures to unvaccinated animals account for half of the cases in the United States. Brucellosis is also the most frequently acquired laboratory infection (Pike 1978). Table 3 outlines the ten most frequent laboratory-acquired illnesses based on Pike's work (Collins 1983).

Spirochetes are generally spread via nonvenereal body contact and include endemic syphilis, lyme disease (*Borrelia burgdorferi*), and rat-bite fever (*Streptobacillus moniliformis*). Tuberculosis, or TB, is associated with three mycobacteria (*M. tuberculosis*, *M. bovis*, and *M. africanum*). TB occurs in developed countries especially via aerosolized droplet nuclei. The case rate of TB in the United States is approximately 8 cases per 100,000 people. The droplet nuclei are generally considered dangerous because they may stay suspended in air for several hours post-generation.

Viruses

Viruses are extremely small (0.02 to 0.3 μm) protein or lipid covers for an RNA or DNA core. Viruses are dependent on host cells for replication. They depend on healthy cells for propagation and reproduction. Typical microbiological analysis via microscopy cannot detect the small virus particles. However, special chemical or biophysical marker tests can indicate the presence of a virus in a host body. Some of the most prevalent viruses encountered by safety professionals involve bloodborne pathogen viruses stemming from blood spills in the workplace (e.g., human immunodeficiency virus (HIV), hepatitis B virus, and hepatitis C virus). Vaccines for many viruses are available and should be emphasized by local public-health officials or occupational health programs. These common viruses include influenza, varicella, measles, mumps, rubella, poliomyelitis, rabies, and hepatitis A and B.

TABLE 3

The Top Ten Laboratory-Acquired Infections

Agent/Disease	Cases Reported	Mortalities Reported
Brucellosis	426	5
Q-Fever	280	1
Hepatitis	268	3
Typhoid fever	258	20
Tularemia	225	2
Tuberculosis	194	4
Dermatomycosis	162	0
Venezuelan equine encephalitis	146	1
Psittacosis	116	10
Coccidioidomycosis	93	2
TOTAL	2168	48

(*Source:* Collins 1983)

Fungi

In humans, fungi are generally seen as co-infections resulting from other underlying health conditions (e.g., immune-compromised patients). Fungi may occur in isolation of other conditions but are normally associated with a particular geography. For example, *Coccidioides immitis* is predominantly found in the southwest region of the United States, whereas *Blastomyces dermatitidis* may be found along the eastern seaboard of the United States.

EVALUATION

Routine evaluation of the occupational environment has been demonstrated to prevent injuries in many different workplaces. The safety professional should be prepared to conduct episodic facility evaluations that may include biological hazards. The anticipation of potential biological hazards should focus resources on engineering and administrative control measures for preventive purposes. Because of the less-than-uniform application of all control measures, the hazard evaluation phase buttresses biological safety programs in prevention and control phases.

The observation and feedback of existing workplace conditions is an important addition to any biological safety program. In common practice, these evaluation plans include visual review of posting, signage, immunization requirements, ventilation, decontamination processes, physical layout, and emergency procedures. Verification of certain biological safety records includes review of training documents, independent facility certifications, biosafety cabinet certifications, inventory records, autoclave or inactivation logs, and written handling and decontamination procedures. The use of some biological agents may require immunizations, medical testing, or routine health examinations. Occupational health records may also provide an understanding of the workplace. Using this type of employee record also poses special privacy challenges that must be thoughtfully considered prior to the evaluation process.

Many facilities employ a *team-based* evaluation approach. The evaluation team should have enough experience to provide diverse feedback on common biological safety principles and workplace operations. A model team might include a laboratorian, safety professional, medical health professional, veterinary health professional, employee union, and management representative. The contribution and viewpoint of each member of this ideal evaluation team assists in improving the overall evaluation process.

Sources for Conducting Biosafety Evaluations

An inclusive list of all biological safety considerations is not available because of the diverse levels of protection necessary for various biological agents. The primary references in the United States are issued by the National Institutes of Health (NIH), the CDC, and the Occupational Safety and Health Administration (OSHA). Each source contains a biological safety aspect that does not apply to all occupational settings. Therefore, while developing an evaluation protocol, refer to each applicable standard or guideline.

The NIH has published guidelines for the safe use of recombinant DNA molecules in research. In Section I of these guidelines, recombinant DNA is defined as either molecules that are constructed outside living cells by joining natural or synthetic DNA segments to DNA molecules that can replicate in a living cell or molecules resulting from the replication of these. This document is commonly referred to as simply the *NIH Guidelines* (NIH 2011) among biosafety professionals. These guidelines apply to all recombinant DNA research in the United States and its territories for any institution receiving NIH funding. Recombinant DNA research may take the form of benchtop science, human testing derived from recombinant DNA, or human clinical trials using recombinant DNA technology. According to Section I-D-2, any institution receiving NIH funding for recombinant DNA research must apply these guidelines to *all* recombinant DNA research irrespective of the funding source (NIH 2011). Because of this fiscal requirement, the *NIH Guidelines* should be interpreted as mandatory in nature if not in substance.

The *NIH Guidelines* require initial procedure and containment assessment by an independent committee called the Institutional Biosafety Committee (or IBC). The IBC is also required to periodically review recombinant DNA research at the institution for compliance with these guidelines. Further, many larger institutions are required to appoint a biological safety officer (or BSO). The general duties of the BSO may be thought of as the daily administration for the IBC. Under Section IV-B-3-c of the *NIH Guidelines*, the BSO must conduct "periodic inspections" to ensure laboratory standards are followed (NIH 2011). No specific guidance is given to the BSO, but the implication is that the periodic laboratory safety inspections are intended to assess physical containment, standard microbiological procedures, special procedures, and specific biological barriers, all of which should be evaluated by the IBC prior to commencing biological agent research.

Conducting Facility Safety Assessments for Biological Hazards

The absence of mandatory regulatory language on biological hazards forces most safety professionals to use alternative resources for developing and implementing a periodic facility safety evaluation program. The two primary regulatory references in the United States are OSHA's bloodborne pathogen regulations (OSHA 2001) and the CDC's guidance document, *Biosafety in Microbiological and Biomedical Laboratories*, 5th Edition (BMBL) (CDC 2009). The design and operation of a facility must, at a minimum, strictly adhere to these parameters (see Sidebars 1, 2, and 3).

The development of a facility safety assessment should include evaluation of notifications to employees.

Notifications are of critical importance with biological agents because of variability of the infectious dose between various agents and the intra-agent susceptibility of human population segments. The notification and posting of mandatory protections yields written guidance before anyone enters a higher-hazard area. The notification generally consists of the *biohazard* symbol in contrasting colors and a written description of the biological agent. The standard biohazard symbol is referenced in 29 CFR Part 1910 (OSHA 1974). Information regarding specialized protective equipment is generally required to be posted at the entrance of biological agent containment facilities. Most protective notifications also include necessary immunizations and emergency response procedures.

The widespread availability of immunizations has reduced the incidence of many occupational biological agents, especially viral agents. The public-health promotion of immunizations is widely recognized as a key life-span factor in developed countries. Immunization public-health promotions are generally aimed at community populations; however, occupational usage is a critical facility safety evaluation parameter that should be included during safety assessments. Immunization of personnel is a complicated and ethical dilemma. The risks of immunization created by negative side effects must be balanced against the protective benefits against the infectious disease. This analysis should involve trained and experienced medical professionals, infectious disease workers, safety professionals, and occasionally local leaders in the public-health area. An important tenet is that not all immunizations are indicated for all employees because of underlying health conditions. Any inadequate immunization processes are critical factors that should be included in the risk assessment conducted by the safety professional.

Laboratory facility design, work-practice controls, and safety equipment combine to form the primary factors. Consolidated tables for evaluating proper measures are available from a variety of sources (Herman et al. 2004). Table 4 outlines general guidance that can be used to evaluate laboratory facility design features at Biosafety Level 2 (BSL-2).

The type of biological agent containment laboratory must be initially defined by the researcher or

SIDEBAR 1: DERIVATION OF BLOODBORNE PATHOGEN REGULATIONS

(Adapted from the CDC MMWR 1988)

1974—Skinholj reported an incidence of hepatitis seven times the general population incidence for Danish clinical chemistry laboratories.

1983—In 1983 the U.S. Centers for Disease Control (CDC) published an MMWR document titled "Guideline for Isolation Precautions in Hospitals," which contained a section on blood and body fluid precautions. Healthcare worker precautions were intended to be implemented when a patient was known or suspected to be infected with a bloodborne pathogen.

The purpose of this critical 1983 CDC publication was the prevention of nosocomial (or hospital-acquired) infections from patients with a variety of infectious conditions. The principal shortcoming of these recommendations was the application of blood and body fluid protections only to those patients likely to be infected.

1987—In August 1987, the CDC published an MMWR document titled "Recommendations for Prevention of HIV Transmission in Health-Care Settings." The severity of this disease was widely recognized in the 1980s, hence the stringent recommendations outlined by this 1987 CDC publication.

These recommendations extended the 1983 blood and body fluid precautions to all patients. Because these safety precautions were being extended universally, the term Universal Blood and Body Fluid Precautions or Universal Precautions was applied.

In October of 1987, the CDC and OSHA distributed a joint federal advisory notice to all state public-health directors, state epidemiologists, and hospital infection-control committees. This notice outlining recommended protections against bloodborne pathogens was the first-ever joint federal notice addressing safety programs for healthcare workers.

1988—The CDC immediately recognized the inherent value of "Universal Precautions" and published an update extending these protections to HIV, Hepatitis B, and other bloodborne pathogens in healthcare settings. The updated pathogen control plan reported:

Blood is the single most important source of HIV, HBV, and other bloodborne pathogens in the occupational setting. Infection control efforts for HIV, HBV, and other bloodborne pathogens must focus on preventing exposure to blood as well as on delivery of HBV immunization.

1992—The U.S. Occupational Safety and Health Administration (OSHA) published the first-ever regulatory standard specifically addressing the occupational hazards of the healthcare worker. The "Bloodborne Pathogens" regulations were developed over a five-year period and were based on physician, scientist, administration, and union consolidated testimony. These regulations were effective in the United States starting on March 5, 1992.

SIDEBAR 2: SYNOPSIS OF BLOODBORNE PATHOGENS RISK AND EPIDEMIOLOGY

(Adapted from the CDC 2003)

Many employees with clinical or research job responsibilities are at risk for occupational exposure to bloodborne pathogens, including hepatitis B virus (HBV), hepatitis C virus (HCV), and human immunodeficiency virus (HIV). Exposures occur through needlesticks or cuts from other sharp instruments contaminated with infected blood or through contact of the eye, nose, mouth, or skin with a patient's blood. Important factors that influence the overall risk for occupational exposures to bloodborne pathogens include the number of infected individuals in the patient population and the type and number of blood contacts. Most exposures do not result in infection. Following a specific exposure, the risk of infection may vary with factors such as these:

1. Pathogen
2. Type of exposure
3. Route of exposure
4. Amount of patient blood involved in the exposure
5. Health status of patient
6. Health status of the clinician
7. Use of post-exposure

Most institutions have a system for reporting bloodborne pathogen exposures in order to rapidly evaluate the risk of infection, inform employees about treatments available to help prevent infection, monitor the employee for side effects of treatments, and determine if infection occurs. This may involve testing the employee's blood and that of the source patient and offering appropriate post-exposure treatment. An injury-reporting system is described in bloodborne pathogens training and outlined in a facility's exposure control plan.

How Can Occupational Exposures Be Prevented?

Many needlesticks and other cuts can be prevented by using safer techniques (for example, not recapping needles by hand), disposing of used needles in appropriate sharps-disposal containers, and using clinical or laboratory devices with safety features designed to prevent injuries. Using appropriate barriers such as gloves, eye and face protection, or gowns when contact with blood is expected can prevent many exposures to the eyes, nose, mouth, or skin.

clinician. For example, clinical testing laboratories and production laboratories differ significantly in terms of hazard potential for the same biological agent. Therefore, the risk-assessment process must include a determination of whether the facility is a clinical, research, animal, or production laboratory. Each facility uses or amplifies biological agents differently; hence, each has specific exposure risks. The safety professional must conduct a risk-assessment process in order to assess the potential hazards.

A risk-assessment process is outlined in the fifth edition of the BMBL (CDC 2009). Stated factors of interest to a safety professional conducting a risk assessment include: pathogenicity of the agent, route of transmission, agent stability, infectious dose, concentration (in units of infectious organism per unit volume), source of the agent, availability of historical human or animal exposure data, medical prophylaxis/surveillance, personnel training, and proposed alterations to the recombinant gene. Another important factor is whether the pathogen is exotic or indigenous to the study location, since employees may have a native immune response and medical professionals may be unfamiliar with the presentation of pathogen symptoms (CDC 2009). This complex process may require the assistance of a team of professionals, including the safety professional. In many instances, a risk-assessment team is formed by the IBC.

TABLE 4

Common Laboratory Facility Design Features to Be Reviewed during the Evaluation Phase

Number	Design Feature
1	Physical separation between the laboratory and remainder of the building.
2	Physical security and restricted access must be maintained between the laboratory and other areas of the building.
3	Doors into BSL-2 laboratories are self-closing and self-latching in places where they intersect a public area.
4	Laboratory furniture is conducive to facilitating agent-specific decontamination.
5	An active vector-control program is established for the facility.
6	Hand-washing facilities are readily available in the laboratory.
7	Protective clothing is worn in lieu of street clothing. Laboratory personnel must have access to a change room or area.
8	Laboratory working surfaces (e.g., benchtops) are easy to clean, impervious to water, and resistant to laboratory chemicals and disinfectants.

Note: These data were intended to be used for Biosafety Level 2 laboratories. Additional facility-design characteristics and work-practice controls are required for Biosafety Level 3 and animal laboratories.

(*Source:* Herman et al. 2004)

SIDEBAR 3: SUMMARY OF OSHA BLOOD-BORNE PATHOGEN REQUIREMENTS

(*Source:* OSHA 2008)

Information and Training

1910.1030(g)(2)(i)

Employers shall ensure that all employees with occupational exposure participate in a training program which must be provided at no cost to the employee and during working hours.

1910.1030(g)(2)(ii)

Training shall be provided as follows:

At the time of initial assignment to tasks where occupational exposure may take place; Within 90 days after the effective date of the standard; and At least annually thereafter.

1910.1030(g)(2)(iii)

For employees who have received training on bloodborne pathogens in the year preceding the effective date of the standard, only training with respect to the provisions of the standard which were not included need be provided.

1910.1030(g)(2)(iv)

Annual training for all employees shall be provided within one year of their previous training.

1910.1030(g)(2)(v)

Employers shall provide additional training when changes such as modification of tasks or procedures or institution of new tasks or procedures affect the employee's occupational exposure. The additional training may be limited to addressing the new exposures created.

1910.1030(g)(2)(vi)

Material appropriate in content and vocabulary to educational level, literacy, and language of employees shall be used.

1910.1030(g)(2)(vii)

[These are the training content requirements.]

The training program shall contain at a minimum the following elements:

An accessible copy of the regulatory text of this standard and an explanation of its contents;

A general explanation of the epidemiology and symptoms of bloodborne diseases;

An explanation of the modes of transmission of bloodborne pathogens;

An explanation of the employer's exposure control plan and the means by which the employee can obtain a copy of the written plan;

An explanation of the appropriate methods for recognizing tasks and other activities that may involve exposure to blood and other potentially infectious materials;

An explanation of the use and limitations of methods that will prevent or reduce exposure including appropriate engineering controls, work practices, and personal protective equipment;

Information on the types, proper use, location, removal, handling, decontamination and disposal of PPE;

An explanation of the basis for selection of personal protective equipment;

Information on the hepatitis B vaccine, including information on its efficacy, safety, method of administration, the benefits of being vaccinated, and that the vaccine and vaccination will be offered free of charge;

Information on the appropriate actions to take and persons to contact in an emergency involving blood or other potentially infectious materials;

An explanation of the procedure to follow if an exposure incident occurs, including the method of reporting the incident and the medical follow-up that will be made available;

Information on the post-exposure evaluation and follow-up that the employer is required to provide for the employee following an exposure incident;

An explanation of the signs and labels and/or color coding required by paragraph (g)(1); and

An opportunity for interactive questions and answers with the person conducting the training session.

1910.1030(g)(2)(viii)

The person conducting the training shall be knowledgeable in the subject matter covered by the elements contained in the training program as it relates to the workplace that the training will address.

Training Records

1910.1030(h)(2)(i)

Training records shall include the following information:

1910.1030(h)(2)(i)(A)

The dates of the training sessions;

1910.1030(h)(2)(i)(B)

The contents or a summary of the training sessions;

1910.1030(h)(2)(i)(C)

Names and qualifications of persons conducting the training;

1910.1030(h)(2)(i)(D)

Names and job titles of all persons attending the training sessions.

1910.1030(h)(2)(ii)

Training records shall be maintained for 3 years from the date on which the training occurred.

1910.1030(h)(3)

Availability

1910.1030(h)(3)(i)

The employer shall ensure that all records required to be maintained by this section shall be made available upon request to the Assistant Secretary and the Director for examination and copying.

1910.1030(h)(3)(ii)

Employee training records required by this paragraph shall be provided upon request for examination and copying to employees, to employee representatives, to the Director, and to the Assistant Secretary.

Control

The control of biological hazards in the workplace begins with the risk-assessment process. Fundamentally, each process or manipulation involving a patient or focused agent must be evaluated prior to employee exposures (Caucheteux and Mathot 2005). Several U.S. regulatory agencies mandate *a priori* review; however, the general practice of biological safety has historically matched administrative and engineered controls against hazard potential.

A system of biological containment is commonly employed to determine necessary laboratory work practices, safety equipment, and facility design. The mandatory controls are designed to be dynamic, based on the hazard posed by the agent. As the hazard of the biological agent increases, additional control measures are required (Richmond and McKinney 1999).

Biological Safety Cabinets

Biological safety (biosafety) cabinets (BSCs) are a class of safety equipment dedicated to protecting the environment, the worker, and even the product contained inside the device from the biohazard. A properly functioning and certified BSC is a central consideration in establishing appropriate physical containment of a biohazardous agent. However, three primary types of biological safety cabinets are available for containment purposes.

Selecting the right biological safety cabinet is inherent to the risk-assessment process for pathogenic agents. Therefore, the safety professional should answer the following questions in order to assess the type of BSC required:

1. Do I need to protect the outside environment or community from the agent?
2. Do I need to protect the worker handling the biological agent?
3. Do I need to protect the cultures or "products" inside the BSC from the outside unfiltered air?
4. Are there other hazardous chemicals, vapors, or radioactive materials present that must be considered in addition to biological agents?

By answering these four questions, the safety professional can easily select an appropriate BSC. Each type of BSC contains inherent features that meet one or more of the containment requirements outlined in these guidelines.

The BMBL compares and describes BSCs. Table 5 compares different types of BSCs (CDC 2009). A Class I BSC is shown in Figure 1. A Class I BSC is under negative pressure with respect to the outside air and has an inward flow of approximately 75 feet per minute (fpm). The Class I BSC does not protect the product (e.g., cultures) contained inside the BSC. The exhaust air leaving the Class I BSC is high-efficiency particulate air (HEPA) filtered. Therefore, environmental protection from the biohazard is offered by this BSC.

The National Institute for Occupational Safety and Health (NIOSH) recently issued guidance on protecting building environmental systems from chemical, biological, and radiological agents (NIOSH 2003). This guidance includes an excellent fundamental review of HEPA air filtration, filter mechanisms, and air purification. The primary difficulty in air filtration involves knowledge of the particle size, structure, and chemical composition of the air contaminants. These parameters may

TABLE 5

Comparison of Biological Safety Cabinets

Type	Face Velocity (lfpm)	Airflow Pattern	Radionuclides/ Toxic Chemicals	Biosafety Level(s)	Product Protection
Class I open front	75	In at front; rear and top through HEPA filter	No	2, 3	No
Class II Type A1	75	70% recirculated through HEPA; exhaust through HEPA	No	2, 3	Yes
Class II Type B1	100	30% recirculated through HEPA; exhaust via HEPA and hard-ducted	Yes (Low levels/volatility)	2, 3	Yes
Class II Type B2	100	No recirculation; total exhaust via HEPA and hard-ducted	Yes	2, 3	Yes
Class III	NA	Supply air inlets and exhaust through 2 HEPA filters	Yes	3, 4	Yes

(*Source:* CDC 2009)

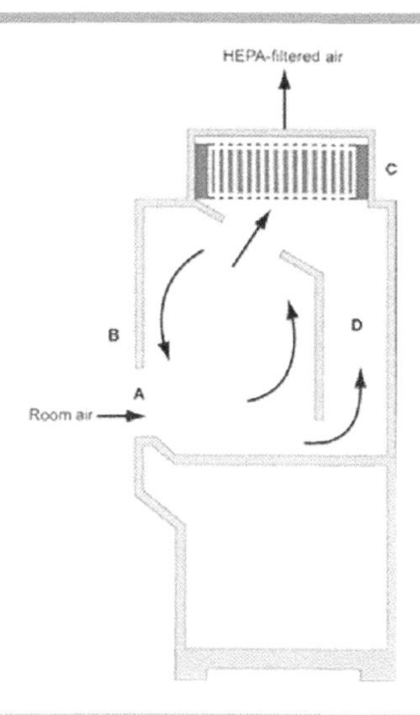

FIGURE 1. **Class I biological safety cabinet**
Legend: (A) front opening, (B) sash, (C) exhaust HEPA filter, (D) exhaust plenum. *Note:* The cabinet needs to be hard-connected to the building exhaust system if toxic vapors are to be used. (*Source:* CDC 2009)

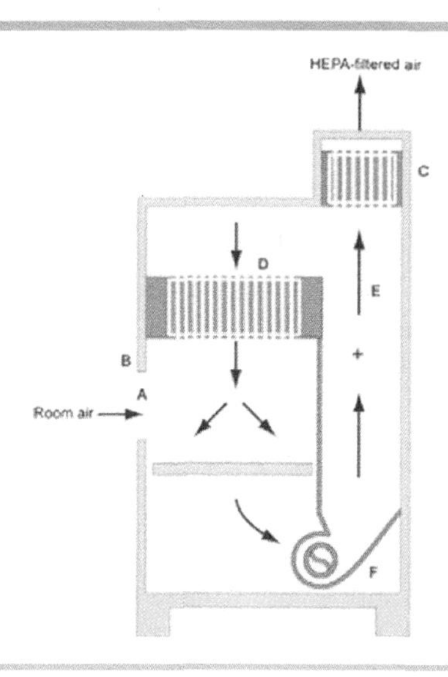

FIGURE 2. **Class II, Type A biological safety cabinet**
Legend: (A) front opening, (B) sash, (C) exhaust HEPA filter, (D) supply HEPA filter, (E) common plenum, (F) blower. (*Source:* CDC 2009)

not be fully known or quantified before engineering controls such as biosafety cabinets are installed. Particle sizes can range from 0.0001 μm (molecular sizes) up to 100 μm (human hair sizes). HEPA filters are designed to filter the particle sizes that are most difficult to remove, occurring from 0.3 μm to 1.0 μm. The NIOSH guidance document on protecting HVAC systems includes a table that compares filtration efficiency, particle sizes, and applications. Applications involving biological agents require the highest filtration efficiency in this document (NIOSH 2003). One important caveat is that air filtration does not alter the oxygen level or significantly change the vapor phase of airborne chemicals. A thorough review of other hazardous materials present in the workplace is highly advisable prior to commencing operations in a HEPA-filtered BSC.

The Class II BSC is the most commonly encountered type of primary containment device. The Class II, Type A1 BSC is shown in Figure 2. The Type A1 BSC sends exhaust back into the laboratory room after the air is filtered via internal HEPA filters. Therefore, the Type A1 cabinet is not appropriate for any chemicals or radioactive materials that would not be readily filtered by a HEPA filter because of the possible recirculation of the contaminant into the room air. The use of natural gas inside a Type A1 BSC is a prime example of how recirculation could significantly impact the workplace. Recirculating natural gas could conceivably build up an explosive atmosphere inside the BSC or the room because natural gas is not filtered by a HEPA filter. The Class II, Type B2 BSC is shown in Figure 3. This containment device offers the usual protection necessary for BSL-2 and BSL-3 laboratories. Room air enters the Class B2 cabinet and is immediately HEPA-filtered. The filtered air blows straight down, creating an air curtain in front of the product, thereby protecting the working surface from outside air. The Type B2 cabinet exhaust is also HEPA-filtered. Therefore, the Class B2 BSC HEPA-filters the incoming room air (for product protection), generates a straight-down air curtain (for product and personnel protection), and finally HEPA-filters the BSC exhaust (for personnel and environmental protection). The exhaust from a Class B2 BSC may be directly connected to the building exhaust system via a *hard* connection to the ductwork. As the name implies, a hard ductwork connection employs mechanical ducting to the exterior of the building. A thimble connection employs a 1-inch air gap between the cabinet exhaust and the building exhaust ductwork. The thimble connection is commonly used to reduce the effect of building exhaust-system fluctuations on the B2 BSC.

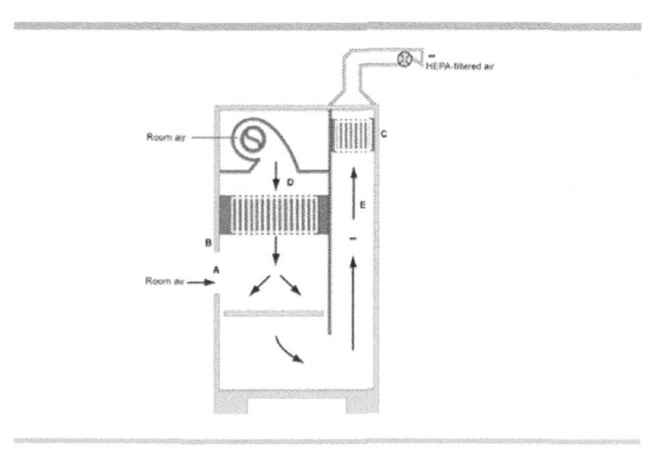

FIGURE 3. Class II, Type B2 biological safety cabinet
Legend: (A) front opening, (B) sash, (C) exhaust HEPA filter, (D) supply HEPA filter, (E) negative pressure exhaust plenum. *Note:* The carbon filter in the exhaust system is not shown. The cabinet exhaust needs to be hard-connected to the building exhaust system. (*Source:* CDC 2009)

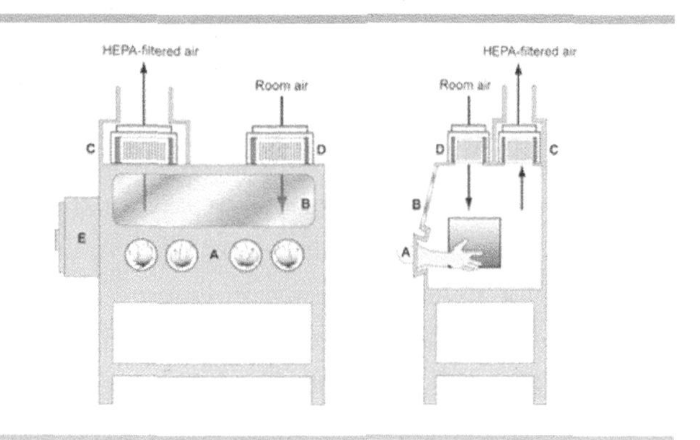

FIGURE 4. Class III biological safety cabinet
Legend: (A) glove ports with O-ring for attaching arm-length gloves to cabinet, (B) sash, (C) exhaust HEPA filter, (D) supply HEPA filter, (E) double-ended autoclave or pass-through box. *Note:* A chemical dunk tank may be installed, which would be located beneath the work surface of the BSC with access from above. The cabinet exhaust needs to be hard-connected to an exhaust system where the fan is generally separate from the exhaust fans of the facility's ventialtion system. The exhaust air must be double HEPA-filtered or HEPA-filtered and incinerated. (*Source:* CDC 2009)

The Class III biological safety cabinet offers the maximum amount of protection for the product, worker, and outside environment. The inside of a Class III BSC may be thought of as totally isolated from the outside environment. Many safety professionals would be familiar with a similar protective device termed a *glove box*. Incoming air is HEPA-filtered, and the contained product has no direct connection outside of the BSC. Figure 4 depicts the Class III BSC. The Class III cabinet is normally found only in the highest level of biological agent containment (e.g., BSL-4). The exhausted air is HEPA-filtered when leaving the unit. Generally, the air is also HEPA-filtered a second time prior to entering the external exhaust fan.

The prudent safety professional also encourages routine testing of primary safety devices such as BSCs. The primary standard for testing BSCs is the National Sanitation Foundations Standard 49 (NSF 2002). This standard is commonly used to evaluate and test the operation of *biohazard cabinetry*. It also specifies training necessary for individuals to conduct assessment or certifications of BSCs.

Training

Employee training encompasses a primary focus of the safety professional for biological hazards. Specific biological safety training is *risk-based* in accordance with the BMBL (CDC 2009). A general rule of thumb is that higher levels of containment dictate additional biological safety training. The frequency of refresher training is also based on the selected level of containment. Training for laboratory staff is based on assumed knowledge and competency of safe microbiological practices.

The following are abridged topics for biological safety training courses (NRC 1989):

1. ***Aseptic techniques:*** Fundamental microbiological techniques require laboratory techniques to prevent cross-contamination. The use of aseptic (or contamination-free) techniques is crucial when propagating infectious substances.
2. ***Laboratory and personnel hygiene:*** A review of historical accidents and exposures shows that failed adherence to good laboratory practices and poor hygiene habits played an important role in laboratory-acquired diseases. Training must encourage safe behavior that is congruent with OSHA regulations, especially in occupations where employees are exposed to bloodborne pathogens (OSHA 2001).
3. ***Laboratory safety practices:*** Laboratory safety practices generally involve the application of

primary containment devices, engineered safety equipment (e.g., sealed centrifuges or eyewashes), and risk assessment. These practices generally become more restrictive with the higher levels of containment.

4. ***Personal protective equipment (PPE):*** The availability of PPE varies as a function of the hazard posed by the pathogen. For example, respiratory protection will be required for any pathogen that could become airborne and infect a healthy adult worker. Additional protective equipment is generally associated with higher levels of biological containment.
5. ***Containment levels:*** The primary levels of biological containment are reviewed in the BMBL (CDC 2009). Higher containment of human pathogens also corresponds with higher hazard pathogens. Infectious diseases with no cures generally require rigorous containment facilities and procedures.
6. ***Decontamination, disinfection, and sterilization:*** The differences among decontamination, disinfection, and sterilization are reviewed in this chapter. Common procedures to monitor the efficacy of *chemical, heat,* and *steam sterilization* are also included.
7. ***Signage, notices, entrance criteria, and postings:*** For hazard awareness and protective equipment-donning purposes, areas that use biological agents must include appropriate notices and postings. Employees must refer to entrance criteria prior to entering a containment facility. These criteria may include protective equipment or immunization requirements.
8. ***Prudent management of biological/infectious wastes:*** Procedures for safe disposal of medical waste and sharps waste apply to many employers in the United States. Improper disposal of contaminated waste materials and laundry have been associated with secondary infections in the recent past.
9. ***Operation and use of biological safety cabinetry:*** The primary containment devices, such as BSCs, represent a fundamental part of biological containment. These devices provide protection to employees, their research specimen, and the surrounding public. An overview with figures from the BMBL (CDC 2009) is included in this chapter.
10. ***Emergency action, spill response, needlesticks and self-inoculation:*** The CDC gives healthcare providers guidance on emergency response and needlestick treatment protocols in an effort to reduce the probability of transmitting a human pathogen. OSHA requires needlestick procedures under its bloodborne pathogen regulations (OSHA 2001).

Institutional Biosafety Committees (IBCs)

The NIH recommends that all individuals, corporations, or institutions not strictly covered by the *NIH Guidelines* establish a properly constituted IBC. Even if an entity is not using recombinant DNA, a properly constituted safety committee should review the presence of biological hazards in the workplace. The IBC is responsible for the following on behalf of the institution:

1. Reviewing procedures, tasks, and protocols involving biohazardous agents, toxins originating from biohazardous materials, and blood and tissues from humans and nonhuman primates
2. Reviewing recombinant DNA research and approving those proposed projects that conform to the *NIH Guidelines*. Specific IBC review items are detailed within those guidelines (2011).
3. Notifying a principal investigator of the results of the committee protocol review.
4. Lowering containment levels for certain agents.
5. Setting acceptable containment levels for experiments involving whole plants or animals.
6. Periodically reviewing recombinant DNA or other applicable research at the institution.
7. Adopting emergency response plans.
8. Reporting significant problems or violations of the *NIH Guidelines* (2011) to the NIH.

9. Not approving certain types of research unless prior approval is given by the NIH.
10. Completing certain other duties as necessary.

These complex duties require a diverse committee structure in order to fulfill the broad scientific and ethical reviews necessary under the *NIH Guidelines* (2011). The IBC must have at least five members who have the collective expertise to review recombinant DNA research and assess the potential hazards presented by the proposed research. Additional experts (e.g., a plant pathogen agronomist) may be a necessary and temporary addition to an IBC depending on the type of recombinant DNA research. A conflict-of-interest resolution is required for IBC members involved in any protocols submitted by a member to the committee. The NIH also encourages institutions to make their IBC meetings open to the public and to release minutes of IBC activities upon request to members of the public (NIH 2011).

Personal and Environmental Sampling/Interpretation

The safety professional may elect to conduct environmental sampling for biological hazards in an occupational setting. The difficulty of personal or environmental sampling is widely recognized in industrial hygiene. Occupational exposures to airborne infectious aerosols may yield disease transmission, hence the motivation to conduct *a priori* sampling of environmental air. Precautions aimed at eliminating or minimizing the spread of infectious diseases are generally termed airborne precautions (Garner 1996). However, airborne precautions are not the solitary protective measure; other types of prevention may also be effective (e.g., hand-washing, social distancing, or prohibitions on eating). The primary risks due to infectious aerosols are associated with speaking, sneezing, and coughing by contagious patients (Lenhart et al. 2004). Research activities outlined in the laboratory-acquired illness section include centrifugation, shaking, and mechanical pipetting. Clinical activities would include aerosolizing medication, airway suctioning, intubation, and bronchoscopy (Lenhart et al. 2004).

The primary methods of controlling airborne hazards generally include engineering controls (e.g., BSCs), standard microbiological practices, proper hygiene, respiratory protection, host immunization programs, training, and antibiotic prophylaxis. Therefore, air sampling is generally not considered a feasible safety practice because of the difficulty in selecting personal air-sampling equipment that is portable and the necessary media to subsequently culture the airborne biological agent. In order to conduct many types of biological air sampling, the safety professional may need to know the suspected agent in order to select an appropriate growth media. Further, long-term time-weighted air sampling is not recommended because of the confounding air contaminants. Air sampling longer than even the shortest duration will result in a large confounding-agent population on the growth media.

Analysis of Air Samples

The analysis or counting of air samples is also a critical consideration when evaluating the occupational environment. False positive readings in sampling are routinely encountered and must be considered by the safety professional. For example, an air sample containing bacillus may incorrectly be interpreted as *Bacillus anthracis* because they are of the same genus. This particular false positive is routinely reported in the news because of the heightened public sensitivity resulting from *B. anthracis* attacks in 2001. Further, surrogate species may produce false positives because of similar toxin productions. An example of this is *B. thuringiensis*, which is used worldwide as an organic pesticide to protect crops from insects. *B. thuringiensis*, which is safe for humans but toxic to insects, belongs to the family of *B. cerus*. If *B cerus* and *B. thuringiensis* were misidentified in an environmental sample, the safety precautions and decontamination efforts would differ significantly because *B. cerus* is known to cause gastroenteritis in humans.

Interpretations

The complications presented by air and environmental sampling dictate strict proficiency in analyzing these samples and interpreting the results. Employing a trained and proficient microbiologist or pathologist is critical when interpreting biological samples. Routine proficiency testing, written test procedures, and previous sampling experience can assist the safety professional in obtaining an accurate hazard-assessment picture and excluding false positive events.

Air sampling is normally conducted to provide negative tests for certain high-risk procedures. For example, if an air hose is designed to carry an infectious dose of a biological agent, sentinel plates may be distributed throughout the work area to monitor airborne concentrations. The aerosols gravimetrically settle onto the sentinel plates, which are subsequently cultured in a controlled environment. The primary concern with sentinel plates is the proper placement of the plates and removal of local air eddy currents that could bypass the sentinel plate, yielding a false negative event.

Environmental wipe tests may also be used to control biological hazards in an occupational setting. The most common example would include a patient diagnosed with a complex respiratory disease that could survive on environmental surfaces (e.g., *M. tuberculosis*). In this situation, the safety professional would oversee the decontamination of a potentially contaminated building space, furniture, toilet fixtures, and so on. However, in order to reassure employees about safe working conditions, environmental wipe tests using sterile conditions would be prudent. The wipe-test media is then specifically cultured for the known infectious agent in order to control possible additional environmental exposures. This procedure is most common for those biological agents with a hardy, long-lasting spore (e.g., *B. anthracis* or *C. immitus*).

Clearance and Decontamination

A primary reason cited for conducting biological environmental sampling is the validation of decontamination or sterilization practices. For example, formaldehyde gas is commonly employed to decontaminate BSCs prior to maintenance work on the HEPA filters. This work would normally be considered highly hazardous because the pathogenic agents are diffused or impacted on the surface of the HEPA filter. In order to assess the positive results of the decontamination process, a biological indicator is commonly employed.

The term *sterilization* means destroying biological life, especially hardy bacterial spores. Sterilization is restrictive and difficult to achieve because it involves the thorough killing of biological life. A related term is *decontamination*, which means reducing or abating the number of biological organisms below the threshold necessary to cause disease. *Disinfection* is generally associated with decontamination because it means reducing all biological organisms below a certain level on an environmental surface. The safety professional must determine which of these goals he or she would like to achieve so that an appropriate methodology and subsequent biological indicator can be selected.

The most common biological indicator involves a 1.25-inch strip of filter paper containing *Geobacillus stearothermophilus* (for validating steam autoclaves and vapor phase hydrogen peroxide) or *Bacillus atrophaeus* (for validating ethylene oxide or dry heat sterilizers). The safety professional places a biological indicator strip inside the equipment to be sterilized prior to initializing the cycle. After completion, the spore strip is sent to a testing laboratory for subsequent culturing. If no growth appears after incubating for 24–48 hours, it is a positive indication that the pathogens in that sterilization cycle were effectively killed. If the biological indicators grow following sterilization, it is an indication that certain parameters were not met during sterilization. Common problems with steam autoclaves include overloading and low temperature. If the effective kill temperature is not achieved, harmful pathogens may potentially remain within the load.

Summary

The complex discipline of biosafety combines a diverse background of microbiology, engineering, industrial hygiene, chemistry, and education. The melding of these talents enables scientists, clinicians, veterinaries, and agronomists to safely engage in the furtherance of their patient care or research goals. The safety professional can better anticipate, recognize, evaluate, and control biological hazards using the topics reviewed in this chapter. However, this information should be combined in collaboration with other competent medical or laboratory professionals to generate a team-based approach to biological safety. Biohazardous agents lead to complex diseases with multifactorial effects on the human population. A team-based approach with knowledgeable professionals will clearly complement the safety professional and lead to a safer work environment.

References

Beers, M. H., and R. Berkow, eds. 2006. *Merck Manual of Diagnosis and Therapy*. 17th ed. Whitehouse Station, NJ: Merck Research Laboratories.

Caucheteux, D., and P. Mathot. 2005. "Biological Risk Assessment: An Explanation Meant for Safety Advisors in Belgium." *Applied Biosafety* 10:10–29.

Centers for Disease Control and Prevention (CDC). 1988. "Perspectives in Disease Prevention and Health Promotion Update: Universal Precautions for Prevention of Transmission of Human Immunodeficiency Virus, Hepatitis B Virus, and Other Bloodborne Pathogens in Health-Care Settings." *Mortality and Morbidity Weekly Report* 37(24):377–388.

______. 2003. *Exposure to Blood: What Healthcare Personnel Need to Know* (retrieved December 14, 2007). www.cdc.gov/ncdid/dhqpl/bbp/Exp_to_Blood.pdf

______. 2009. HHS Publication No. 21-1112, *Biosafety in Microbiological and Biomedical Laboratories (BMBL)*. 5th ed. Washington, D.C.: CDC.

Collins, C. H. 1983. *Laboratory Acquired Infections: History, Incidence, Causes, and Prevention*. Boston: Butterworth.

Garner, J. S. 1996. "Guideline for Isolation Precautions in Hospitals: Parts I and II." *Infection Control & Hospital Epidemiology* 17(1):53–80.

Gilligan, P. H., and M. K. York. 2004. "Sentinel Laboratory Guidelines for Suspected Agents of Bioterrorism: Brucella Species." *American Society of Microbiology*, pp. 3–4.

Herman, P., Y. Verlinder, D. Breyer, E. Van Cleemput, B. Brochier, M. Sneyers, R. Snacken, P. Hermans, P. Kerkhofs, C. Liesnard, B. Rombaut, M. Van Ranst, G. van Groen, P. Grombau, and W. Moens. 2004. "Biological Risk Assessment of the Severe Acute Respiratory Syndrome (SARS) Coronavirus and Containment Measures for the Diagnostic and Research Laboratories." *Applied Biosafety* 9:128–142.

Heubner, R. J. 1947. "Report of an Outbreak of Q-fever at the National Institutes of Health." *American Journal of Public Health* 37:431–440.

Holmes, G. P., J. K. Hilliard, and K. C. Klontz. 1990. "B-Virus Infection in Humans: Epidemiologic Investigations of a Cluster." *Annals of Internal Medicine* 112:833–839.

Lenhart, S. W., T. Seitz, D. Trout, and N. Bollinger. 2004. "Issues Affecting Respirator Selection for Workers Exposed to Infectious Aerosols: Emphasis on Healthcare Settings." *Applied Biosafety* 9:20–36.

Martini, G. A., and H. Z. Schmidt. 1968. "Spermatogenic transmission of the 'Marburg virus.' (Causes of 'Marburg simian disease')." *Klinische Wochenschrift* 46(7):398–400.

National Institute for Occupational Safety and Health (NIOSH). 2003. DHHS Publication No 2003-136, *Guidance for Filtration and Air Cleaning Systems to Protect Building Environments from Airborne Chemical, Biological, and Radiological Attacks*. Washington, D.C.: NIOSH.

National Institutes of Health (NIH). 2011. *Guidelines for Research Involving Recombinant DNA Molecules* (retrieved July 22, 2011). oba.od.nih.gov/oba/rac/guidelines/NIH_Guidelines.htm

National Research Council (NRC), Committee on Hazardous Biological Substances in the Laboratory. 1989. *Biosafety in the Laboratory: Prudent Practices for the Handling and Disposal of Infectious Materials*. Washington, D.C.: National Academy Press.

National Sanitation Foundation (NSF) and American National Standards Institute (ANSI). 2002. *Class II Laminar Flow Biohazard Cabinetry. Standard 49*. Ann Arbor, MI: Academic Press.

Occupational Health and Safety Administration (OSHA). 2001. *Occupational Exposure to Bloodborne Pathogens; Needlestick and Other Sharps Injuries; Final Rule*. 66:5317–5325. Washington, D.C.: OSHA.

______. 2008. 29 CFR 1910.1030, *Toxic and Hazardous Substances*. Washington, D.C.: OSHA.

Oliphant, J. W., D. A. Gordon, A. Meis, and R. R. Parker. 1949. "Q-fever in Laundry Workers, Presumably Transmitted from Contaminated Clothing." *American Journal of Hygiene* 49:76–82.

Pike, R. M. 1976. "Laboratory-Associated Infections: Summary and Analysis of 3,921 Cases." *Health Laboratory Science* 13:105–114.

______. 1978. "Past and Present Hazards of Working with Infectious Hazards." *Archives of Pathology & Laboratory Medicine* 102(7):333–336.

______. 1979. "Laboratory-Associated Infections: Incidence, Fatalities, Causes, and Prevention." *Annual Review of Microbiology* 33:41–66.

Public Health Agency of Canada (PHAC). 2006. *Infectious Diseases* (accessed April 26, 2011). www.phacaspc.gc.ca/id-mi/index-enf.php

Rao, G. G., B. P. Saunders, and R. G. Masterton. 1996. "Laboratory-Acquired Verotoxin Producing Escherichia coli (VTEC) Infection." *Journal of Hospital Infection* 33(3):228–230.

Richardson, J. H. 1973. "Provisional Summary of 109 Laboratory-Associated Infections at the Centers for Disease Control, 1947–1973." 16th Annual Biosafety Conference, Ames, Iowa.

Skinholj, P. 1974. "Occupational Risks in Danish Clinical Chemistry Laboratories." *Scandinavian Journal of Clinical and Laboratory Investigation* 33:27–29.

Sulkin, S. E., and R. M. Pike. 1949. "Viral Infections Contracted in the Laboratory." *New England Journal of Medicine* 241:205–213.

______. 1951. "Survey of Laboratory-Acquired Infections." *American Journal of Public Health Nations Health* 41(7):769–781.

Wedum, A. G. 1997. "History and Epidemiology of Laboratory-Acquired Infections (in Relation to the Cancer Research Program)." *Journal of the American Biological Safety Association* 2:12–29.

Appendix: Recommended Reading

Budavari, S., M. O'Neil, A. Smith, P. Heckelman, and P. Merck. 1996. *Merck Index: An Encyclopedia of Chemicals, Drugs, and Biologicals*. 12th ed. Whitehouse Station, NJ: Merck Research Laboratories.

Centers for Disease Control and Prevention (CDC). 2006. *Diseases and Conditions* (retrieved November 15, 2006). www.cdc.gov/node.do/id/0900f3ec8000e035

6

Best Practices

S. Z. Mansdorf

Learning Objectives

- Become familiar with the definitions of industrial hygiene.
- Know the five basic tenets of industrial hygiene.
- Become familiar with the best practices for industrial hygiene as categorized by the key elements of the practice of industrial hygiene.
- Understand the basis for inclusion of the listed programs, approaches, and methods as best practices.

INDUSTRIAL HYGIENE (also referred to as occupational hygiene) has been defined as the science of protecting and enhancing the health and safety of people at work and in their communities (ABIH 2010). The practice of industrial hygiene (IH) is commonly described as the science and art devoted to the anticipation, recognition, evaluation, prevention, and control of those environmental factors or stresses, arising in or from the workplace, which may cause sickness, impaired health and well-being, or significant discomfort among workers or the citizens of the community (AIHA 2010). IH has been a recognized profession since the 1940s, allowing for the growth of best practices in the profession as the science has developed. *Best practice* can be defined as the best means to achieve a desired goal (i.e., health and safety). There are only a few technical references that identify approaches, tools, or methods as being a best practice. The majority of best practices listed in this chapter are those identified over 35 years of experience by the author in a variety of sectors and roles. Where the tools and methods for best practice are stated or implied as a best practice, they are referenced.

This chapter summarizes these best practices within the context of five recognized aspects of IH (see Figure 1):

- anticipation
- recognition
- evaluation
- prevention
- control

Anticipation

Anticipation is probably the most difficult aspect of industrial hygiene. It certainly requires the most experience and technical

Anticipation	• Reviewing all new chemicals and processes (including significant modifications of processes) in advance of their use • Performing either a quantitative or qualitative assessment annually (or a combination of the two) of processes and procedures • Using control banding, a best practice where there is limited information or technical resources available • Actively integrating industrial hygiene practices and procedures into other related business processes
Recognition	• Establishing a file or database that contains all the required (legal requirements) and recommended practices for the substances and processes of concern • Risk-ranking operations and establishing an assessment or audit plan based on that ranking
Evaluation	• Having a justifiable exposure assessment strategy • Documenting hazard evaluations in a detailed and standardized way
Prevention	• Ensuring effective hazard communication • Demonstrating the effectiveness of all health and safety training
Control	• Following the hierarchy of controls • Having an active product stewardship program • Using a recognized safety and health management system

FIGURE 1. Best practices for industrial hygiene

knowledge (Mansdorf 1999a, Perkins 1997). Anticipation is essentially the *estimation* of exposure and response to one or more hazards. A simple example of a solvent can illustrate the concept of anticipation. To estimate the level of risk, the safety professional would need to know the nature of the hazard (composition of the solvent of concern), the physical conditions (evaporation rates, room size, ventilation, and work practices), the toxicity of the solvent (TLV, PEL, and toxicological effects), protective measures (engineering controls, administrative controls, and PPE), other potential hazards in the use of the solvent (e.g., fire or explosion), and other facts. Combining this information with use conditions, one must estimate the level of risk presented. It is also quite common to have some of this information, but not all of it. This further complicates the task of anticipating a potential hazard. This is also why estimation (anticipation) of the risk requires the most knowledge and experience.

The best practice in anticipation is the review of all new chemicals and processes (including significant modifications of processes) in advance of their use (Hansen 2008). This practice can be done at the organizational and local level. It should involve a multidisciplinary team approach (typically involving safety, environmental, and engineering experts) and can be based on various criteria to limit the number of reviews. For chemicals, it could be limited to those of concern (health hazard, environmental hazard, or fire hazard). For processes, it could be limited to those of most concern (high temperature, high pressure, chemicals of concern, or physical hazards), or it might be based on the size of the project. For potential high-hazard processes, best practice is to use one of many available tools, such as the hazard and operability (HAZOP) approach. Best practice is to review all new chemicals and processes or major process modifications for risk at the local level (where it is used) and at the organizational level (when they are to be implemented at multiple sites).

Another best practice is to perform a quantitative or qualitative risk assessment of all processes and procedures (Wallace 2008). These assessments should be performed annually. The ideal approach would be to perform a quantitative assessment, as described in the previous paragraph, for potential high-hazard situations and to perform a qualitative risk assessment on a "wall-to-wall" basis annually. There are a number of published approaches and tools for risk assessment on both a quantitative and qualitative basis. Quantitative approaches include HAZOP, hazard analysis (HAZAN), fault-tree analysis (FTA), failure mode and effect analysis (FMEA), and others (Manuele 2008, Cantrell and Clemens 2009). See also the section "Risk Analysis and Hazard Control" in this Handbook, particularly the chapters "Systems and Process Safety" by Hansen and "Basic Safety Engineering" by Mroszczyk. These process safety procedures are usually limited to high-risk operations. Quantitative approaches require a significant level of effort and expertise, while qualitative approaches are relatively easy to perform and usually involve workers more directly, since less technical skill in safety and health is needed. Qualitative approaches include many variations on the common theme of likelihood (frequency) and severity.

While there are a number of varying approaches to qualitative risk assessments, the basic concept can be described in six steps. The first step is the formation of a team to conduct the assessment. Ideally, this would involve a technical expert or someone with safety, industrial hygiene, or similar experience joined by supervisors and workers that actually perform the procedures in the areas being evaluated. An ideal team would include at least five persons but not exceed ten members. Team composition can vary from department or operational area, depending on the breadth of knowledge of the workers in the procedures and processes in the areas under evaluation. Step two is to collect and review all the procedures and processes in the area under evaluation with the team. At this stage, the team can also decide the order of analysis. This can be based on product flow, physical layout, or other factors. Stage three is identification of potential hazards. This usually involves a walk-through of the area, brainstorming on what could go wrong and the consequences, and a listing of all the potential hazards considered, even though potentially remote or unlikely. Step four is a more systematic evaluation of each hazard, given in terms of frequency, severity, and potential controls. Step five is a mapping of frequency against severity (see Tables 1 and 2) in a risk matrix (see Figure 2). Table 1, reflecting frequency of the hazard, can be altered to fit the needs of the organization, as can Table 2,

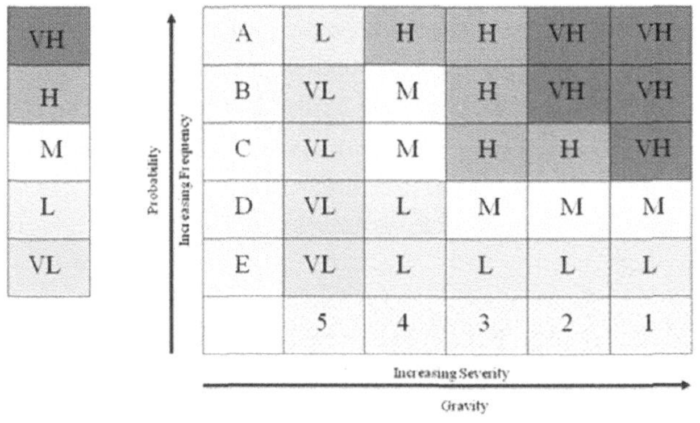

VH
H
M
L
VL

Probability / Increasing Frequency

A	L	H	H	VH	VH
B	VL	M	H	VH	VH
C	VL	M	H	H	VH
D	VL	L	M	M	M
E	VL	L	L	L	L
	5	4	3	2	1

Increasing Severity
Gravity

FIGURE 2. Risk-assessment matrix of frequency and severity (*Source:* L'Oreal 2001)

TABLE 1

Frequency of the Hazard

Description	Code	Definition
Frequent	A	once per week
Probable	B	once per year
Occasional	C	once per 3 years
Rare	D	once per 10 years
Improbable	E	once per 100 years

(*Source:* L'Oreal 2001)

TABLE 2

Severity of the Hazard

Description	Level	Definition
Catastrophic	1	• Single or multiple deaths • Severe and immediate operational difficulties • Site closure
Critical	2	• Severe multiple injuries or potential mortal disease • Severe operational difficulties • Severe reputational damage
Major	3	• Severe injury or disease • Loss of critical equipment
Minor	4	• Minor injury or disease • Irritation • Loss of productivity
Negligible	5	• No injury or disease • No significant impact on production

(*Source:* L'Oreal 2001)

showing the severity of the hazard. The risk matrix (Figure 2) is the outcome of the intersection of frequency and severity. This is shown as ranging from very low (VL) to very high (VH), depending on the level of acceptable risk for the workers and the organization. One can also decide on the time constraints for lowering risk levels based on the risk. For example, a very high risk (HR) would require immediate attention, while a very low risk (LR) could be accepted. Low (L) and medium (M) risks are those that commonly dominate in most organizations.

Another approach is *control banding*—a variation of the classical risk-assessment approach—which uses chemical classes and the Global Harmonization System (GHS) for grouping and labeling chemicals. At present, it is primarily used in Europe and based on the current "R" phrases, which will be integrated into the new GHS system under their registration, evaluation, authorization, and restriction of chemicals (REACH) requirements (Zalk and Nelson 2008). It places hazards where the actual potential severity is not well known into control bands, and control strategies are then defined based on these bands. While NIOSH (2009) and others view this approach as having some limitations, it has been successfully applied in a number of European countries, with the United Kingdom being one of the leaders in its use. This practice is best applied to chemical exposures where there is no occupational exposure limit (OEL) or limited toxicological data, as well as in situations where there is limited or no sampling or analytical method available. A good example of the application of a control-banding approach is found in nanotechnology, where the toxicological data is limited and sampling and analysis difficult (Paik et al. 2008). Control-banding applications with examples can be found on the Health and Safety Executive (HSE) Web site. Control banding is a best practice used where limited information or technical resources are available (NIOSH 2009, HSE n.d.).

Active integration of industrial hygiene practices and procedures into other related business processes is a best practice (Leibowitz 2003). It is listed in this section on anticipation since effective integration could be considered a measure that anticipates hazards, although it could also fit within the section on prevention as well.

SIDEBAR

An Example of the Six-Step Qualitative Risk-Assessment Process

The qualitative risk-assessment process example scenario is a nonautomated hand-washing (cleaning) operation where the wash water is 160°F. This example focuses on a single operation within a department and a single risk to make it simple to follow.

Step 1: The team of six persons is formed. It includes several workers from the area, the area supervisor, and the team leader, who is a safety and health professional.

Step 2: In their walk-through survey, the team inspects the area where small irregular vessels are hand washed, using a water hose and large sinks. The team notes that it is a continuous operation with one person per shift assigned to this task. The team talks with the washer and studies how the operation is performed. They also note that the washer wears a face shield, apron, rubber gloves, and rubber boots.

Step 3: Among a list of ten possibilities for injury or illness, the team's analysis of the potential risks includes slips due to the wet floor and the potential for workers to be splashed with hot water and/or get soap in their eyes. They note that there have been some previous incidents, but none of a serious nature.

Step 4: The team focuses on the hot-water burn potential first. They learn that body contact with water at 160°F can result in second- or third-degree burns in less than one second of contact. They discuss all the ways the water could scald the worker, such as by a splash, by the hose breaking, by equipment malfunctioning, or by failure of the worker to wear the proper equipment. They conclude that the potential probability of a splash occurring is once per year (for all three shifts) and that its severity is in the "major" category. They also note that the personal protective equipment (PPE) might not fully protect the wearer as he or she could be splashed on the arms, lower legs, head, or back. Initially, they talk about potential additional controls, such as automating the process, providing more protection for the worker, and using lower-temperature water.

Step 5: The risk is mapped, using charts provided. As discussed, the frequency is judged to be once per year, which is "B" on the chart for frequency. The severity is judged to be major, which is a "3" on the severity chart. The intersection of a "B" frequency and "3" severity on the risk-assessment matrix is "high." This makes the risk unacceptable.

Step 6: The team, after consulting with the quality, engineering, and operations departments, determines that the process cannot be automated, and that lowering the water temperature would not diminish the cleaning of the vessels. It is concluded that the water temperature can be lowered to 120°F, and the worker could be protected by use of a thermostatic value that protects against scalding and thermal shock. The scenarios are again tested using a lower frequency (failure of the valve controlling temperature) and severity (10-minute exposure to 120°F water to produce a burn). The new frequency is judged to be rare ("D") and the new severity is considered to be minor ("4") since the flow and contact would need to continue for 10 minutes to result in a burn. In the risk matrix chart, the intersection of "D" for frequency and "4" for severity results in a "low" risk result. This risk is found to be acceptable.

It is recognized as a best practice by the National Safety Council (NSC) and the Robert W. Campbell award (NSC 2010). An example of the application of such integration would be to have an new operational process approval method that incorporates the procedures and requirements for new processes from an industrial hygiene perspective. This would mean that the process engineers or others (e.g., business owners) developing the new process would know the industrial hygiene requirements from the very beginning of their work, not just in a review. The same principle would apply to other business processes, such as research and development processes and procedures, quality and maintenance processes and procedures, new product launches, and so on.

Recognition

The second aspect of the practice of industrial hygiene is recognition, which has traditionally been based on standards of practice and regulations from local, state, and national organizations, such as the Occupational Safety and Health Administration (OSHA). Standards of practice come from a wide variety of groups and organizations, including industry groups (e.g., Chlorine Council); voluntary standards from consensus standard groups (e.g., American Society for Testing and Materials (ASTM) and the American National Standards Institute (ANSI)); governmental organizations (e.g., NIOSH); nongovernmental organizations, such as the World Health Organization (WHO) and the International Labour Organization (ILO); and professional organizations, such as the American Society of Safety Engineers (ASSE), the American Conference of Governmental Industrial Hygienists (ACGIH), American Industrial Hygiene Association (AIHA), and American Institute of Chemical Engineers (AIChE). Recognition of hazards presented from chemicals can be found in literature on the subject from a wide variety of sources listed above, with special emphasis on OEL information, whether regulatory or advisory. Process controls and standards of care for equipment and processes are typically available from industry groups (e.g., Compressed Gas Association). Best practice is to have a dossier (file or database) containing all the legal requirements and recommended practices for the substances and processes of concern. The dossier can also be used to develop inspection guidelines and the necessary frequency of inspections. Additionally, it is common for litigation cases where there is an "accident" or occupational disease involved to focus on what are considered "standards of practices," so it is quite important to be aware of recommendations of trade and professional associations along with those practices that are legally mandated.

Once the requirements for safe operations are known, it is necessary to assure that all the required and recommended standards of use are being followed. A world-class, written program is certainly a plus but is of little value if there are not "boots on the ground." Audits and inspections detract from normal production in any organization. They also tax the resources and person-power of any industrial hygiene team. Therefore, it is necessary to establish a schedule that provides assurance of the recognition of existing or proposed hazards in an efficient manner. Conventional wisdom and common sense suggests a risk-based approach (Hollenbeck 2007). Routine inspections on a local or corporate level can be done annually, as discussed previously. For substances or processes of most concern, the frequency of inspection or assessment should be based on the level of risk presented or in response to incidents or to new practice or regulatory requirements. Best practice is to rank risk operations and establish an assessment or audit plan based on this ranking. It is quite common to require auditing and other inspections be done on a management-systems basis (management-systems approaches are discussed later in this chapter). For example, a process utilizing sodium cyanide would require a regular, formalized and detailed on-site process inspection, while a reverse osmosis of waste water would only require infrequent and less detailed inspections. System audits without specific technical expertise in the risks identified would not meet the requirements of this best practice.

Evaluation

Best practice here is to have a justifiable exposure-assessment strategy (Mulhausen and Damiano 2003). An integral part of the practice of IH is to perform exposure assessments. These may include a number of statistical considerations in order to identify the workers at highest risk (with the assumption that the others would have less risk) in operations that are too large to do documentary quantitative evaluations on all workers. This process is inherent, for example, in sampling for asbestos content of materials in schools and public buildings under the Environmental Protection Agency (EPA) rules where there are established statistical sampling requirements for both the number and location of samples (USC 1986). There are also a number of other references for exposure-assessment strategies, such as those contained in the field operations manual of OSHA (OSHA 2011). The essential issue is that the exposure-assessment strategy must correctly identify or estimate the level of exposure of those at risk. It is therefore important to be able to show that the sampling strategy is designed to accomplish this purpose.

Best practice is to document hazard evaluations in a detailed and standardized way. For a number of reasons, it is not unusual that a company be required to answer questions on hazard evaluations many years after conducting the original assessment, including documentation for a retrospective study, documentation of the changes in risk level to employees, or documentation for legal actions. The only way to effectively meet these demands is to carefully document the basis for and conduct of the studies in a uniform way. For air monitoring and personnel monitoring this requires the basis for the sampling strategy (as described above) as well as all the details of the actual air monitoring, laboratory work, and analysis of results. Technical reports form a good basis for this requirement, but it is necessary to have the backup information as well, since most technical reports are summaries of the work done. It is particularly important to give the basis (rationale) for why the evaluations were done, who requested them, the choice of approaches, work-practice observations, and so on. Some regulations govern the retention of records (e.g., lead standard, asbestos standard), while most companies have an internal standard on retention of records not governed by regulation. Ideally, records dealing with hazards to employees would be maintained indefinitely. As an example, the author was recently asked about air sampling that he had conducted more than 30 years ago. It was for a retrospective study that had significant legal implications. Needless to say, most industrial hygienists and safety professionals today have worked for several companies, and that was the case here. There was no recollection of the details of the study; therefore, they would have to rely totally on retained records.

Prevention

Prevention (for the purposes of the organizaton of this chapter) is presented as a discrete aspect of industrial hygiene. Anticipation and recognition can both lead to prevention (avoiding or hindering the unwanted event). For example, substitution of a less troublesome chemical for a more hazardous one is both an aspect of anticipation (knowing it could be a problem) and a control strategy. Best practice for prevention is effective hazard communication (Silk 2003). Hazard communication is regulated by OSHA. It includes many different aspects of worker information and training, which will not be repeated here. What is important is that the workers know the potential hazards they may encounter and the means to protect themselves from them. It is most difficult to assure that the information and training provided is effective. For some hazards, the risk may involve a significant level of technical information to assure that the hazard is communicated and understood. It is important to have a means of assuring that the information is understood and demonstrated on both a theoretical and practical basis. This requires both written and on-the-job testing of worker knowledge. Everyone has experienced situations where a worker has "passed" a test but demonstrated a total lack of understanding of the risks involved. The key to this best practice is to use a method that actually demonstrates that workers know the practical requirements for the tasks they perform. For example, workers could be asked to respond to an emergency and actually carry out an exercise or drill that shows they understand what is necessary.

Best practice is to demonstrate the effectiveness of all health and safety training (Samways 2003). Health and safety training is a common theme in all health and safety programs. Informed workers, supervisors, and managers are critical to understanding safe and unsafe practices. There are some aspects of industrial hygiene that can be quite technical and difficult to understand for those not trained in the sciences. Hazard communication is the example given in the previous paragraph. However, there are other hazards not covered by hazard-communication requirements, such as what to do in a fire emergency. As previously discussed, it is best to actually have workers demonstrate they have understood the training. A practical example of this principle applied to a safety topic is to test forklift drivers and their supervisors while drivers are actually operating the forklift. Both can demonstrate their skills and knowledge of the rules.

Control Strategies

The last element of the practice of industrial hygiene is control. There are a large number of potential approaches to control hazards; these have traditionally been grouped into classes (see Figure 3).

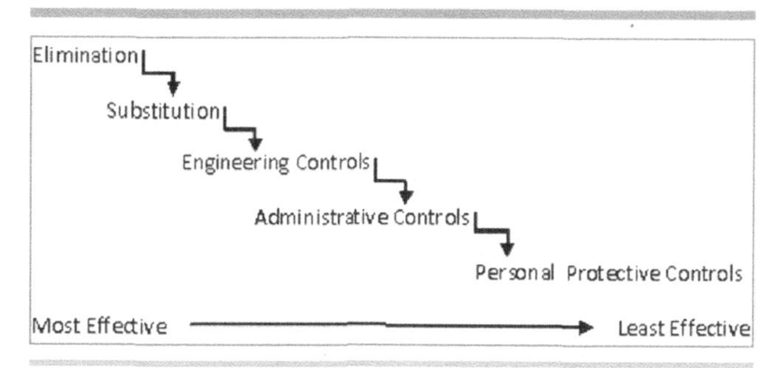

FIGURE 3. Hierarchy of controls (*Source:* Mansdorf 2011)

The categories in Figure 3 are ranked by preference (listed in order of effectiveness) and are known as the hierarchy of controls. While elimination and substitution (with a less hazardous material or process) might not appear to be *controls*, they are generally classified this way. Best practice is to follow the hierarchy of controls (May 2008, Blayney 2008, and Mansdorf 1999a). This means elimination of the problem or substitution with a less problematic chemical or process whenever possible. This is followed by various engineering controls that do not rely on worker intervention (such as ventilation, interlocking, or noise damping) and administrative controls (e.g., worker rotation or work practices). The last method of control recommended would be PPE use (e.g., hearing protection or respirators), even though it is the one most commonly applied.

Best practice is to have an active product stewardship program (Agopsowicz and Grumbles 2010). The most progressive companies have such programs to assist their customers in the proper use of their products. This includes products used by other manufacturers, as well as suppliers and end-use consumers. Certain products (such as those that are inherently hazardous due to toxicity, flammability, corrosivity, reactivity, and environmental sensitivity) naturally lend themselves to support in their use by the manufacturer. Nevertheless, even commonly used consumer products such as soaps, shampoos, cleaning products, and so on, need some level of support to assure that they are stored and used properly. Best practice is to have an active customer support program; specialized training and auditing programs may also be required. As an example, hypochlorite, used as pool chlorine, is a common product that can be purchased in many different types of consumer stores as a liquid or as a solid. It is an inherently hazardous product due to its reactivity. It is usual for companies to provide specific instruction to those that store the product, as well as those that use it, rather than simply relying on the MSDS to convey the warnings and instructions. The programs of the Spray Polyurethane Foam Alliance for Product Stewardship is another example of product stewardship undertaken by an industry association (i.e., alliance), where the industry has jointly developed programs to assure the safe use of their products. The American Chemistry Council Responsible Care program has had a longstanding and significant program for product stewardship. In 2006 they implemented a Global Product Strategy within Responsible Care and have announced a plan to have "100% of high priority chemicals covered by publically available product stewardship summaries by 2012" (ACC 2010). These are all examples of proactive product stewardship.

The final best practice is development of a management system. It is placed in the prevention category since one could argue that an effective management system will prevent incidents. The three major management systems for industrial hygiene (and safety) are the OSHA Voluntary Protection Program (VPP) (OSHA 2010), the American National Standards Institute/American Industrial Hygiene Association (ANSI/AIHA) Z10 standard (ANSI/ASSE 2005), and the *Occupational Health and Safety Management Standard* (OHSAS 18000). It should be noted that the OHSAS is also called the OHSMS; however, the British standard uses the OHSAS acronym (BSI 2007). There are other privately sponsored systems as well; however, this section focuses on the ones listed as they are the most widely used.

All three systems have claimed some level of improvement with their application. For example, the OSHA VPP program states, "The average VPP worksite has a days away, restricted, or transferred (DART) case rate of 52% below the average for its industry" (OSHA 2010). The disadvantage with the OSHA VPP is that it is limited to the United States and is not as widely recognized by external organizations internationally. There is also some evidence for the effectiveness of OHSAS and the more recent ANSI Z10 standard, but the evidence is mostly anecdotal (ASSE 2009). The biggest advantage of the three safety and health management systems listed is their recognition as a best practice by stakeholders, including workers, government agencies, nongovernment organizations (NGOs), financial analysts, and others. Like the companion environmental management standard (ISO 14000), a safety and health management system is considered to be a minimum standard for "corporate social responsibility" (ASSE 2009).

A second reason for listing an occupational health and safety management system as a best practice is that it can provide the basis for a common approach across businesses and organizations, including diverse multinational locations. The two independent management systems (OHSAS 18000 and ANSI Z10) are similar but not identical, while the OSHA VPP is government-sponsored and -administered. OHSAS 18000 (available through the British Standards Institute) would appear to have the most registrations as it tends to be more globally applied and was developed earlier (originally in 1999, with the latest edition in 2007, while the ANSI Z10 standard was published in 2005). Best practice is to have a recognized safety and health management system.

Conclusion

These best practices will be beneficial to those desiring the highest level of performance and effectiveness in their industrial hygiene programs. The best practices given are not an all-inclusive listing nor are they applicable to all situations. However, they do provide the professional practice benchmark.

References

American Board of Industrial Hygiene (ABIH). 2010. "What is an industrial hygienist?" (retrieved June 30, 2010). www.abih.org/general/cihcaih.html#defining

American Chemistry Council (ACC). 2010. "Product Stewardship" (retrieved June 30, 2010). www.americanchemistry.com/s_responsiblecare/sec_members.asp?CID=1320&DID=4863

American Industrial Hygiene Association (AIHA). 2007. Hollenbeck, Craig, ed. *Industrial Hygiene and Safety Auditing-A Manual for Practice*. 2d ed. Fairfax, VA: AIHA Press.

______. 2010. "What is an industrial hygienist?" (retrieved June 30, 2010). www.aiha.org/aboutaiha/Pages/WhatIsanIH.aspx

American National Standards Institute/American Industrial Hygiene Association (ANSI/AIHA). 2005. *Z10-2005 Occupational Health and Safety Management Systems*. New York: ANSI.

American Society of Safety Engineers (ASSE). 2010. "Implementing OHSAS 18001-A Corporate Perspective" by S. Z. Mansdorf. Best in Class: Safety Management Virtual Symposium, April 23, 2009.

Blayney, Michael B. 2008. "Personal Protective Equipment—Best Practices." In Joel Haight, ed., *The Safety Professionals Handbook: Technical Applications*. Section 5, pp. 731–835. Des Plaines, IL: ASSE.

British Standards Institute (BSI). 2007. BS OHSAS 18001-2007 *Occupational Health and Safety Management Systems: Requirements*. London: BSI.

Cantrell, S., and P. Clemens. 2009. "Finding All the Hazards—How Do We Know We Are Done." *Professional Safety* (June) 54(11):32–35.

Agopsowicz, Daniel, and Tom Grumbles. 2010. "Product Stewardship." In Rose, Vern, and Barbara Cohrssen, eds., *Patty's Industrial Hygiene and Toxicology*. 6th ed., Vol. 4, Chapter 46. Hoboken, NJ: Wiley.

Hansen, Mark. 2008. "Systems and Process Safety." In Joel Haight, ed., *The Safety Professionals Handbook: Technical Applications*. Section 1, pp. 37–69. Des Plaines, IL: ASSE.

Health and Safety Executive (HSE). n.d. *The Technical Basis for COSHH Essentials—Easy Steps to Control Chemicals* (accessed September 8, 2011). www.hse.gov.us/coshh/essentials.index.htm

Leibowitz, Alan. 2003. "Program Management." In Salvatore DiNardi, ed., *The Occupational Environment: Its Evaluation, Control and Management*. Chapter 37, pp. 958–984. Fairfax, VA: AIHA Press.

L'Oreal. 2001. *Safety Hazard Assessment Procedure Handbook* (SHAP). Paris: L'Oreal.

Mansdorf, S. Z. 1999a. "Introduction-VIII. The tenets of industrial hygiene." In Marty Stern and S. Z. Mansdorf, eds., *Applications and Computational Elements of Industrial Hygiene*. Chapter 1, pp. 1–19. Boca Raton: CRC Press, LLC.

______. 1999b. "Personal Protective Equipment." In Marty Stern and S. Z. Mansdorf, eds., *Applications and Computational Elements of Industrial Hygiene*. Chapter 11, pp. 583–627. Boca Raton: CRC Press, LLC.

Manuele, Fred. 2008. "A Primer On Hazard Analysis and Risk Assessment." In *Advanced Safety Management Focusing on Z10 and Serious Injury Prevention*. Section 4.2, pp. 111–145. New York: John Wiley & Sons.

May, David. 2008. "Personal Protective Equipment." In Joel Haight, ed., *The Safety Professionals Handbook: Technical Applications*. Section 5, pp. 851–858. Des Plaines, IL: ASSE.

Mulhausen, J., and J. Damiano. 2003. "Comprehensive Exposure Assesssement." In Salvatore DiNardi, ed., *The Occupational Environment: Its Evaluation, Control and Management*. Chapter 6, pp. 103–112. Fairfax, VA: AIHA Press.

National Institute of Occupational Safety and Health (NIOSH). 2009. Publication 2009-152. *Qualitative Risk Evaluation and Management of Occupational Hazards: Control Banding (CB): A Literature Review and Critical Analysis*. www.cdc.gov/NIOSH

National Safety Council (NSC). 2010. Robert W. Campbell Award (retrieved June 2010). www.nsc.org/safety_work/NSCAwards/Pages/Campbell(RobertW)Award.aspx

Occupational Safety and Health Administration (OSHA). 2010. "All About VPP" (retrieved June 2010). www.osha.gov/dcsp/vpp/all_about_vpp.html

______. 2011. *Field Operations Manual* (FOM) (accessed September 8, 2011). www.osha.gov/OshDoc/Directive_pdf/CPL_02-00-15-.pdf

Paik, S., D. Zalk, and P. Swuste. 2008. "Application of a Pilot Control Banding Tool for Risk Level Assessment and Control of Nanoparticle Exposures." *Ann. Occup. Hyg*. 52(6):419–428.

Perkins, Jimmy. 1997. "Principles and Focus of Industrial Hygiene." In *Jimmy Perkins, Modern Industrial Hygiene*. Vol. 1, pp 29–45. New York: Van Nostrand Reinhold.

Samways, Margaret. 2003. "Worker Education and Training." In Salvatore DiNardi, ed., *The Occupational Environment: Its Evaluation, Control and Management*. Chapter 30, pp. 775–792. Fairfax, VA: AIHA Press.

Silk, Jennifer. 2003. "Hazard Communication." In Salvatore DiNardi, ed., *The Occupational Environment: Its Evaluation, Control and Management*. Chapter 40, pp. 1019–1030. Fairfax, VA: AIHA Press.

United States Code (USC). 1986. 40 CFR Part 763.86. *Sampling for collecting bulk asbestos samples*. (Asbestos Hazard Emergency Response Act).

Wallace, Stephen. 2008. "Risk Assessment and Hazard Control-Best Practice." In Joel Haight, ed., *The Safety Professionals Handbook: Technical Applications*. Section 1, pp. 243–292. Des Plaines, IL: ASSE.

Zalk, D. M., and D. I. Nelson. 2008. "History and Evolution of Control Banding: A Review." *J. of Occup. Env. Hyg*. 5(4):330–346.

INDEX